By William L. Shirer

Novels

The Traitor
Stranger Come Home

Nonfiction

Berlin Diary
End of a Berlin Diary
Midcentury Journey

Stranger Come Home

Stranger
Come Home

by

William L. Shirer

Little, Brown and Company • *Boston*

Published simultaneously in Canada
by Little, Brown & Company (Canada) Limited

PRINTED IN THE UNITED STATES OF AMERICA

AUTHOR'S NOTE

This is the imaginary journal of an imaginary person, and all the other characters in its pages are likewise imaginary. If there is any resemblance whatsoever to persons living or lately dead, it is purely coincidental.

Stranger Come Home

GENEVA, SWITZERLAND, AUGUST 7, 1949

AT LAST! I am going home! For good!

I don't know why I should feel so excited about doing what I planned to do ten years ago — and would have done had the war not intervened. Last night I tried to finish the report for Washington on Afghanistan. But Kabul, though I left it but a fortnight ago, seemed beyond the grasp of my memory. I finally gave up. I must have sat for hours gazing across the lake. There was a bright light high up in the Juras — some inn on fire probably. I shall never tramp through those mountains as I first planned . . . ten, no twenty years ago. I was twenty-six then, and it seemed easy. So much seemed easy then. . . .

I must sell this villa. It isn't much of a place, except for the view over the lake in the front, and of Mont Blanc — its snows took on a bright pink this afternoon — in the back. But it's the only somewhat permanent home we ever had. . . . A letter from Yvonne today. She thinks she has found an apartment in an old house on the East River, though she neglects to say just where. The youngsters are away in camp losing, presumably (I hope), some of their French accent. They will be back in New York by Labor Day for school — the first American school they will ever have attended, and about time too, since Dick is fourteen and Maria, twelve. Yvonne in raptures over America. "A fabulous land!" says she. I was a little worried on that score. When am I coming? she asks. I telephone a cable: Labor Day.

AUGUST 8

WORKED all day on the Afghan report, but I must confess my mind was unco-operative. A good thing, I guess, that I left the diplomatic service years ago for writing and journalism, which I love. Since the end of the war, though, I have let the State Department hook me for one temporary mission after another. But this is the last. Two months ago the secretary asked me to go to Kabul for a little private snooping into what the Russians were up to in that part of Asia.

I am telling the secretary the Russians are up to plenty. Old Radislav, the best man in the Soviet Embassy, a great authority on Central Asia and a charming ruffian, did his best to find out what *I* was up to in Kabul, attempting to load me with vodka, caviar and other nice things every time I dropped by the embassy to have a game of chess with him. I told him I was on the wagon — a good place for an American to be whenever he spends any time snooping around a Soviet Embassy.

AUGUST 9

THE decision to go back for good is really not new, and I wonder why I should feel so wrought up. It is what I badly wanted to do, beginning ten years ago when I finally made up my mind. It was not, I admit, an easy decision to make then. The first fifteen years in Europe, as a youthful foreign service officer, to begin with, and then as a newspaperman and writer, were certainly pleasant and often absorbing. Gradually I came to feel at home not only in this peaceful little corner of Switzerland to which I had first come as an American observer at the League of Nations but wherever else my work, in the more turbulent moments, took me: Paris, London, Berlin, Warsaw, Prague, Vienna, Rome, Madrid. I must admit that very little I saw at home during my occasional visits those years kindled much of a resolve to hasten my eventual return. Life in America seemed either drab or glossy. In both cases there was an emptiness. I felt a gulf growing between my family and friends and me, and, what disturbed me most, between my

[4]

country and me. I felt less and less at home there. I remember I hardly set foot on the dock in New York before I began counting the days until my boat sailed back to France. One day, I knew, I would have to come back to work and live. I didn't want to die in lonely exile. But for a long time that day seemed far off, buried in the dim and uncertain future. For thirteen happy, eventful years I scarcely gave it a thought.

I had resigned from the foreign service, after a five-year stretch, in 1929 and taken a job with the *Times*. Diplomacy, at least as it was practiced by the State Department and its permanent missions abroad, was not, I saw, for me. I had not gone to the right colleges (Yale, Harvard, Princeton). The formal social life — the snobbery of it, the boredom — killed me. And, to confess a weakness, the Department did not appreciate my prose. My reports were too literary, they said. Would I please conform to form? That was what I rebelled at most: the deadly conformity of the work, of the life. It was one long, dreary confinement. Even working for the sedate *Times* was a release, and after three years as its roving correspondent, I thought I had learned enough to go on my own. Thereafter I lived fairly decently off the magazines and a book every two or three years.

AUGUST 10

JUST as I was sweating out the final section of the report, Steve Burnett called up from Berne to say the pouch wouldn't be going until the evening of the 12th — which gives me a day or two of grace. Steve sounded worried. Wonder if he's having troubles with the minister, or with the Department, or what. I shall find out when I see him day after tomorrow. . . .

Dining tonight with Elsie McCabe. She will be angry and nagging about my going. But then she is cantankerous about everything and almost everybody nowadays. God spare me from these old Communist fanatics who have suddenly — so late — seen the light. Someone just arrived in Kabul from the States told me the other night that they were the new heroes at home, though I cannot imagine why. He said you practically had to be an ex-Communist to be accepted as an authority on world politics. If true, that explains how Elsie has become the darling of the *World Review* — its star correspondent and greatest pundit. She was almost breathless when she phoned this morning.

"What brings you here, Elsie?" I asked.

She had come, she said, to see me and do a piece for *World Review* on the Communist menace in Switzerland.

"There isn't any — in Switzerland, Elsie."

"Oh, Raymond, when will you wake up!" she exclaimed.

Years ago, when I liked her, Elsie did not forgive me for two things: my refusal to follow her into Communism, which she embraced with a female ferocity I have never seen in any other woman; and my marrying Yvonne.

AUGUST 11

ELSIE was just as I expected. We dined at the Bavaria where we had often gone in the late Twenties when she came out to Geneva to cover a League meeting for the *Moscow News*. I had not quite remembered how enormously fat she had become in recent years. She claimed she was down to 200, and dieting, though she gobbled down a mountain of food and complained of thirst after her third big stein of beer. I tried my best to recall — what was true — that in the Twenties, despite her fanaticism in politics, she was a very attractive young American woman — slim, black-haired, vivacious — and that we had had some very memorable week ends together up at Mégève and Chamonix, to mention two places, and that probably we were in love then.

She quickly reminded me of it before we were through with our soup. For the hundredth time — or the thousandth — she swore that she never would have married Sobolev if I hadn't ditched her for Yvonne. (That "bourgeois bitch," I remember, Elsie had called my bride-to-be at the time.) The story wasn't true, but Elsie always has had an immense capacity to distort a fact and to furiously believe in her own distortion. Poor old

Sobolev — as decent a Russian as I ever met. He was liquidated in one of the Moscow purges just before the war. That was when Elsie began to wake up about Bolshevism. I always wished she had had better reasons, though that one was understandable, of course. He was her husband, and he was taken away from her one night in Moscow — forever.

Elsie has taken to shouting. She kept screaming that everyone in the room was a Communist, and when I pointed out that most of the diners were folk I recognized as U.N. officials who were stationed here, she yelled that the U.N. was full of Communists and when in hell would I wake up to the Red danger?

"I never closed my eyes to it," I said. "— from the beginning, when you were giving your life to it. Remember, Elsie?"

But she had forgotten. She ranted on and on so that there was no opportunity for me to tell her about my going home, which probably was just as well. Though I have seen her only infrequently during the seventeen years since I married, she has never ceased trying to maintain a proprietary interest in me. I could imagine her accusing me of deserting her by my going home now, and even making threats. I wonder why she has stopped using powder and rouge. Her obesity has made her skin very oily and her thin lips always needed a little pointing up. Rouge is red, of course. But powder is white. She could at least use a little to dust her shiny nose.

AUGUST 12 (NOON)

FINISHED the Afghan report and will drive up to Berne after lunch. Steve will put me up for the night, and perhaps I will learn what's troubling him. Elsie insists on coming along. Weak fool that I am, I agreed.

BERNE, AUGUST 13

AN AWFUL row with Elsie last night. I thought I acted decently enough by bringing her up here in the first place and then taking her along to dinner with Steve, whose

[7]

children are still in the States. But she insisted on my spending the night with her at the Schweizer Hof. I refused — not because my record is spotless in such matters — but simply because I didn't want to. That was over between us long ago. She wouldn't listen to reason. She raved and ranted and swore she would get even. I have never seen her so repulsive.

Sat up most of the night chewing the fat with Steve. He says he is in bad with some Senate committee over his record in China. I told him he was taking it too seriously. After all, he had been proved right, which doesn't always happen to a diplomat. All that he had done was to warn Washington right after the war that if Chiang didn't clean up the mess around him, kick out the crooks and strengthen his regime, the Communists would destroy him. What was wrong with that? Steve, who is just back from home-leave, said I was awfully naïve, that I had been away too long. Despite his worries he looked fit enough. I was struck by how well he had matured. His thin, bony face has an ascetic quality rather unusual for an American, and as he grows older, his eyes take on more fire and his long nose grows a little sharper. He is beginning to stoop slightly, as am I. We joked about midde-age having crept up on us unawares, but perhaps it is not very funny.

GENEVA, AUGUST 14

I WENT down to the American Express this morning and booked a seat on the New York plane for the first day of September. No word from Elsie. When I phoned yesterday morning in Berne — determined to do my duty, that is, to ask her if she wanted to drive back with me — the hotel clerk said she had left.

AUGUST 16

I THINK I sold our villa this morning. A young Swiss banker and his wife drove up shortly after breakfast. He liked the house, which is not much; she liked the view. She was French, I gathered, and reminded me of Yvonne (the same black hair, very white complexion, brooding eyes), though she was not as attractive, being subject to some strain, some deep frustration, I thought. It showed like a cloud on her face. The banker didn't seem to have a worry in the world. Sometimes I envy men like that, though not often.

AUGUST 17

      I READ something in Stendhal last night that moved me enormously. This great writer, whose genius was only recognized after he died, had just returned, down at heart, from his beloved Paris to his meager job as French consul at Civita Vecchia, northwest of Rome. Looking out from the dusty port to the clean calmness of the blue Tyrrhenian Sea he exclaimed:

Am I to live, am I to grow old far from my native land? Am I to live and die by this solitary shore?

About two years before the war I began to face Stendhal's question. I had been over here thirteen years — since I became of age. Along in 1937, the year Hitler gave Europe a brief breathing spell and there was a little time to pause in one's work and take stock, I began to wonder about my own future and that of my family. Yvonne, being French, was perfectly at home in Europe, and I felt I had become so. The children were too young to be aware of where we lived, Maria having just arrived that year and Dick being only a couple of years old. Still, there was the question to be faced soon: where would our children grow up? In what land? In what language? I wanted them to be American, and Yvonne agreed.

I must try not to be hypocritical. The children were a factor in my decision. But they were not the most important consideration. I myself was. It sounds egotistical to say so, but it's the truth. (In your own private journal, at least, you can afford to be truthful.)

A certain truth began to dawn on me toward the end of the Thirties: however pleasing the life, I really was not so much at home abroad as I imagined. I might master the Continental languages, French, German, Italian, Spanish, and absorb a reasonable amount of the culture and the spirit of Western Europe, as I had done. I might marry into an old European family, as I had also done. And yet, in spite of all this, I remained a foreigner, uprooted and rootless, destined by circumstance to be the eternal observer and therefore prevented from belonging to the society in which I passed my days and from participating, however humbly, in its life. It wasn't the loneliness that I minded. Such loneliness as came over me I coveted, for it was necessary to my kind of living. It was the exclusion, the apartness, of exile that began to weigh upon me. Could one go on to the end that way?

One could, of course, but I had no burning desire to. Having reached that much of a conclusion, I faced another question: what was the deadline for a voluntary exile, that point in time and experience beyond which it was too late to go home?

For apparently there was a deadline. I had seen that in the case of Wendell Lewis Philpots. He had remained over here beyond it. When he went back it was too late. I began to think a good deal of Wendell in those days before the second war. He was perhaps my oldest friend in Europe. He had befriended me when I first came over as a greenhorn, and I came to have a deep affection for him which grew with my admiration for him as a fine human being.

Wendell belonged to that tiny band of American correspondents who had come over to cover the first war in 1914 and remained in Europe to write of the peace. On the whole, they were a distinguished lot, and Philpots was easily the most distinguished of them all: a graceful writer, profound and yet urbane, a man of wit, charm, refinement and cultivation. He moved with confident but quiet ease in the circles of European statesmen, politicians and intellectuals; and in Paris, at least, where he spent most of his life, he frequented the literary salons and cafés, and the world of the theater. He was an imposing figure in that first postwar decade, tall, always immaculately — though not showily — dressed, with a finely chiseled nose and clear, blue, inquiring eyes dominating his thin, sensitive face.

A few American diplomats, businessmen and journalists in Paris and Geneva thought that Wendell went rather European, as they put it, in the Twenties. My own judgment was that he had absorbed the best of both worlds — American and European. The experience over here had rounded out his Yankee character and deepened it. He was at home wherever men were civilized and cultivated. His one mistake, I can see now, was not to have gone home on leave often enough to renew his roots, to become reacclimatized to a rapidly changing America, to retain his journalistic "contacts" and to see what was happening to his once great newspaper on which, of course, he depended for his very good living.

His first marriage, I gathered, had broken up partly because of this failure. His first wife, who was American, the daughter of a Chicago packer, had not liked Europe. In order to be with him, she had stuck the first war out in Paris, which by all accounts was quite a pleasant place despite the proximity of the fighting — there was no bombing, to speak of, in that war, and no rockets, and the food and wine were good. But she was always homesick for Chicago, and a couple of years after the Armistice she went back there, demanding that Wendell go with her. He declined to do so, and she promptly divorced him. Shortly afterward he married a Polish beauty whom he had met on an assignment in Warsaw. Wanda, with shiny black hair, high cheekbones and large, luminous black eyes, was one of the most attractive women I ever knew, for besides her looks, she had a warm, passionate nature and an intelligence almost as keen as her husband's. They were a popular couple in the European capitals and their marriage always seemed to Yvonne and me, who had our difficulties, to be almost too good to be true.

One day at the beginning of the Thirties, Wendell's newspaper suddenly went under. It was a terrible shock to him, but as the dean of the American correspondents in Paris, so to speak, he was confident that one of the other great New York dailies, probably the *Times*, would take him on. But this did not happen — such are the mysteries of American journalism. I urged him to speed home and talk to the editors of other newspapers in New York. But he lingered on in Paris, and slowly, I could see, a certain resentment — or perhaps it was more a bewilderment — began to sprout in him. Pretty soon he took a job at a small salary with one of the American press associations, and he and Wanda moved out of the big house near the Etoile where they had entertained the great of Europe and took a small apartment on the Left Bank. Wendell, it was obvious, was ill-fitted for work with a news agency. The pace was too fast; he was too contemplative.

When he finally returned home in 1935 at the age of fifty-one, broke, bewildered and with the self-confidence built up over two decades of solid achievement shattered by events he could not comprehend and which seemed to him senseless, he became the tragic figure of a decent, distinguished returning American lost and unappreciated in his native land.

There had been no place for him at home that he could find, and finally he had gone back to Paris where Wanda opened a hat shop; Wendell, philosophically accepting his fate, spent his mornings writing articles that occasionally he sold and his afternoons reading in the Bibliothèque Nationale.

The experience of Wendell hastened my own decision.

AUGUST 21

A LAZY, sultry Sunday, the mountains hidden in a haze. I spent most of the day clearing out my papers and — my mind.

It was just ten years ago this month that we were all set to go home. I had no idea of how I was going to earn my living, but it didn't worry me very much. The important thing was that I had finally made up my mind to get out of Europe and that Yvonne had concurred. Along in June of that year, Yvonne and I began to make plans. We would leave Geneva at the end of the summer, spend a fortnight with her family at Versailles, and sail for New York in the middle of September.

Then, at the end of August, the war came, smashing our plans, as it did those of hundreds of millions of other persons, into smithereens.

In July that summer I broke into broadcasting. A representative of the Federal Broadcasting Company called me up from Paris one day and asked me to do five minutes on how the war clouds looked from peaceful Switzerland. Fletcher — Robert A. Fletcher was his name — kept asking me for more. By mid-August I was on the air every day.

I could, of course, have gone home anyway that fall. Most Americans caught in Europe did. But I convinced myself that it would be cowardly to do so, that it was my professional duty to remain over here and do what I was asked to do: cover the war. Surely that was where my experience had led me. Fletcher came down from Paris and insisted that I join up as a regular correspondent with F.B.C. for the duration, which I did. The editor of *U.S.A.*, for which I had been writing regularly, made a similar request. I thus found myself with two jobs.

AUGUST 22

A SENATOR O'Brien, of whose existence I'm afraid I was woefully unaware, phoned this morning from the Beau Rivage to ask if he could drop by to see me. I told him I was flattered that a solon should seek me out. He was not a very impressive figure — not what I imagined a U. S. Senator should look like. He was rather short and flabby-faced: there was something shifty, I thought, in his eyes and the curl of his lips. However, he was pleasant enough. He asked me what I knew of Steve Burnett. Since Steve is about due to be named a minister, an appointment which has to be approved by the Senate, I was glad to put in a good word for my friend. I told the Senator Steve was one of the few really outstanding men in our diplomatic service, that he probably knew more about China than any other living American, and that if his advice had been taken in 1945 and 1946 the Communists wouldn't be gobbling up China. He thanked me, asked perfunctorily about Afghanistan — whether I had seen any Russians there — stayed briefly to wash down a second quick drink — and then left.

AUGUST 24

BOB FLETCHER wired he was coming to Geneva tomorrow, and could I put him up? He has become a big shot in F.B.C. in New York. Vice-president of something — a fancy title such as the radio people, who Bob used to say never quite grew up, like to bestow on their top executives. His letters have sounded slightly stuffy of late — most unlike Bob, whom I got to know very well during the war, and liked and admired for his intelligence, his fierce integrity and his decency and modesty as a human being.

Bob is largely responsible for my going home now. Last June he got me a contract for a weekly Sunday broadcast starting in October, and originating in New York. It will give us our living and leave me some time for writing.

Bob's offer brought me to my senses, for I was adrift again and didn't realize it. I had forgotten all about my resolve to go home; or at least I had lost my resolution. Though most of Europe was shattered at the end of the second war, the people — victors and vanquished — weary, hungry and cold, my own life was pleasant and interesting enough. Once or twice Yvonne did try to remind me of what we had planned that summer of 1939, but, cockily, I reminded *her* that the war had destroyed everyone's plans, that we had to accept fate, that I had now been abroad so long it was probably too late to go back, that we were doing quite well over here now, the children liked it, the Swiss schools were fine, and all that.

One evening last winter, after we had put the children to bed and were sitting before the fire in the living room, Yvonne suddenly interrupted a conversation that had concerned itself with nothing more weighty than where the skiing would be best that week end.

"Raymond!" she said. "Do you remember something you once said shortly before the war, that for Americans like you there was a thing called 'point of no return'?"

"I remember — vaguely," I said.

"I've been thinking of it lately."

She said no more and we dropped the subject. But in the next few weeks I began to turn it over a little in my mind. Then, in March, I think it was, two letters strangely identical in content came: one from Steve Burnett, who was home on leave; the other from Bob Fletcher. They had both read a piece of mine in *U.S.A.*, they said, and it had set them to wondering whether I ever considered coming home for a while. I wrote Burnett asking what was in the back of his mind. To Fletcher I wrote facetiously:

Bob, you are the one who argued me into staying over here when I was all packed to go back for good in August 1939. You insisted it was my duty to help cover the war for dear old F.B.C. So, if I'm still here, you're largely to blame.

That, I suppose, is how the broadcasting offer originated. Bob took me seriously. Soon he was writing and cabling about my taking on a Sunday broadcast from New York. In June a contract came — I am even to have a sponsor — and I duly signed it.

Once that was done, I was impatient to go. I began to see how shabby Europe had become. Two world wars had ruined it. One day it might revive if America helped enough and Soviet Russia did not in the meantime overrun it. All depended on the United States. My own land had become the center of the world. Since the war I had, as a journalist, been frittering my time away by remaining in Europe.

The day I signed the contract, Yvonne and I decided to leave by the end of the month — the sooner the better. Then came the cable from the Secretary of State practically ordering me to go to Afghanistan for him. I tried to beg off, but he would not listen to reason, even when I telephoned him. In the end it made little difference. By the end of June, I had packed off

Yvonne and the children to New York, she to find lodgings, they to start learning the language and get ready for school in the fall. I flew off to Kabul.

AUGUST 26

BOB FLETCHER was his old self. There was no trace of the stuffiness that had crept into some of his recent letters from New York. He has plenty of self-confidence, of course, and his words tend to come out a little more clipped and crisp than in the old days. Probably that comes from having to throw his weight around in the innumerable conferences of radio and advertising executives — vice-presidents, mostly — which Bob says take most of his time — and waste it.

By the time we got to the golf course over at Divonne he had completely relaxed. He began to hit a long ball — much too long for me to keep up with; but we paid little attention to the score. I could feel that he had, for the day, anyway, shed some immense load that was weighing him down. The curious frown he had worn when he alighted from his plane at the airport — and that I was sure was a mask he had acquired for business purposes after his return to New York — gradually lifted. He seemed genuinely happy and carefree. He kept gazing up at the Juras that rose steeply from the edge of the course and at the High Alps beyond Lake Geneva, breathing in the mountains and the fine fresh air.

"And you're leaving all this," he exclaimed, "for the dreary canyons of Madison Avenue and Radio City — for the bloody rat race there!" He smiled, but there was a sadness in his sensitive face, which seemed much more lined than when I had last seen him.

"It's your fault, Bob." I kidded him.

"Raymond, you're a fool," he said. "And maybe I'm one too."

"But it's pretty good to be back home again, isn't it? You've been raving about it for years in your letters."

"I suppose it is." He smiled faintly, looking away toward the mountains.

[16]

"Of course, it is," he said a moment later. "And it will be good for you, Raymond. Only, I can see what you're giving up. And I don't think you know what you're getting into."

"Whatever it is, Bob, I'm looking forward to it," I said. There were no reservations in my own mind. I was quitting Europe clean.

Later, tacking up the lake in my boat, and then at dinner, and finally last night to the small hours here on the veranda finishing up the Scotch, we continued our torrent of talk. There is something in Fletcher that always draws me out, making me more talkative than I ordinarily am; and apparently I have the same effect on him. He was brimming over with thoughts about America, New York, his work, his life. He was modest about his own success, but not about his ambition, which was driving and passionate, to transform radio and develop television into something far more imaginative and exciting and adult and honest than they promised at the moment to be.

"They call me an idealist, and they mean no compliment," he said, and there was just a bit of sadness in his smile, as there had been, I noticed, all day. "But perhaps in the end I'll get somewhere. Perhaps. Especially if I can bring more dopes like you back home to help me."

He was so eloquent on the subject, so engaging, so fiercely sincere, that he soon had me swearing that I would, if necessary, abandon my writing, curtail my family life, and give up all else to enlist at his side in the great crusade.

I wondered a little, though, why he himself had given up broadcasting to become an executive. He explained that it was the only way he could get anything done in the medium, as he called it. I could see the point, but nevertheless I regretted his banishing himself from the airways. During the war he had developed into one of the best commentators we had. In the continued confusion of the world, I argued, there was still need for such voices as his: clear, honest, independent, fearless.

"Besides, Bob," I said, "now that TV has come, you're about the only old hand with a mug that won't frighten the viewers."

He laughed. It was true, of course. He is a handsome bastard, with a finely chiseled face, strong and manly and yet intelligent. It is a brooding, almost melancholy countenance, like Lincoln's, without Lincoln's homeliness.

Long after midnight Bob got around to giving a little advice about the broadcast he has arranged for me. The sponsor, one of the big tobacco firms, will be no worse than the average. Bob will back me in standing up to it and to some of the F.B.C. executives who kowtow to the advertisers. I will be free, within limits, to say what I like.

"It isn't complete freedom of speech," he warned. "As you will find, there are a number of pressures at home besides that of the sponsor, especially if you have an opinion that is currently unpopular. But perhaps it's more freedom than you'll find anywhere else in the world. And if you don't take advantage of it, Raymond, I'll fire you."

Bob Fletcher will be a rare person to work with. He's a good friend to have, and no doubt I will lean on him heavily during my first confused months at home.

AUGUST 27

GOT our books packed today, and it was a wonder I did. I kept browsing through one after another before I slipped it into a box. We do not have many — seven or eight hundred tomes at the most — but they are like old friends that have become a part of our life, and I would not lightly part with more than a few of them. However, I did not discard even those few, as I perhaps should have, to save on the freight bill. I would feel an irretrievable loss should the ship carrying them home go down. Probably they could all be replaced, if I had a little extra money, but not the underlining and the comments I have scribbled over the years in so many of them and which often guide me when I go back to them.

A number of books I glanced through today set me to thinking. For years I failed to appreciate the greatness of Emerson. Frankly, he bored me. I found his essays ponderous and dull. There seemed to be nothing poetic about his poetry. Recently, I took to rereading him. What a fool I was! The worth of his poetry still eludes me. But his essays now strike me as the work of a fresh, original, unorthodox, independent mind which had a respect for style in our language. And I warm to his passionate belief, a hundred years old though it is, that a rich and unique civilization could flourish in America if we only broke away spiritually from Europe and grew up as a vigorous, free, literate people. Last night Bob quoted a wonderful paragraph from "The American Scholar," written in 1837:

> The spirit of the American freeman is already suspected to be timid, imitative, tame. Public and private avarice make the air we breathe thick and fat. The scholar is decent, indolent, complaisant. See already the tragic consequence. The mind of this country, taught to aim at low objects, eats upon itself. There is no work for any but the decorous and the complaisant. . . .

Bob said he was going to use it as the theme of a speech he has to make at some broadcasters' convention when he gets home.

AUGUST 28

SUNDAY — my last over here — and I felt a great loneliness in this house. I kept thinking of the life we have had in it — Yvonne and I and the children — the storms, the calamities, the crises, and the good times, the hours of wonderment, the periods of contentment, the days and nights of happiness, the growing and the knitting together.

It was often difficult, like all worth-while ventures.

I never found marriage easy, and ours has had its full share of ups and downs. Still, we never subscribed to the practice which is said to be prevalent — or at least fashionable — at home that either a marriage be fabulously happy, or you go to Reno. We've stuck it out — Yvonne and I — but there were crises. And there was one nightmare of a separation that lasted the better part of a year.

One cause of our trouble — and, curiously, of our remaining together in a bond which is pretty close, I think — has been my work, which often took me away from my wife for several months at a time.

Is a man supposed to remain celibate on these occasions? And a woman?

We found no acceptable rules to govern us in this matter, stumbling over the years amid not a little anguish toward our present understanding and adjustment.

There were advantages, of course, to our being separated often by the exigencies of my work. At least we escaped that mean existence of a husband and wife, who no matter how great their love are never out of one another's sight day and night, month after month, year after year, We never had to take each other for granted. Once the first mighty passion of the early years had subsided I know that I only began to appreciate Yvonne — her complicated nature, her unique personality, even her beauty — after I had gained the perspective of distance linked with time.

Today I felt a great longing to be with Yvonne, to have her here these last days in this home. She will be forty-two next month, but I honestly believe she is more beautiful and certainly more attractive than she was at twenty-five, when we were wed. Hers is not the type of beauty found in our women at home. It is too French for that: the buxom but still trim figure, the coal-black flaunting hair, the black, large, dancing eyes, the satin-white complexion. I love her eagerness for life, her warmth, her spunkiness and her passion.

Dick, at fourteen, is a good deal like her; Maria — God help her! — more like me. It will be wonderful to be back with them.

AUGUST 29

A BLUE Monday. I suddenly remembered that in four years, come November, I shall be fifty. It was a depressing thought. I must have been kidding myself that I would be young forever. What was it that Stendhal wrote on approaching that age? I scribbled it down somewhere:

I shall soon be 50, it is high time that I got to know my-self. . . . Have I had a talent for anything? Am I clever or a failure? Have I been happy or sad? It is important to know in the end. . . . What have I really been? To what friend, however enlightened, can I appeal for knowledge?

Elsie phoned, and in a moment of weakness I invited her in for a drink.

AUGUST 30

ELSIE was unusually calm. She apologized for her outburst in Berne, explaining she was upset by my telling her I was going home for good. But now, she said, she was glad — for several reasons. It was wise for me to go back. She was sure America would bring me down to earth and awaken me to the only thing that mattered: the threat of Communism.

"But there are only a handful of Communists at home, aren't there?" I asked.

"Yes. But they're all-powerful."

"Where?" I persisted. "Since they can't even elect a dog catcher, let alone a Congressman."

Elsie gave me a glance of exasperation, but I could feel she was trying to keep her voluble temper under tight control.

"My dear Raymond, haven't you heard about them in the government, especially the State Department? Even worse, they've infiltrated into the press, radio, the movies, the colleges and universities. That's why they're such a danger at home."

"But certainly they're more of a threat over here in Europe, where they have a mass following, especially in France and Italy. Now that they've got China, Western Europe is their big prize."

"America too," Elsie insisted. "We're the Kremlin's Enemy Number One."

The chief prize and the chief enemy were not the same thing, but I did not persist in the argument. Elsie obviously was hipped on the subject. I, of course, was out of touch with what went on at home.

Elsie will never abandon the pretense that she still owns a chunk of me, of my life. She said she assumed I would continue to find time to see her regularly at home — "without Yvonne."

"Those days were over long ago, my dear," I said, but she did not seem to hear. It was almost as if she were becoming a little deaf.

"Of course," I said, "you are always welcome to drop in on us."

"It will work out nicely, Raymond," she said, "because from now on I myself will be spending more and more of my time at home."

Her work at *World Review*, she said, warranted it. And her presence as a witness before the various Congressional committees investigating Communism. Also, she said, she was much in demand as a speaker before various patriotic groups.

Apparently she has become, among other things, a professional informer, but I did not chide her about it. I was in no mood for another scene. I have seen the informer exalted in Soviet Russia and Nazi Germany as the highest type of citizen and patriot. It seems incredible that it can be likewise at home.

After she had downed her third whiskey and soda — I am down to my last two bottles which I am saving for my farewell here with Steve tomorrow — Elsie left. She was not so repulsive this time. She says she is dieting. She did not seem quite so hefty, or so greasy as at Berne. And she shouted less. She can behave decently if she half tries. But I shall try to steer clear of her at home. I wouldn't mind very much if I never saw her again.

SEPTEMBER 1

I PUT Steve Burnett on the morning train to Berne just now. We never got to bed last night. We didn't finish the whiskey either, being too full of talk, I guess. We covered about everything under the sun and, of course, settled nothing.

It seems incredible that a man of Steve's caliber and of his record in the service can be in the doghouse with Congress. But apparently he is. That Senator O'Brien who called on me the other day is back of it all. Steve, with his acute sense of fairness and his genius for taking the long view, said the Senator was merely a product of the uneasy climate at home. Such men, he reminded me, always sprout up in times like these.

Steve is not so much worried that O'Brien's committee will succeed in getting the Senate to block what would have been his first appointment as a minister after twenty-five years in the career service. He is too honest not to admit, though, that this is a blow.

"It squelches my career," he put it. "But I guess I can take a personal disappointment like that. What I can't take — or at least won't take lying down — is O'Brien's attempt to drive me, along with a dozen other career officers, out of the diplomatic service on the trumped-up lie that we're Communists or fellow travelers or just plain disloyal."

It was difficult for me to grasp what my friend was saying. It seemed like a bad joke that one could not possibly take seriously.

"But O'Brien knows, or could easily find out," I protested, "that it's absurd to call you a Communist or a fellow traveler. Why should he pick on you then?"

"Probably he does know," Steve said. "But that isn't the point, as you will learn now that you are going home. O'Brien thinks he has hit upon something, given the fear of Communism in the States, that will gain him overnight a national reputation, that he can make political capital of, that perhaps will sweep him higher, even into the White House. No doubt he will get the reputation. Probably he has it already. To the majority of people it's a reputation as a patriot, as a savior of his country from the wicked, scheming Bolsheviks in the State Department."

"But there are no Communists in the sedate State Department." I could not help feeling that Steve was exaggerating the menace of O'Brien. The Senator had struck me as being a small potato.

"Not that I know of. There were maybe three or four. Men who came in during the heady days of the New Deal from other departments. But they're not there now. However, that doesn't prevent O'Brien from charging that the Department is riddled with them."

"Well, in a free country, I suppose," I said, "anyone — and a Senator first of all — can make any ridiculous charge that floats across his mind. But a charge is one thing. And proof is another. I should think the Department could sit back calmly — and you too — and ask the Senator to produce his evidence."

"You could think that, but you would be wrong. As things are at present at home — and I am sure it is only temporary — a mere charge can convict a man in the public mind. To be charged with Communism — even though there is not an iota of proof — is enough to destroy him — his name, his reputation, and his livelihood."

"Steve," I said. "I just can't believe it."

"All right," he said, breaking into a laugh. "Write me in six months what you believe."

He dwelt no more on the subject. In fact, most of our talk was about other things. We spoke of what we had most missed, living our lives away from America, and he thought one thing was big-league baseball in the summer and college football in the fall and the magnificent autumns in his native New Engand when the maple leaves turned red; also, he said, in Asia, where he had spent most of his life, he missed classical symphonic music, but was making up for it now by stealing away to Zurich or Salzburg or even to Vienna and Munich to catch up on Beethoven, Mozart and the others.

"Of course," he laughed, "you will get the best in that in New York — at the Philharmonic. In fact, Raymond, you will get the best in a lot of things at home. I'm really envious of you. I wish I were going back for good myself. And at this time of the year, Raymond! Soon the Met will be opening and Broadway coming to life with the fall plays and the Philharmonic resuming at Carnegie Hall, and college football getting under way and the pennant race in the big leagues approaching a climax — it's nip and tuck in both of them, the Yankees and the Red Sox, the Cardinals and the Dodgers. . . ."

He paused, as if to halt his daydreaming.

"Hell, Raymond! Maybe Senator O'Brien will prove a blessing in disguise — by getting me retired so I can go back."

Now I must toss a few things into a bag and see that I get out to the airfield by two P.M., when the plane departs. The house is unbelievably lonely this last day. I am no doubt a sentimental fool, but I keep thinking of a hundred and one things that happened here; the times I came back from the hospital after each of the children was born; the night we thought Dick was dying — he had a fever of 105 and the doctor kept wrenching his hands; the beauty of Yvonne and the eagerness of the children when I came back from a long trip; the evenings before the log fire reciting fairy tales to the kids and, after they were abed, the talks with Yvonne over our problems and over the mystery of life itself. Now, this place where so much happened that is a part of me, and of them, recedes out of our life, forever.

NEW YORK, SEPTEMBER 3

YVONNE was right. "Fabulous" is the word for it. People here haven't the faintest idea how well off they are — at least, compared to those in Europe, not to mention Asia where the squalor would be beyond the comprehension of our well-fed, neatly dressed, cleanly housed, gaudily entertained, automobile-owning citizens, unless they saw it, which they have not.

Excited as I was at the sight of Yvonne and the children, I could not keep my eyes off, as we drove in from La Guardia, the display of luxury — or what struck me as luxury. I gawked at the fruit stands, at the unbelievable piles of fresh fruit in the stands and windows: mountains of red, purple, yellow plums, pink peaches, yellow and red apples, oranges and grapefruit, fresh pineapples, bananas — and all the rest.

"What's so unusual about that?" Dick, noticing the wonder in my eyes, asked. He has been here only three months, and has already forgotten the frugal fare we had in Europe, where the taste of a fresh orange, grapefruit, pineapple or banana has been all but forgotten.

"Such windows, darling!" I must have exclaimed to Yvonne a

[25]

hundred times in the twenty-four hours since I've been back. "Look at all the fruit, the piles of vegetables, all that meat!"

"And none of it rationed!" she said, smiling.

Such windows! Before lunch today we strolled down Fifth Avenue from the tip of Central Park to Forty-second Street. I must have looked like a genuine hick from Podunk — the way I gaped and stared at each shop front: the elegant dresses, the mink coats, the chapeaux, the variety of men's suits, overcoats, hats, shirts, pajamas and dressing gowns, the furniture, the leather goods, the glassware, the jewelry, the shoes! Perhaps Regent Street and Oxford and Bond Streets in London before the war were a little like this, but in the postwar austerity of rationed and utility clothing and the shrunken incomes, halved by taxes, they remain only a memory.

Workers were tearing up the pavement near Forty-fifth Street (in New York they are aways tearing up the pavement — this much had not changed). Four or five of them, besides the foreman, puffed on fat cigars. Our taxi driver, who took us to the park, had also been chewing a cigar. In Europe, as the Communist press never tired of depicting in its cartoons, only a few cheating plutocrats could afford cigars. I thought of some of my English friends who have had to give up not only cigars but their beloved pipe-smoking because taxes and the lack of dollars have made the price of tobacco in England almost prohibitive. (Many of them have had to give up Scotch too, since most of it is exported for dollars to America, as one glance at the windows of the liquor shops here, piled high with a dozen famous brands, shows.)

Along Fifth, Madison and Park, a fantastic air of prosperity and well-being in the people thronging the sidewalks at the luncheon hour. They were pouring out of their skyscraper offices and into the restaurants, and the eating places in the hotels: the Ritz, the Roosevelt and Biltmore on Madison; the Waldorf and Ambassador on Park. Not even in Paris — and certainly nowhere else — do the women dress with such chic.

The men, I must confess, looked a little too much like the figures in the advertisements of men's clothing, shirts and hats:

[26]

too neat, a little smug. They were hurrying out of the caverns of Radio City and out of the C.B.S. building on Madison, carrying their self-confidence, their aggressiveness, a little too noticeably on their faces and in the way they walked and talked. Still, many of them had a worried air, as if the burden of whatever they were up to was almost too great. A remark of Bob Fletcher's flashed through my mind. "A rather ulcered lot," he had called them once. However, they're the men I must work with — so far as the Sunday broadcast is concerned. They are probably no worse nor better than those I have labored with in the past, in other fields — diplomats for example. From their demeanor I gather they take themselves rather seriously, as they do their business problems, though the latter must not be exactly world-shattering nor even worth an ulcer.

We found a pleasant place to lunch in the open air of a court off Park. Actually Yvonne had discovered it some weeks earlier. She was soon discussing the menu with the headwaiter in voluble French. I noticed that when the old man addressed the children in French they replied tartly in English. (Their accent, I saw at once on my arrival, has improved, or, rather, diminished.)

"Don't tell me, Yvonne, they've forgotten their French already," I said.

"It isn't that. Something happened at camp. I'll tell you later," she replied, hurriedly.

The children, however, were not for keeping the secret.

"They called me 'Frenchy,'" Maria blurted out. "Dick, too. At the camp. So we stop talking the French."

The pressure of conformity, always strong among children, was at work already.

"We're not 'Frenchies,' are we, Papa," Dick said. He did not put it as a question.

"You're Americans," I said. "And this is a free country. You talk French whenever you feel like it, regardless of what names they call you."

I could see, though, that the damage had been done. Still, I could not hide from myself a certain pleasure that at last my children would be living in the land of my native tongue. I had never quite become adjusted to them speaking English as if they were foreigners. It made them seem as if they were not quite mine. A matter of vanity, perhaps. Actually, Yvonne still retains a slight accent, which I love, of her native land. But with your own children, it is different.

After lunch we walked home, which is right off the East River. The streets were full of sleek convertibles apparently conveying their owners to the country for the long Labor Day week end. We ourselves are going out this evening to the Bob Fletchers in Connecticut.

The "lodgings," as Yvonne keeps calling them, in fun, are perfect. They are part of an old house on Sutton Place that looks down the East River toward the Williamsburg Bridge. The river will be a wonder to live with. As I write this, the tugs, lashed to barges, are plying up and down. I can see five of them between here and the bridge. A moment ago a trim little freighter, immaculately white and flying a Norwegian flag, glided down the river. There have been a dozen sailboats making for the Sound — for a final holiday outing, I suppose. And several motor boats — cruisers, I believe they are called — that look ample enough to sleep a family.

Yvonne has furnished the place with her usual good taste — and thrift. She haunted the auctions, she says, and picked up a number of things in Washington from friends in the State Department who were being reassigned abroad. She has fixed up a fine study for me on the third floor. It is wood-paneled and has a fireplace (I never saw one before on the *third* floor) flanked by bookcases going up to the ceiling. And there is a view down the river. If the mood of a room counts for anything, I shall have no excuse for not settling down to some writing here.

We finally got the children quieted down and to bed and went out to a little garden on a terrace at the rear of the house above the river to consume a highball and have a few words to ourselves. High above us the lights of the Queensborough

Bridge swept across the night sky. I didn't have to ask Yvonne how she liked it here. I had sensed from the first minute that she loved it.

"It has been a long three months, darling," she half whispered, leaning toward me, and putting her arm on my shoulder.

"For me, too," I said, putting my arm about her.

"But it has been such fun here, I must admit, dear. Everything is so exciting and new and — in many ways — different."

"It seems to have agreed with you, Yvonne." She really looked five years younger than when we had parted in June.

"I love it!" she exclaimed. "And with you here now, it will be —" she hestiated and I could feel her smile without seeing it. "Why shouldn't I say it, darling? — it will be perfect . . . it will be wonderful."

I cannot remember twenty-four hours of such happiness as we have had. Nor have I ever felt such zest for what lies ahead. No doubt there will be setbacks, disappointments, defeats. What of it? The main thing is to be home again. And was there ever a more auspicious time to return? This country, as someone in the plane said, is lousy with greatness. I can feel it already.

I wish we could skip Labor Day with the Fletchers, as much as I love Bob. Barbara, his wife, I scarcely know — she remained over here during most of the war — but everyone agrees she is lovely. As Yvonne says, however, it would be a shabby gesture not to go. And there will be a houseful of broadcasting and advertising people there, Yvonne tells me. As long as I have to make a living — or a part of it — before a microphone, I will have to meet such people, and learn how to get along with them. I wonder what sort of folk they will turn out to be.

SEPTEMBER 6

        I WAS not prepared to find Bob Fletcher's place anything like it turned out to be. I don't recall that he even mentioned it the other day in Geneva.

The house, high up in the Connecticut hills, is a replica of an old English manor house: stone, crossbeams of stained oak, steeply slanting red tiled roof, chimney pots galore, and with wings enough to house five families. Yesterday they were full of guests as they are, I take it, on most week ends. The lawn, acres of it, sloped down from the house to woods of hemlock, pine and birch and there were groves of great, stately maples here and there. There was a great deal, here and there: a blue-tiled swimming pool, three tennis courts, a couple of croquet lawns, the grass rolled smooth like a golf green. In fact, Bob has his own private golf course, which starts just beyond the stables and curls over the hills and through fairways cut in the woods for nine holes. I was a little taken aback at *that*. Even on the ten-thousand-acre estates of millionaire English press lords, I have never seen a private golf course.

Bob was certainly modest about it all, even a little apologetic when he got me alone for a few minutes to show me around.

"It comes to around eight hundred acres," he explained. "There were three or four run-down farms. I picked them up cheap. Hired a chap from the agricultural college to help restore them. The golf course, Raymond, is mostly for business. Impresses the clients, as you'll probably see before the week end is up. I rarely get time to play it, myself. What free time I have goes to farming."

"Farming?" I said, a little surprised.

"Horses and blooded cattle. I'll show you over the fields this afternoon — the part most of our guests never see, and aren't interested in. One day, Raymond" — he smiled, the old half-sad smile I had so often seen on his face in the old days — "it will pay for itself. Then I can thumb my nose at some of these people."

They were — most of these people — I must say, a curious lot. Not all of them stayed at the Fletchers'. Some had country places nearby, or what they called "nearby," which seemed to take in most of Connecticut and adjoining Westchester and Putnam counties in New York. I was fascinated by their restlessness and drive — qualities, I suppose, which well served them, the women as well as the men; for quite a few of the wives, it came out, and most of the single ladies were "career women" — in the world of radio, advertising and that relatively small group of big businesses which can afford to sponsor programs nationally over the major networks.

It did not take long to realize that apart from a handful of close friends of Bob, and their families, most of whom were his house guests, the majority of those who swarmed about the grounds had been drawn here over the Labor Day week end by more than the lovely physical attractions or their feeling for the Fletchers. They had come for more pragmatic reasons: to make or develop what they called "business contacts" and "social contacts" — obviously the two blended — and to pick up what I have learned this week end are a phenomenon of American life at the moment, *celebrities.*

At the Fletchers' the celebrities were, as someone said, a dime a dozen. Not that I recognized even the names of many of them. In this field, I am still a hick. I've been away too long. But thanks to Yvonne, who has picked up a lot of Americana quickly, and to Bob and Barbara, I quickly became orientated, as they used to say in the army. Over the week end there fluttered in and out, I should guess, at least four film stars (my own Dick and Maria were terribly impressed by them), half a dozen Broadway actors and actresses of renown, a pair of playwrights whom I remembered as having collaborated on one smash hit after another, a Broadway critic famous for his caustic tongue, three best-selling novelists, a dozen radio stars, not to mention a notorious commentator, and an equally notorious (but more obnoxious) newspaper columnist. Numerous other faces were pointed out to me as belonging to big shots in the business and advertising worlds. And I was surprised yesterday afternoon to see Senator O'Brien show up in the company of Bert Woodruff, the embittered and half-demented columnist of the Clark newspaper chain.

Bob Fletcher said he was surprised, too, to see the Senator, since he had not been invited, nor his coming even signaled.

"But whom else," he added glumly, "would you expect a heel like Woodruff to bring along?"

"Still, who invited Woodruff?" I wondered.

[*31*]

I must confess that Woodruff, whom I have read on and off for years, and will probably, for my sins, have to read regularly now in order to get the full American picture, is a phenomenon that is beyond my comprehension. Daily he spews out a venomous column of complete tripe, full of insults of everyone — and vituperation against everything — decent in American life. He despises our democracy, loathes organized labor, likes Franco, thinks Franklin Roosevelt was a crook, and despite the fact of Pearl Harbor and the fact of Hitler's declaration of war on us still maintains that the United States started the war with Japan and Germany. And he has more readers than any other newspaper columnist in America!

There were three men who did not come over to Bob's to drum up any contacts, bask in the light of any celebrity, or seek out any person or favor. Tycoons, I suppose, you could call them. Their tremendous self-confidence, the sense of exerting power which exuded from them in differing ways, was impressive, I must say. I don't recall any figures in Europe quite like them. They all motored over for cocktails yesterday.

One was Bob Fletcher's boss (and mine too now, I suppose). Mark Robson, president of F.B.C., struck me at once as an extremely pleasant and personable fellow, almost boyish in his manners and looking five or ten years younger than his fifty-odd years. He had a genial grin on his face a good deal of the time that puzzled me because it reflected such a contradiction: a smooth self-confidence and yet a seemingly genuine modesty. Sometimes, though, I noticed, when he was talking with someone he considered important, or with some of the advertising men, the grin would melt away, his face would harden and the warm, laughing eyes grow cold.

Robson was disarming in his welcome to me. Bob had scarcely started to introduce us before he was saying: "Whitehead — hell, I'm going to call you Raymond, if you don't mind — we're certainly glad to have you back with us. You did a fine job of broadcasting from over there during the war. And Bob Fletcher says you'll do an even better job here at home. When does your show start?"

[32]

"The first Sunday in October, I believe," I said.

"That's right," Bob added — friendlily, but a little crisply, I thought. I suppose I must get used to my friend being a big-shot executive.

"Come up and see me, Raymond, before you start," Robson said, smiling and shaking my hand heartily.

"Thank you, sir."

"And don't 'sir' me," he laughed.

Bob obviously — from what he has said and the way he acted over the week end — worships the man. And Robson leaves no doubt of his tremendous admiration and affection for Bob.

General Cyrus Field Clark — at least everyone addressed him as "General" — head of the newspaper chain bearing his name, turned out to be about what I expected from all I had heard. He is a giant physically and a pigmy intellectually. He was pretentious, overbearing, sour, stupid, opinionated — if you could dignify his medieval prejudices as opinions. Why Bob invited him over I haven't the least idea. In Bob's job, I suppose, you have to move among the great and powerful, no matter how much you despise them.

The General took a dim view of me, or, rather, my background.

"You been in Europe too long, Whitehead," he said. (You couldn't help but admire his bluntness in a group most of whose members spent the week end slapping one another's backs.) "It showed in your broadcasts and the stuff you wrote. Some of my damn-fool editors bought some of it, didn't they?"

"A piece or two," I said.

"We printed it," he went on. "But I thought it was terrible. . . . Well, glad you're back anyway. Are you staying, this time?"

"I hope to, General." (I would like to know what he was ever General of.)

"It's about time, Whitehead. Maybe you can be saved yet."

I thought for a moment he was joking, but there wasn't a trace of humor on his solemn, pretentious face.

"Trouble with Europe," he exclaimed — as if he were laying

[*33*]

down some great uncontradictable truth from the Olympian heights — "is it's been ruined by socialism. Here in America we're being ruined by it too. The whole gang in Washington — nothing but Reds."

He looked at me with piercing eyes. "You're not a Socialist, are you, Whitehead?"

"Hardly," I laughed.

"Nothing to laugh at," he grunted. "Most Americans who come back from there are, you know. Damn fools, most of them. Damn Reds."

You would almost think the man was loony if you didn't remember how shrewdly he operates his papers. I mean, he makes millions out of them without ever printing the news. His journals are given over strictly to his personal prejudices, his hates and his loves, with plenty of cheesecake thrown in. And people buy them. I was curious to see whether he had brought along his famous mistress, Madeleine Marlowe, a bad actress but a fabled courtesan, whom he flaunts in public as if he were above the restraints imposed on the rest of us, which, of course — with his millions and power — he is. (She always accompanies him to Europe.) But this time he had brought along his wife, a middle-aged lady with a sad, sensitive face, who seemed to me to be much more attractive than the faded, pouting, vulgar Marlowe of the photographs and the gossip. The General treated Mrs. Clark, I thought, like a subordinate employee — as if she did not exist. The only time I saw him address her was just before dinner when he abruptly announced that they were departing.

The third tycoon was a man who is bound to influence my living (though not my life, I am determined), at least for a time. He is William McKinley Forbes, President of United Tobacco, which sponsors three big programs on the networks and which will foot the bill for my Sunday-afternoon broadcast. Forbes struck me right off the bat as a colorful old rogue. He's a rugged man, with a thick mane of iron-gray hair, an unkempt walrus mustache and a weather-beaten face, resembling a little the photographs of Mark Twain, though he is tougher, and I believe he is almost totally illiterate. He has an interesting vocabulary of profanity, though, which he indulges whenever the ladies are out of earshot.

It was something to see, the way the advertising men and the network executives bowed and scraped to him, all except Fletcher, who was merely respectful — as indeed were F.B.C.'s president and the General. For Forbes is a prodigious advertiser, though, I gather, a temperamental one.

The obsequiousness of the ad men kept turning my stomach. Some of them don't seem to have the dignity of a Paris pimp — at least in the presence of the big-time "clients." Besides Forbes, there was a scattering of other clients: a kindly old gentleman out of a liquor ad — one of the "men of distinction" — who was vice-president of some big food processing concern which, Bob said, sponsored a number of morning soap operas on the air; and a rather hard-bitten, cigar-chewing fellow, who turned out to be a vice-president (Fletcher's world seems to be made up largely of vice-presidents — aren't there any other other titles in American business?) of one of the major automobile corporations in Detroit — also a heavy advertiser.

In their presence the ad men — and, for that matter, some of the radio executives — seemed to be frightened of their own shadows and particularly of their own voices. They would wait for a cue from Forbes or the food fellow or the motor-car magnate before daring to mouth the simplest expression, as if they lived in mortal fear of saying the wrong thing — the "wrong thing" being, I soon sensed, what displeased the advertiser. They gave you the impression of being in a continued state of panic lest some *faux pas* might cost them their "account."

I believe William McKinley Forbes is the sort of robber baron I can get along with, as I did once with some of the tribal bandit chiefs in Afghanistan. What is going to be more trying is to have to stomach regularly one Archy Oakes, Assistant Vice-President of Dunsany & Dunne, who is to handle my account; that is, he is the advertising intermediary between the United Tobacco Company and F.B.C. and me for my Sunday broadcast.

I got quite a dose of Oakes over the week end. In fact, he

moved in and tried to take me over — lock, stock and barrel, as it were. We had a few Oakeses in the diplomatic service when I was young: oily sort of men, obsequious to their superiors, rude to those they thought were their inferiors, and without any guts or ideas of their own. Above all he is devoted to what he kept calling the "science" of advertising, which, according to him — and his lingo on the subject is inexhaustible — is "the greatest phenomenon of American civilization," "the power that makes the wheels go round," "the watchspring of our free-enterprise system," "the foundation of American journalism," "the basis of modern psychology," "the main reason for the matchless American Standard of Life" — and I don't know what else, for I soon became immune to his gibberish. He also told me he thought William McKinley Forbes was "one of the greatest Americans of the age," and that he was sure I would become as devoted to him — and to selling his cigarettes and tobacco — as was he.

"Am I supposed to sell?" I asked, not as innocently as he thought. "I thought I was supposed to broadcast."

"It's the same thing, Whitehead!" he exclaimed, though his enthusiasm, I must say, was too ersatz to be catching.

"Broadcasting is selling!" he went on. "Right now it's doing the greatest selling job in the world."

"Aren't we to have an announcer, Mr. Oakes?" It was my understanding that I would give the news and comment, and the announcer would bellow the sponsor's message.

"Of course, Whitehead! Of course! But let me tell you one of the little secrets of broadcasting. It will be *you*, with your unique personality, your voice of authority, your tremendous background in world events, your personal friendship with the great statesmen abroad, which, my good friend, will really sell the cigarettes and the tobacco for William McKinley Forbes."

Oakes shadowed me throughout the week end. He acted as if he owned me. I became so desperate yesterday — after a couple of days of it, that I even sought out Senator O'Brien in order to shake him momentarily.

[36]

"Excuse me, Oakes," I said, "but I have to speak to the Senator — confidentially, if you don't mind."

"Of course, of course, Whitehead. I quite realize you fellows have to keep up your contacts. Great statesman, O'Brien. Doing a wonderful job cleaning the Communists out of Washington. He's a great friend of Forbes. Remember that, Whitehead."

He smiled knowingly, and I felt his beady eyes on me as I meandered across the lawn in search of the Senator whose resemblance to a statesman, incidentally — Archy Oakes to the contrary notwithstanding — I have yet to discover.

I found the solon communing with Verne Gibson, the owner and publisher of *World Review*. I ought to have included Gibson with the three tycoons, for *World Review* is another one of the fabulous American successes. But Gibson impressed me as being quite different from the other three. He is just as powerful through his magazine and the way he slants everything in it to his narrow view of the world; but you would never guess it from his demeanor or from talking to him. He is a small, slight man, probably in the middle fifties, and pleasant but completely undistinguished looking. You could easily take him for a teller in the neighborhood savings bank or a middling certified public accountant. He seemed very shy and even self-effacing. I concluded that all his genius goes into the magazine and that he is like a renowned actor who is overwhelming on the stage but quite uninteresting as a human being once the footlights have gone out.

"Welcome home to God's country, Whitehead," O'Brien fairly shouted as I approached. "Meet a great American and a great publisher," he said, introducing Gibson.

"I know your voice," Gibson said quietly in a tone that was friendly and yet somehow conveyed a reservation. "From the radio. And I've followed your articles. I don't believe we've had the honor of publishing any of them — yet."

I knew from Elsie, and from my agent, that he had personally turned down three or four pieces of mine. He had not liked my views, which did not surprise me. I had not felt offended.

[37]

"No, I don't believe you have published anything of mine. Not that it is any loss," I said.

"We were just discussing one of Mr. Gibson's famous collaborators — Elsie McCabe," O'Brien said. "You may have run into her over there."

"Long ago," I said, watching Gibson's face for a reaction. But there was none. I'm not sure he got it: that I had known Elsie when she was a red-hot Communist.

"I was just telling Mr. Gibson what a wonderful job Miss McCabe has been doing," O'Brien went on.

"Do you think so?" the publisher interrupted, fixing his not very strong gaze on me. I think I know what was in the back of his mind. And I can see already that it is going to be a temptation — if I want to get ahead in journalism, especially radio, here at home — to jump on the bandwagon. However I decided to give an honest and a truthful answer.

"I'm afraid I haven't followed her articles," I said.

"You ought to," O'Brien hastened to say. "She's been a great help to me — rooting out the Red scum in Washington."

"She's coming home, I believe," I ventured to say.

Gibson's ears picked up. "You've seen her recently, then?"

"Yes, in Geneva. A few days ago. She said she would be spending more of her time here at home."

"Don't you think there is a lot for her to do in this country right now?" Gibson persisted. He kept trying to feel me out.

"I wouldn't know, Mr. Gibson," I said. "I've been away a long time. She certainly thinks so, herself. I know that."

"We'll be glad to have her back," he beamed.

"Me too," the Senator chimed in.

As we talked I kept wondering about Verne Gibson's success. Like General Clark's newspapers, *World Review* attracted an enormous number of readers — millions of them. Yet, like Clark's journals, Gibson's magazine gave them a deliberately distorted picture of America and the world. This was not due entirely to his own warped, shallow views. He was greatly abetted by a curious group of reformed Communists, Socialists and left-wing Liberals, which largely edited the magazine and wrote most of its contents and whose members seemed to tumble over themselves in its pages to prove they were now properly conservative and fashionably orthodox. They had had, most of them, a distorted vision in their "radical" years of protest. The distortion remained with them after they turned.

Bob Fletcher waved at me to come over to a table on the edge of the lawn away from the throng where he, Mark Robson and the inimitable William McKinley Forbes were gathered. As I took leave of Senator O'Brien and Verne Gibson I had the feeling, despite their apparent cordiality, that once I was out of earshot they would turn to each other with expressions of reservations about me.

It was pleasing to note that neither Fletcher nor Robson fawned on the great tobacco entrepreneur, as the advertising men and the other F.B.C. executives had done. Forbes was quite obviously aware of this and actually, I gathered, liked it. Like all tycoons he had to have his sycophants, but there were moments when it was a relief to be rid of them.

"We were just talking about you, young man," he said, moving the fingers of his right hand along his rebellious walrus mustache. His weather-beaten face was attractive after the smooth emptiness of O'Brien's countenance.

"I've been trying to tell him," Mark Robson said, with his infectious grin, "that sponsoring news and comment on the radio is a little different from sponsoring a variety show."

"They're trying to tell me I can't be boss," the old man said, with feigned indignation. "I tell them if I can't be boss, maybe I don't play."

"All you've got to do is *pay*!" Bob Fletcher laughed.

"Seriously, Mac," Robson said. The "Mac" must have come from "McKinley."

"The man wants me to be serious, just because he is president of a lousy network that sponges up all my profits," Forbes interrupted to say. Well, at least the old man has a sense of humor and he's not stuffy, I noted to myself. That was more than you could say for most of the radio and ad men I had met so far.

[39]

"Mac," Robson said. "You know damned well that you've gotten away with murder in radio. I admit you're a genius at selling tobacco. But you're terrible in show business."

"I know what I want," Forbes grunted.

"Yes, but not what the public wants. By insisting on casting your own shows, not to mention trying to write them — or rewrite them — and direct them — which you have no business doing, United Tobacco has the lousiest, corniest shows on the air. We let you get by with it in the beginning, Mac. And it's too late to change now."

"They sell cigarettes, Mark — you have to admit."

"Not as many as they would if they were any good," Robson said. The spirit, you could see, was genial on both sides. The two men probably had bantered like this, I gathered, for years. You were scarcely aware that three or four million dollars of United Tobacco's money, which Robson annually collected for two big network shows, was continually at stake.

"The point is, Mac, on a news and comment program you won't be able to call the tune. Bob and I just wanted to make that clear at the beginning," Robson said.

"You mean," Forbes exploded, his big eyes flashing from underneath the shaggy eyebrows, "I can't tell the guy what to say?"

"That's right," Bob said quickly.

It was all banter, of course, But beneath it, I felt, was a half-seriousness. The tobacco king, for all his good nature with men like Robson and Fletcher, whom he respected, was too used to having his own way, especially where his millions were concerned, to accept any limitations on his freedom or his license.

"Archy Oakes — the little worm —" Forbes said, and I couldn't have agreed with him more. "I tell you, Archy never mentioned any restrictions. He said it would be good business to put on a distinctive kind of news show."

"I think it will," Robson said quietly, and now his grin was gone, though not his genial air. "But, Mac, we have an iron rule at F.B.C. On news and comment, the sponsor stays strictly out."

"The hell you say! Well, gentlemen," he sputtered, "I'll have to reconsider the whole matter."

"You can't," Robson said, smiling benignly at the old codger. "You signed the contract. For a year."

"I signed?" he yelled. He looked around furiously. "Where's that little bastard Oakes? Wait till I get my hands on him! Bob, in God's name, give me another Scotch. You fellows have swindled me!"

"The bar's over there, Forbes," Bob said. "I need one myself, after your outburst."

Later, after we had had another drink, Bob and I finally got away for a moment together.

"It was largely in fun," Bob said, "but not quite."

We wandered into the big house and up two flights of stairs to what formerly had been an attic. At one end Bob had fixed up a sort of a den, with odds and ends picked up in his travels. Autographed photographs of Roosevelt, Willkie, Truman, Dewey, Justice Douglas, Eisenhower, Churchill, Attlee, Bevin, Herriot — and to come down a little, Robson, Clark, Forbes and some I did not recognize, adorned one wall behind a big Spanish-oak table. The bookcases were well stacked, mostly with encyclopedias and standard works of history. It was an ample, comfortable, restful room, with three or four plush chairs and a thick, green carpet. One corner was stacked with radio gadgets: recording machines, a radio control-board, mikes and a loud-speaker. There was also a television set.

"Here's where I do my real work," Bob said, collapsing into one of the overstuffed chairs, and propping his feet up on a small table. He looked weary. ". . . or at least my thinking, or what passes for thinking in this business." He pointed to the corner. "With that gear over there, I can catch all the network shows. And see what TV's up to. At least here I don't have a dozen vice-presidents and advertising men in my hair." He smiled wanly, wearily.

"By the way, Raymond, I forgot to tell you," he said after a while, and now the sadness was gone, replaced by an eagerness in his eyes. "Mark Robson had a little surprise for me when I got back from Europe the other day."

"What was that, Bob?"

"He has made me vice-president and general manager in charge of the whole shebang."

"Congratulations, Bob." I was really happy at the news. He was so different, so superior to the type of network official I had been meeting over the week end. To my surprise, his face reverted to its gloominess. He glared darkly at me.

"I'm deep in this thing, Raymond. Deeper than I ever expected to get."

I think I know what he meant, and I could feel how he feared it and I could even understand, vaguely, why.

"It won't swallow you up, Bob. I'm sure of that," I said.

There was a sound of footsteps outside. Barbara Fletcher and Yvonne burst in.

"Sorry, Bob," Barbara said. "But people are starting to leave. Thought you might like to say good-by to them."

"Suppose I'll have to," Bob muttered. He pulled his long legs slowly off the table, started to get up and then relaxed back in the big chair, looking up at his wife. "Darling, how do you manage it?"

"Manage what?"

"To look so damned pretty and unruffled this late in the week end?"

She bent over him fondly and kissed him, and then gently pulled him to his feet. "Actually, I look horrible, and you know it, Mr. Fletcher," she said. "Don't I, Raymond?"

"You look wonderful, Barbara," I said.

She had grown on me tremendously over the week end. I had scarcely remembered what she was like from the one time we had gone to dinner with them in Paris two or three years before. She was not exactly pretty, in the conventional sense; not as pretty, say, as Yvonne, whose striking features she lacked. But she had an attractive, well-balanced face, illumined by what I can only call an extremely sweet nature. It was not sickly sweet, but warm and robust, and you felt it in her clear blue eyes and in the rich

timbre of her voice. And behind the kindliness and the consider-
ateness, you felt a keen intelligence — that, and an utter lack of
cant and pretense, which had been rather prevalent, I thought,
in a number of the wives gathered here. It was easy to see that
she was a stabilizing influence on her somewhat mercurial and
moody husband. As she stood there I noted again her trim figure,
which was rather athletic, and how golden her hair was.

Apparently, even before my return, she and Yvonne had hit
it off well, and over the week end they had been inseparable. I
was glad to see it, for I was not sure how Yvonne, with
her rather Gallic ways, would get along with American women.

We adjourned to the lawn where Yvonne and I watched Bob
and Barbara say their farewells. They made a congenial
and handsome couple, and they had a natural graciousness that
would have set them apart from most of the others even if they
had not been hosts. Whether in their hearts they enjoyed what
they were doing as much as they appeared to, I couldn't tell.
Perhaps not. At any rate, their remarkable social talents obviously were helpful to Bob in his career, and at his stage it was
difficult and perhaps not even desirable to separate the business
life from the social life. As he had said, he was deep in the one,
and, being so, had become immersed in the other. There was no
stopping, no drawing back, now — even if he wanted to, and, as
he had implied a moment ago, he knew it. The stake was too big,
and it was growing bigger. His mounting position at F.B.C. was
it; and this show place in the country; and his relation to these
people; and his growing reputation and his success.

All the week end long the atmosphere of what these people
kept calling "success" lay thick and sweet over Fletcher's green
lawns. Almost all of them obviously considered themselves and
each other a "success." I was learning quickly what it meant. It
meant, I began to muse, that . . .

Christopher Chambers, the drama critic, came up, interrupting
my thoughts. He must have been reading them. A boyish-looking
man, despite his white hair and his sixty-odd years, he had an
impish air I liked. I had read him occasionally in Europe. Not
only his caustic wit appealed to me but his passion for some of

[43]

the playwrights I liked: Ibsen, Strindberg, Chekov, Shaw, Pirandello, Sean O'Casey and O'Neill. They say he has almost, singlehanded, saved Broadway from becoming completely trivial. And even in Europe, one heard of his unceasing war on our native complacency and smugness. He slid into a chair beside us.

"Did you ever see anything like this in France?" he said to Yvonne, glancing disdainfully at the departing guests. Some were lingering around the Fletchers, taking their time to say good-by. Others were climbing into their sleek convertibles, filling the air with the thunderous, impatient and — it seemed to me — unnecessary roar of the engines.

"Not quite," Yvonne smiled. We had agreed to be careful in intimating that Europe had its points in comparison to this country. We had decided not to get off on the wrong foot that way.

"It's all new to us — especially to me," Yvonne said pleasantly. "In fact, Mr. Chambers, I find it quite fabulous."

"I admire your French *politesse*, madame," Chambers said. "I find all this a little revolting, myself. They're lousy with success — so-called," he went on, casting his sharp dark eyes at various knots of people making their way toward the Fletchers or their cars. There was no resentment in his kindly but strangely high-pitched voice, but only a sort of ironic amusement. "Success is what knits them together. Making money, getting their names in the paper, becoming vice-presidents of this or that, writing hit plays or acting in them, turning out best-sellers, adding another million suckers to those who buy their publications — in short, being at the top of whatever heap they're swarming in. But, brother, it's a changing crowd. Half the people you see today won't be here next year, or the year after. Bob Fletcher himself may not be here. The turnover is terrific. They're in the limelight today, and forgotten tomorrow. The slightest fall — and out they go. They can't forgive what they call 'failure' in others, and they're easily broken when it comes to them. A playwright comes up with a couple of flops, a novelist fails to hold his audience or get a book club selection for two or three books, a radio commentator loses a sponsor or his Hooper rating — and they're quickly dropped from this august circle. The same with all these strutting radio and advertising executives. Sooner than later they get caught in what they call, I believe, a shake-up. The business apparently is one long series of shake-ups. No matter how good they are, most of these v.p.'s soon get shaken out on their behinds. And you don't see them anymore at parties like this. Their place is taken by whoever is the next occupant of their desk.

"Whitehead," he said, turning to me in a sort of fatherly way. "It's a bloody rat race. And if you will pardon an old hack for giving a little advice, stay out of it, for God's sake — if you can."

"I'm sure that will be easy," I said — rather lamely, I fear.

Bert Woodruff, the columnist, passed by, and a moment later Bob waved to me to come over and meet him.

"There goes perhaps the most successful worm of the day," Chambers mused. "His particular mixture of venom and bile nets him $150,000 a year, even after taxes, which he denounces as 'communistic.' And it gives him power — power, Whitehead, is what all these people crave — to destroy the decent people."

"How can a columnist be that powerful?" I asked.

Chambers looked at me rather benignly. "You'll see," he smiled.

"It was good to talk with you," I said. "I hope we can meet again."

Bert Woodruff glared as Bob presented us to him. On close inspection, he turned out to be a dumpy little man with a swarthy complexion and small, black eyes burning with suspicion and hostility. He had a pinched, angular nose and a large mouth with thick lips. Woodruff struck me as an uneasy and unhappy man and a distinctly unpleasant one.

"What kept you in Europe so long?" he snapped at me.

"Work," I said.

"You spent most of your life over there, didn't you?"

"That's right," I said.

"Strange for an American."

"Perhaps." I was determined not to give him an inch.

"You're going to have a Sunday broadcast, aren't you?" Woodruff said, as he turned to go.

I admitted it.

"I'll be listening," he said, and I swear he smacked his lips.

I have no doubt he will be listening, not for any enlightenment but because of the prospect of taking on still another victim to smear with his poisonous pen.

Another man will be listening. I almost forgot to mention him, though his figure bulked large over the week end. Whitney Shuttleworth came over Sunday from his place on the North Shore of Long Island, crossing the Sound, he told everybody, in his fast motorboat cruiser. A big, genial, simple-minded man, he has a peculiar way of speaking into a microphone and a gift for simplifying the most world-breaking news and injecting a homespun humor into it, that has endeared him to the public and brought him the largest audience of any commentator in America. Though he broadcasts on another network, he appears to be a good friend of both Fletcher and Robson, who I suspect are in the stage of wooing him (and his wealthy sponsor) over to F.B.C. I found him surprisingly likable as a human being and unbelievably ignorant as a pundit — a role he obviously relishes and is accorded not only by his mass audience but by the good folk who swarmed over Bob's acres during the week end, though it seemed a ludicrous one to me.

Yesterday when he had finished holding forth on the state of the world — and there was no country, no subject, no situation, he did not pose as an expert and scholar on, abysmal though his ignorance of all them was — he took me aside, patted me on the back and wished me well in my Sunday broadcast. He was a bit condescending, to be sure. But Yvonne says I must live here a while to appreciate his enormous position and reputation in this country.

"Always glad to have some competition, Whitehead," he smiled, making it clear that he did not consider that he had any competition and that he expected none from my little, unknown voice. "You'll do well, I'm sure," he said, adding the final touch.

"You'll do better than he suspects," a familiar voice behind me chirped, as soon as Shuttleworth was out of earshot. It was Archy Oakes, who apparently had been eavesdropping to satisfy

[46]

his curiosity as to what the famous commentator had to say to me. I took a good look at Oakes's face to see if there was anything one might remember him by, but there wasn't. It was fleshy and unmarked beneath a shiny, bald dome.

"Great broadcaster, of course, that Shuttleworth," Archy Oakes said. "Great figure in America. Sells a lot of oil too. His position in the industry is something for you to shoot for, Whitehead. And, by God, I think you'll reach it. I honestly do."

It was the last thing in the world I wanted, but I was not going to goad Oakes on if I could help it.

"How are you fixed for tomorrow?" he said. "We ought to have a talk. Really get going on your Sunday show. How about lunch?"

"I'm sorry, I can't make it," I said, searching desperately in my mind for an excuse.

"Well, after lunch, then. Two-thirty, say, at my office."

"I'm sorry, Oakes, but Mark Robson asked me to keep the day free for him and the others at F.B.C.," I lied.

"That's the way to start out," he beamed. "Glad to see the chief taking you up like that. Well, phone me tomorrow, anyway, and we'll fix something for day after. Got to get going on the format, you know."

"The what?" I asked.

"Format. Every show has to have a format, Whitehead. I've got some ideas."

"I'll phone you, Oakes," I said. "And if you'll pardon me, I've got to start trying to find my youngsters. Yvonne," I exclaimed, "have you seen them?"

We broke off that way and Oakes went over to bow and scrape to the Fletchers in farewell.

"What *have* the youngsters been up to, Yvonne?" I said, as we made our way to the house. I regret to say I had scarcely seen them all the week end.

"Riding Bob's ponies, for the most part," she said. "Like they were glued onto them. They've had a wonderful time, Raymond."

"And have you, darling?"

Yvonne had been, I thought, a striking figure as she moved about during the whole week end. No doubt I am prejudiced, but, aside from Barbara, and two or three of the stage and Hollywood stars, she had been, it seemed to me, the most attractive woman present and quite a few people must have agreed with me, judging by the way they flocked around her.

"I loved every minute of it, darling," she said, her fine black eyes sparkling. She took my arm and we skipped off to find the children.

SEPTEMBER 8

GOT the youngsters off to school. They were a little nervous — since it is their first American school — and they covered it up with a certain aggressiveness that did not make an altogether pleasing impression on the headmistress. I would have preferred sending them to public school, but a teacher in the one in our neighborhood warned me that it was a disgrace, overcrowded and unsanitary. She said it was one of the worst slum schools in New York. That seems a strange phenomenon in the wealthiest city in the world.

The Baldwin Day School to which young Richard and his sister Maria repaired, seems democratic enough and even liberal. I noticed a dozen or so Negro youngsters and the headmistress said nearly half the enrolment was Jewish — as was natural in New York. It was devilishly difficult to get into, though. We had to enlist not only the Fletchers but Mark Robson and even old Forbes himself to get our two brats admitted. It wasn't a question of snobism. It was just, as the good mistress explained, that there were over a thousand applications for a hundred and fifty vacancies in a school of five hundred.

It is shockingly expensive. It costs as much as it would to send the children to college, and Dick is only in the eighth grade and Maria in the sixth. I begin to see the pressures on midde-class folk here to make money, even if they merely want to live on a modest scale. Yvonne told me this morning a maid would cost us fifty dollars a week. That's all we paid per *month* in Europe.

[48]

It was a top salary there, too. As soon as the Sunday broadcast is licked, I must get busy on some magazine articles; and start a book.

SEPTEMBER 16

THE initial rubber-necking having subsided — I can now pass the Empire State Building, Radio City and the Chrysler skyscraper without craning my neck — I have spent most of this week getting acquainted with the Federal Broadcasting Company. It is quite a beehive. There is a great deal of running around — sometimes in circles. All day long there are "conferences," which generate a lot of heat but only a feeble light. I must have sat in on a dozen, most of which concerned my modest little broadcast. I couldn't agree with Bob Fletcher more: they are almost a complete waste of time, and boring beyond bearability.

Mark Robson and Bob Fletcher are an unusual pair to work with. They seem to have integrity, guts, ideas — especially Bob. Some of the executives, I gather, have little love for Fletcher. They are envious for one thing; they resent his passing over them to the top spot under Robson. And they seem contemptuous of his ideas because they are contemptuous of any ideas — and of anyone harboring ideas. But they fear him. These things you come to feel. They go on underneath. On the surface most of the executives of F.B.C. give an impression of belonging to one, big, happy family and of being full of brotherly love for one another. Without exception they have treated me royally, and while I am not naïve enough to take them at their word I admit I have been pleased by their interest in my home-coming radio debut two weeks from Sunday.

I will work directly with Mark Robson himself and with Bob Fletcher. They have promised me, as they put it, complete freedom — but not license — to interpret the news.

"You'll have to stand up to old Forbes," Bob admonished me today. "And, if you take my advice, you'll suitably flatten out that little Oakes fellow from the very start."

[49]

I doubt if that will be necessary. In the few conferences Oakes was invited to this week, Robson and Fletcher did it for me. Oakes seemed so frightened of them he rarely opened his mouth. In fact at times he has seemed scared of the whole project, and I suspect that Forbes mopped the floor with him, as he threatened that Labor Day week end to do, for having got United Tobacco involved in so controversial a business as uncontrolled news comment.

However, Archy Oakes, as salesman, cannot be flattened by anyone. Yesterday, after a session with Robson and Fletcher in which they warned him to stick strictly to his knitting — to the commercial — he said as soon as we were alone: "Whitehead, I'll tell you one thing. We're going to sell a lot of cigarettes."

I must try not to forget that if we don't I won't be long on the air, at least not for United Tobacco. But I suppose Oakes will keep reminding me of that.

OCTOBER 3

THE first home broadcast yesterday, and I was nervous as a coot, though I suppose I have faced a microphone a thousand times abroad in the last ten years. You never overcome a certain tenseness just before air time no matter how often you broadcast. What made me fidgety, I guess, was the frenzied atmosphere of a gala opening which F.B.C. and the sponsor insisted on whipping up for the occasion. Forbes and Oakes dragooned a score of celebrities, Mark Robson an equal number, not to mention a gang of photographers, reporters, columnists, publicity hounds and network sycophants.

Afterward we adjourned to the Somerset Club, where Robson and Forbes were joint hosts at an elaborate buffet dinner. The food was piled high, the drinks poured as from Niagara and there were some maudlin speeches, one of which, I fear, I made myself. Bob Fletcher says it is all part of the game and urged me to submit as patiently and as gracefully as possible, which I tried to do.

But what ballyhoo in this town on the slightest excuse! Yvonne thinks I did all right but that I will do better.

OCTOBER 4

I HAD one little item on my broadcast Sunday which everyone else seems to have overlooked. I ferreted it out of the United Nations, though there was nothing secret about it. It is the report of the U.N. Commission for Korea, which on September 8 (the item was a little stale, and I hesitated about using it) warned that there was danger of what it called "a barbarous civil war" in Korea. It said bluntly that the Chinese Communists might help the North Koreans invade South Korea.

OCTOBER 16

ELSIE phoned immediately after the broadcast today. So she is back! She said she had to see me immediately about some of the things I had said. I put her off; said I was catching a train for Washington. Somehow, her call upset me. I did not mention it to Yvonne this evening.

OCTOBER 19

A RATHER snide column in the Clark press today by the inimitable Bert Woodruff about my radio debut. He informs his readers that I am off to a bad start. He accuses me of "straddling" on the Communist issue, though I do not recall even mentioning the subject. He concludes: "Our returned exile — why did he stay over there in Europe so long in the first place? — will learn sooner than later that there is no place on the air in America for appeasers of Communism. If he doesn't know that, his boss, the Federal Broadcasting Company, and his sponsor, United Tobacco, ought to lose no time in telling him."

No word yet from William McKinley Forbes about Woodruff's

snarl, but there was a bit of a flurry at F.B.C. One or two vice-presidents gave me a curious look. Bob Fletcher, however, as I expected, said there was nothing to worry about.

"You see the technique of the guttersnipes, though," Bob said. "They try to get you through your sponsor. Being rabbits, sponsors don't like controversy."

"Forbes is no rabbit," I said.

"Let's wait and see," Bob said. There was an air of faint amusement, I thought, in his handsome, brooding face as he turned to gaze out the window at the spires of Manhattan. Perhaps, it occurred to me, he was thinking of how much went on beneath them that I was not yet aware of. In the end he advised me not to dignify Woodruff's little thrust by mentioning it on the air.

OCTOBER 24

THE permanent headquarters of the United Nations here was dedicated today with President Truman making the main address at the ceremony of laying the cornerstone. Ever since I came home I have watched from the window of my study the thirty-nine-story frame of the U.N. Secretariat taking shape like a huge oblong block along the river's edge. For years, from another home we had, I could look across another body of water in Geneva and glimpse the marble palace of the old League of Nations beyond the lake. Will history repeat itself? And another hope, another great dream, fade into limbo?

NOVEMBER 24

THANKSGIVING DAY, and we are celebrating it up here at the Fletchers'. Yvonne and I agreed this evening that we had much to be thankful for: above all, the coming home.

This autumn here in New England has been a glory. I had forgotten how magnificent it could be. I have seen nothing in Europe or Asia to equal the sight of the maples on a Connecticut hillside, their thick foliage a lavish orange, or more often a flaming red, on a sunny, October afternoon. And there is the clear, cool, invigorating autumn air and the wonderful smell of leaves on the lawn or in the woods, and of the smoke from the leaves burning, and from the hard maple crackling in the fireplace. The subtle aroma envelops the Fletchers' acres on a frosty, moonlit evening.

There is a quiet, soothing mood to the autumn here that recalls one's childhood, that induces reflection and contemplation and that no doubt prepares one's body as well as one's mind and soul for the rigors of winter.

Because of the Sunday broadcast, I could not make it up here — or anywhere else in the country — for week ends. But Bob, with typical thoughtfulness, suggested that whenever we liked we could come up with Barbara Thursday evenings. He would bring up the youngsters, his and ours, Friday afternoons after school was out. This we have often done, and I have skipped back to New York Saturday afternoons to begin writing the Sunday broadcasts, the background for which I prepare earlier in the week.

The three Fletcher children, about the same age as ours, get along famously with Dick and Maria. All five are nutty about horses — a mania, apparently, of this particular young generation.

The first two months of the Sunday broadcast are over and Bob says I am in. I have a fair audience-rating and what is more important, he says, it is gradually rising each week. That's the main thing with the sponsor, he says. Even Archy Oakes seems fairly pleased though his pleasure may be due partly to the fact that Bert Woodruff has ignored me in his column since his first little outburst.

Now that I have the broadcasts licked, I must get down to some writing: a book perhaps and some magazine pieces. Henry Wadsworth Prentice wants me to resume with *U.S.A.*, which has taken most of my meager output since the war. And Verne Gibson has invited me to lunch next week. Perhaps he has something in mind, though I cannot imagine what, since *World Review* is so confoundedly smug, narrow and depressingly reactionary. Elsie's piece in it this month on "The Communist Danger in Switzerland" is pure hooey.

NOVEMBER 30
          LUNCHED with Verne Gibson in the Rainbow Room atop Rockefeller Center and, as I anticipated, Elsie was there with him when I arrived. However, she let her boss do most of the talking. He wanted to explore, he said, the possibility of my becoming a regular contributor to *World Review*.

"Now that you are building up a nation-wide radio audience, Whitehead, how about adding a ready-made nation-wide magazine audience?" he proposed, a smile breaking over his face. He was conscious, I could see, of the bait he was dangling. Had he not baited most of the writers of America into his camp, especially the former liberals — and even more — the former Communists?

I stalled on an answer. My decision, though, is this: I shall take the *Word Review* money if they want to publish what I write. But I will not trim my sails to Gibson's views.

After luncheon I foolishly let Elsie lure me to her flat. We started walking up Fifth Avenue together and two or three blocks beyond the beginning of Central Park, we turned into one of the streets in the Sixties; before I realized it she was saying that an apartment building before which she paused was hers and that I must come up for a moment.

"There is something I couldn't say before Gibson that you ought to know, that you *must* know, Raymond," she insisted.

DECEMBER 1
          THE session with Elsie yesterday has greatly depressed me. It isn't only that I want done with her and yet seem unable somehow to shake myself completely loose. She had something to say that was quite disturbing.

At first I was furious with her.

As soon as we sat down on her overstuffed sofa in a large, impersonal living room that looked out over the park she fixed her gaze on me with ferocious intent and said: "Raymond, I've been *appalled* at your broadcasts!"

"They must be even better, then, than I thought," I replied.

"Seriously, my dear," she said. "You just can't go on that way. Not in this country."

"And why not?" I asked. "It's a free country, isn't it?"

"Not for what you've been getting by with. Not for playing into the hands of the Communists, as you've been doing!"

"For God's sake, Elsie, don't give me that bloody rot," I said, getting up angrily and moving to the window.

The park below looked bare and I noticed for the first time what a bleak day it was. I glared back at Elsie, who remained perched on the sofa looking like a sly old cat. It was, I have to admit, a more attractive cat than had pounced on me in Geneva a few months ago. She had shed a few more pounds and obviously had spent considerable time since her return at one of the beauty establishments with which this city abounds and to which the professional women like Elsie (they swarm through the halls of F.B.C.) apparently repair regularly and often. In fact, my first glance at her with Gibson as I strolled into the lounge of the Rainbow Room had almost taken me aback. In the face, at least, which had lost much of its greasy fleshiness, and in the hair, which she must have had freshly dyed, for it was jet black again and glistening instead of stringy and colorless, I saw instantly, as if the years had been suddenly rolled back, a striking resemblance to the Elsie of old — of her old Communist days, that is.

"What you've been saying recently about the strikes!" Elsie shouted across the floor, though we were only a few feet apart and she knew I was not hard of hearing.

"I played them down the middle," I said, returning to the battle and resuming my seat beside her.

"The middle! You were way over on the extreme left, Raymond. You were behind the strikers, both in coal and steel. It was the straight Communist party line."

[55]

The strikes had had nothing to do with any party line since both unions are completely dominated by anti-Communists, and, besides, I had been completely objective, I thought, between them and the companies; but this made no difference to Elsie. I was surprised, though, that she should have followed my broadcasts so closely.

"I feel rather flattered," I said. "You must have listened to me faithfully every Sunday."

"Not by any means." She smiled knowingly, as if to put me in my place. "I have listened to some of them, Raymond, out of my interest in you and —" for the first time she relaxed a little and a trace of a smile melted her belligerent features —"my affection. But it wasn't necessary in order to learn what you were up to."

"How else would you know? I asked.

She looked at me quizzically for a moment.

"Raymond," she finally said, not without a certain air of anticipated triumph, "let me fill you in with a few facts of life. In the first place, all your broadcasts are monitored."

"By whom?"

"By a number of people or organizations."

"What kind of organizations, for God's sake?"

"Well," she said, a slight smile creasing her face. "Let's call them patriotic organizations."

"I didn't know I was that important to them, or to anyone else."

"Everyone," she said, rather solemnly, "is important who has the ear, as you do, of the public."

"All right," I said. "They listen. So what?"

"So what! My dear Raymond, must I start in at the bottom with your education?"

"Don't bother, Elsie," I said. "It really bores me."

"Bores you!" she cried, angrily. "Let me tell you something, Raymond. I'm positive it won't bore you, as you say."

It didn't. But it perplexed me. And, I suppose, even shocked me. And still does — today.

According to Elsie, some of her friends are diligently preparing a black list of alleged Communists, fellow travelers and their sympathizers in radio.

I didn't catch the import of it at first; it sounded sort of silly — in this country. "Your former masters in Moscow have black lists," I said. "And Mussolini's Fascists and Hitler's Nazis had them. But those are, or were, official, backed by the state. Here in America, Elsie, where they would have to be private, the work of frustrated crackpots, I can't believe anyone takes them seriously."

"Well, try to believe it, Raymond, because it's a fact. Incidentally, I've seen the first tentative list."

"What on earth has it got to do with me?"

Elsie eyed me with unconcealed exasperation. "They're debating you."

"For what?"

"For a place on the list, Raymond."

"Who is 'they'?"

"Oh, some of my friends. People who are trying to save this country."

Elsie was getting hard to bear, as all self-appointed saviors of their countries usually are, but I was determined to keep my temper.

"Not that I care," I said, "what any noodle-headed zealots do — but why should I be on such a list? You know my feelings toward Communism. For years you wouldn't forgive me for not falling, as you did, for it."

She didn't give me much of an answer. How could she? But from what she said — and from what I'm beginning to feel since I got back — anyone who questions the *status quo*, from a liberal viewpoint, runs the risk of being denounced as a "Red" and a "subversive." Curiously, this latter epithet does not apply to the extreme reactionaries, who certainly denounce the present state of things. *These* questioners of the *status quo* find a friendly press and radio for a forum. I do not believe their names — and there are more of them than of us on the radio and writing newspaper columns — will appear on any black list.

I got up to go, but she insisted on a drink first. She said she had forgotten the drinks. So I stayed on a little longer, kicking myself the while. A highball seemed to mellow Elsie.

"You don't have to worry, for the time being, at least," she said after a while. "I can fix that."

"I certainly hope you won't," I protested.

"You mean, you want them to ruin you at the very start of your new career over here?"

"I don't think they will," I said. "In fact, Elsie, I don't think they can."

"Don't kid yourself, my dear. The networks are scared to death of them. The advertising men even more so, and the sponsors, worst of all."

"A great industry afraid of a handful of crackpots? I'll believe that when I see it," I persisted.

"Keep your eyes open, darling. It won't be long."

I got up again to go and she followed me to the window where I had tossed my hat and coat. Down in the park near Fifty-ninth Street, workers were assembling a shed by the duck pond. Probably for the ice skaters, I thought. The days had raced by since my return. It was difficult to realize that winter was at hand.

Elsie put her arm around my waist. "We have our differences, darling, but I know you will come down to earth."

"Not to yours, my dear," I said. "No more than in your Bolshy days."

"It's different now. We're on the same side of the fence."

"I wonder. I . . ."

"Hush," she whispered, coyly, throwing the other arm around me and kissing me. For the sake of old times, I suppose, I did not resist.

In the hallway before the door she released her grip. She seemed to be in a happy mood.

"Do you get to Washington much, Raymond?"

"Not as much as I should."

"You need to," she said. "We all forget that Washington is the capital, not New York. By the way, Raymond, anytime you wish, you can use my little apartment down there. *World Re-*

view *p*ays for it, so you might as well get some benefit too."

I haven't the slightest intention of taking advantage of her hospitality, if it is that and not something else. But I thanked her and fled.

DECEMBER 6

DOES the public, I am beginning to wonder, distinguish between Communists and those who are recklessly charged with being such — but aren't? Does a mere accusation, without the shred of any evidence, convict one in this country's court of public opinion!

I talked with Bob Fletcher about that for a few minutes after work today. He walked part way home with me — up Park to Fifty-seventh Street and across to the East Side. I thought he looked a little worn. He spoke of feeling a bit weary from the battles on the twenty-ninth floor, where most of F.B.C.'s vice-presidents are concentrated in their thickly carpeted, chromium-adorned, Venetian-blinded offices.

Bob suggests that I take into account the "climate" in this country today.

"I don't like the current hysteria any more than you do, Raymond," he said, his dark eyes and his dark features combining in a melancholy smile. "Sure, a hell of a lot of people confuse a charge with a conviction. But I think the climate will change, as it did after the first war. In the meantime, Raymond, you and I, and a lot of others like us, have to be smart. We have to realize what the score is — that at the moment it's against us."

I don't recall Bob talking exactly like that before. Perhaps the strain of his job — of those inane battles he has to fight incessantly on the twenty-ninth floor — has him down at the moment.

However, he said not to worry about any black list. From time to time, he said, some zany outfit gets one out and sends it to the networks. But F.B.C. pays no attention to them.

"If it ever does," he said, rather grimly, "I get out."

DECEMBER 7

BARBARA dropped by this evening and mentioned that Mark Robson is ditching his wife, Colette, the former actress, for a pretty young ballerina who is presently married to some English lord. Apparently the divorce will cost Mark a pretty penny — one million dollars, in fact. F.B.C. must be doing very well.

DECEMBER 9

THERE was an El Greco-like winter sky over Central Park this afternoon. The kind you see above Toledo, above Madrid, in December and which El Greco caught so memorably. The great clouds bleak and cold against the gray heavens.

DECEMBER 10

THE first thirteen weeks' cycle for the Sunday broadcast will be up Christmas Day. I thought we had signed a year's contract. Bob explained to me last night that we had but that, notwithstanding, the sponsor may renew or cancel every thirteen weeks. On the other hand, I am stuck for the year if the sponsor so desires. That's a curious kind of equity, but Bob admonished me that that's the way radio contracts run. No word from the high and mighty Forbes as to whether or not he will renew. He has until day after tomorrow to decide. Bob says not to worry.

DECEMBER 11

OAKES seemed plenty worried at the broadcast today. But I did not mention the question of renewal to him. I did explain the situation to Yvonne after dinner tonight. She seemed a little surprised.

"It is a little like a Damocles sword held over you every thirteen weeks, isn't it?" she said.

DECEMBER 12

ARCHY OAKES was on the telephone, breathlessly, before I had a chance to take off my overcoat at the office this morning.

"They've renewed!" he cried.

DECEMBER 13

THIS evening, after we tucked the kids in bed, I had a frank talk with Yvonne about Elsie. She has been phoning me daily at the office insisting I come around to see her and I have refused. Sunday, just after the broadcast, she phoned to say that it was too bad I was giving her the run-around since the Red black-list thing was getting serious.

"I'm not sure, after all, Raymond, that I can keep you off," she said.

"I've told you a hundred times, Elsie, not to try."

"I'm trying to help you in spite of yourself," she insisted.

"Please don't," I repeated.

But Elsie, as I ought to know by now — after all these years — is not so easy to put off.

"Listen here, Raymond," she said, sharply. "I want you to come to cocktails here tomorrow to have a talk with these people. I'm sure after they've heard you they will keep your name off."

"Sorry, Elsie. Not interested." And I hung up.

I recounted all this to Yvonne tonight.

"So far as the list is concerned, I don't know enough about this country to even try to advise you," Yvonne said. "It sounds incredible, but so do a lot of other things here. As for Elsie McCabe," she added, breaking into a smile, "she's your problem, Raymond, as she has been since we married. You must leave me out of it."

From the start Yvonne had insisted on that. She had been faintly amused at Elsie's dislike of her, which she reciprocated. And she had never worried over Elsie's attempts to thwart our marriage in the first place or to break it up later. Not that

Yvonne had much reason to worry so far as I was concerned.

"Perhaps," Yvonne said this evening, "if you could make up your mind — once and for all — about the lady, you would be happier."

"I made it up long ago," I said. "That summer you and I decided to get married."

"Then why is there any difficulty?"

DECEMBER 23

MARK ROBSON presided over F.B.C.'s annual Christmas party this afternoon in one of the big studios. It turned out to be a dull affair. Several vice-presidents got roaring drunk, but I did not find this as funny as some others did.

The drinking in New York puzzles and fascinates me. There is much more of it than I have seen in Paris, London, Berlin or Vienna. But for many it seems to be not so much a pleasure in itself as a means to escape the pressures one lives under — not only in business but in one's personal life. And from what little I've seen so far in this wondrous metropolis I suspect it is also the basis of what people in this town call love, or what I would call the sex life. The men and women scamper off to bed together only after they've downed a dozen cocktails or highballs. Off to bed, or off to the marriage registry — or to the one after the other.

What was that wonderful line of Shakespeare — in *Macbeth*, I think — about the effect of alcohol on the urge to go to bed with a woman? Very bawdy, as I recall.

DECEMBER 25

WE HAD a fitting Christmas Eve, singing Christmas carols before the fire and exchanging presents there. The Fletchers had sent us an enormous tree from their farm and we spent the afternoon with the youngsters decorating it. Now that Dick and Maria (with surprising speed) are becoming at home in my language, I could read them Dickens's *A Christmas Carol*. They sprawled on the floor utterly entranced by it, in contrast to last Christmas in Geneva when I had tried to read it to them and they had been unable — or unwilling — to follow. Fired by my success, I tried "the night before Christmas" verse on Maria. She loved it; in fact she demanded two encores. This evening after the broadcast, though it was a bit late for the children, we had our big dinner.

It was a happy holiday. It belongs, of course, to the youngsters, but I guess that includes me. I always feel terribly sentimental on this day and for some reason recall nostalgically all the other Christmases: the ones of my boyhood in Indiana (we always had a white Christmas out there, with the snow piled high in the tree-lined streets of our town; I remember vividly the full moon above the sparkling snow one bitterly cold and beautiful Christmas Eve when I trudged through the snow with my father distributing presents in our neighborhood); and the ones Yvonne and I had before the children came, when we were young and madly in love (we spent them in the mountains, Chamonix, Mégève, Villard, Gstaad, skiing and skating and making love); and I remember, especially, the sad Christmases when I was away from my family and desperately lonely (there was one in the Balkans, in Sofia, where I got caught on some mission, and the loneliest one of all in Kabul where, as Americans invariably do when this day catches them in some forlorn and distant outpost, a handful of us tried desperately to engender some Yuletide spirit).

After the children were finally goaded to bed, Yvonne and I sat before the fire relaxing over a nightcap highball, I noticed tears welling up in her eyes. Yet her face was aglow, I could see, with a deep happiness.

"*Je suis tellement heureuse,*" she said, wiping away the tears. I sprang up to embrace her.

DECEMBER 28

I FOUND that piece from Shakespeare today. It *is* in *Macbeth* — the famous porter's scene. The porter is pickled and sounds off to MacDuff on drink being "the great provoker."

[63]

Lechery, sir, it provokes and it unprovokes; it provokes the
desire, but it takes away the performance: therefore much
drink may be said to be an equivocator with lechery: it makes
him, and it mars him; it sets him on, and it takes him off; it
persuades him, and disheartens him; makes him stand to, and
not to stand to; in conclusion, equivocates him in a sleep, and
giving him the lie, leaves him.

JANUARY 2, 1950

A NEW YEAR, and as usual I have tried to take
stock in my fumbling way.

The figure — 1950 — stared at me all day from the calendar on
my desk. Here we are at the mid-century — so soon. You cannot
help but wonder whether the second half will be as bad as the
first, plagued by total war, obscene destruction, tyranny, fratri-
cide, hysteria, intolerance. It is almost a consolation to think
that those of my age will not live to see this bloody twentieth
century out.

We went to the Fletchers' for New Year's Eve. There was
quite a party, gay and, as the evening wore along into the morning, rather noisy. At times there seemed to be almost as many
people crowded into their spacious Park Avenue apartment as
at their country place the Labor Day week end.

At such moments as these we return to our childhood. It
would be easy for a man from Mars — or even from some distant place on earth — dropping in on such a gathering, to ridicule us and to wonder how silly American adults can get. On
the other hand, I myself was relieved to see the American businessman become, for the moment at least, a human being again,
letting down the barriers which make him such a boring robot
most of the time. Even old General Clark, who had brought his
mistress, the faded Madeleine Marlowe, with him this time
seemed a more genuine member of the decent part of the human race than usual. He was in a gay mood, dancing a lot and
cutting up. Call it horseplay. Call it childish. At least here, for
this moment, these tycoons and their sycophants dropped the
hard-bitten, aggressive roles they play in their offices.

[64]

Only a few, like Bert Woodruff, seemed incapable of unshriveling themselves for the gala evening. The infamous columnist stalked around with a frown frozen on his face as if it made him boil to see anyone in good spirits. I wondered how I should behave toward him if he accosted me, whether to turn my back on him, insult him, or merely act as if I hadn't read his column that morning. For he had not left me out of it. Yvonne had espied the item at breakfast.

"Did you see our friend Woodruff's list of New Year's resolutions?" she asked.

"No. And I don't want to," I said.

"One of them concerns you, Raymond."

"Me? How could that be?"

She had read it:

My Own New Year's Resolutions . . . (9) not to waste any more time listening to Raymond Whitehead Sunday evenings. It's a New Deal, Fair Deal, ordeal. The guy lived abroad too long.

"Well, at least he didn't call me a Communist," I laughed.

Once Archy Oakes, who kept saying the paragraph had him worried, tried to steer me over to Woodruff, but I declined.

"If you two only would get together," Archy pleaded. "I'm sure your little misunderstanding would be cleared up."

Something else made him nervous before the evening was over. Sometime after midnight, after we had welcomed in the New Year, he came up to me fairly trembling.

"The boss says he would like to have a word with you," he whispered. His eyes had an anxious look.

"What boss, Archy?"

"Forbes."

I had had a drink earlier in the evening with my tobacco king. He had seemed to be in good spirits. He was drinking heavily and his robust face was full of fine color. We had exchanged pleasantries, and I had reflected again what a personable old ruffian he was. I had not seen him since the party he and Mark Robson had thrown after my opening broadcast and

[65]

if he had had any opinions about my subsequent shows they had not sifted down to me.

"No news from the old man is always good news," Archy had aways said, as if he lived in fear and trembling of receiving any kind of word from the president of United Tobacco.

I sauntered over toward the bar where Forbes was standing, somewhat unsteadily.

"Wanted to have a nightcap with you, Whitehead, before I left," he greeted me, cordially. A waiter in a white coat perked up.

"What will it be, Mr. Forbes?" Even the waiters, I reflected, know what a big shot William McKinley Forbes is.

"Two Scotches, son. Double," Forbes ordered. Then he turned to me.

"Nothing like Scotch to start the New Year right — eh, Whitehead?" His voice was as big and as robust as his body.

"By the way," he said, after we had had a swallow, "I was just telling that little Oakes fellow, you and I haven't had a get-together since that first show you did for us."

"That's right," I said.

"How about lunch this week?"

"I'd like it," I said.

"Good. Day after tomorrow then . . . What is it? . . ."

"That would be Tuesday," I said.

"Good. Tuesday. 1 P.M. At the Union League Club. Some things I want to talk to you about."

"Fine," I said. "I'll look forward to it."

We finished our drink, and he left.

Archy Oakes was upon me immediately.

"Well?" he said, as if his life depended upon a quick and satisfactory answer.

"Well, what, Archy?" I said.

"The old man! What was the word?"

"He invited me to lunch. Day after tomorrow."

"Oh!" His relief was immense, and color began to return to his pallid face.

[66]

In the hallway I ran into Barbara Fletcher. Surprisingly, she was alone, sitting in a high, straight-backed Spanish chair, calmly drawing on a cigarette, and smiling, as it were, at the opposite wall, though I do not believe she saw the faded old piece of tapestry which her eyes seemed to be focused on. Her face was flushed with exhaustion.

"Happy New Year, Raymond! Are you having a good time?"

"Wonderful," I said. "And a good New Year to you, Barbara."

I had never seen her in exactly this subdued mood before, but it became her surprisingly well, somehow intensifying the genuineness of the human being that made her so attractive. Her blue eyes were warm, her balanced, wholesome face relaxed. I was puzzled, though, to find her sitting so contentedly alone, for the rest of the house was a noisy bedlam of alcoholic conviviality.

"Are you all right, Barbara?" I asked, realizing before the words were out of my mouth that six months ago I would not have said such a thing on such an occasion, realizing suddenly how quickly I had acquired the viewpoint of this frantic city, to which a person who took a moment's repose from the frenzy was regarded with alarm, causing you to ask almost automatically whether he was all right.

"I'm fine, Raymond," she said, softly. "Just pleasantly tired. Catching my breath. Do you think everyone is having a good time?"

"They certainly act like it, Barbara."

"And you, Raymond?" she asked again, with a quizzical smile that came mostly from her expressive eyes.

I repeated that I had had a wonderful time. "After all, Barbara, it's my first New Year's Eve at home since I was a youngster. You can imagine what a kick I'm getting out of it."

"Of course," she said, eying me with a warmth and a sympathy that made her seem more lovable and close than I had ever felt before. And yet I was aware of a question forming in her brow.

"Your job, Raymond. Do you like it?"

"It's fascinating."

"But a bit of a rat race, just the same, isn't it? I know it is for Bob."

"True," I said. "But I'll survive. And Bob, of course, better than I."

She did not say anything for a moment, but I could feel that she was mulling over something in her mind, perhaps debating with herself whether to enunciate it.

"Why don't you join them, Raymond?" she asked.

"Whom?"

"Bob and Mark. I think you'll find them in Bob's study."

I found Bob Fletcher, Mark Robson and some of the other executives of F.B.C. in Bob's study toasting the New Year. It was going to be a big one for the Federal Broadcasting Company, they said. Television, Robson beamed, was going to come of age this year and burst forth in all its glory.

"It will revolutionize our civilization, I'm telling you, Raymond," he said, addressing me. "And for the first time, gentlemen," he said, turning to the others, "we won't lose money on it. In fact, I think we may make a couple of millions this year."

Everyone else agreed. Everyone at F.B.C., I had noticed, with the exception of Bob Fletcher, always agreed with the president, even when they were sober, and now that they were a bit in their cups they fairly roared their tribal approval of everything he said.

Bob Fletcher was delightfully tight. There was no trace of his habitual frown nor of the sadness which filled him so much of the time. He was in high spirits.

"Brother," he kept saying, "we're going places this year."

Does he know where? Do any of us?

JANUARY 4

SO THE New Year, for me, gets off to a lousy start. William McKinley Forbes was blunt enough. He says he cannot continue to sponsor my Sunday broadcast unless I change my line. How can I change — and live with myself?

"I get complaints, Whitehead," he said. "That you're off the beam. That you're too tolerant of this New Deal, Fair Deal nonsense. Too tolerant of the sinister influence of the United Nations; of all those alien philosophies which emanate from it and from other foreign sources and which are corrupting this great land of ours. In short, that you're too god-damned European and not enough American. What about it, Whitehead?"

"Before I answer you, Forbes," I said, "let me remind you of one thing: in our contract, I believe, there is a stipulation that you, as the sponsor, have nothing to say about the content of the broadcast. That's my business, exclusively."

I wasn't very diplomatic, I suppose. I could have kidded him along, made a joke of the asinine charges and insisted that his complainants were spoofing him. But why should I be any less blunt than he?

He had a perfectly good answer, of course, as soon as he had calmed down.

"True enough, Whitehead," he said, "that's what it says in the contract." He hesitated, smoothed one of the points of his handle-bar mustache and smiled, as though he felt just a bit sorry for one so ignorant of the rules of the game, such as they were, in his jungle world. "But it also says in the contract, if I am not mistaken, that I have the right to renew your services, Whitehead, or not to renew them, every thirteen weeks. Is that correct?" The question was put with studied innocence.

"Correct," I said, trying to match his smile.

I repeat, I have almost an affection for the old scamp, and I believe he has a sneaking liking for me.

"You know, Whitehead," he said, "my own feeling about you is that you were away so long you really need more time to get both feet planted firmly on the ground here. So I tell you what I've decided to do. Your second thirteen-week cycle is just beginning. We'll wait a couple of months and see what happens. Personally, I have great confidence in you, once you've got your bearings."

I had no doubt about the bearings I was expected to get. They were the bearings all the well-fed figures in this great dining hall had come upon and which they would defend to their last yacht. But they were not likely ever to become mine.

A rather mellow mood came over the old man as we sipped our coffee in the lounge, and he smacked his lips on an enormous cigar. He had a case to make, I had to admit, if you accepted our system of broadcasting. And had I not accepted it when I signed the contract in Geneva and came home? Was it not accepted — without reservations — by almost all the citizens, poor as well as rich, in the country?

"The way I see it, Whitehead, is this," Forbes said, tilting his cigar at a smart angle. "It isn't up to me, as you point out, to tell you what to say in these broadcasts. But it isn't up to me, either, to pay you good money to say a lot of things that I honestly think are bad — bad for business, bad for the people, bad for the country. I don't think even you would expect me to go on doing that, would you?"

"No," I said. "I wouldn't."

I hadn't quite seen it that way until now. It was all right, I thought, for Bob Fletcher and Mark Robson to prattle about the freedom of speech on the air and to boast, as both of them had, that the sponsor couldn't meddle with it. It said so in the contract. But, as Forbes now made clear, the sponsor didn't have to meddle with it. He didn't have to tell you what to say, or what not to say. He could simply suppress you by not renewing you at the end of a thirteen weeks' cycle.

JANUARY 5
            AT BREAKFAST this morning Yvonne spotted an item buried in the back page of one of the morning papers which troubles us. It said that Stephen A. Burnett, counselor of the U. S. Legation at Berne, had been subpoenaed to appear before the Senate Committee on Security and Americanism. I see the slimy hand of Senator O'Brien, who heads the committee, in this. We cabled Steve that he could put up with us whenever he is in New York.

LAKE PLACID, JANUARY 9

MY AMERICAN education continues apace. On the train this morning on the way to Lake Placid, where Yvonne and I are taking three or four days off for skiing, I read with interest an editorial in *World Review*. It was entitled: "The Insufferable Long-Hairs."

Yvonne, noticing the head, said: "What on earth are 'long-hairs'?"

"I'll tell you in a moment — after I've read the piece," I said, plunging into Verne Gibson's purple prose.

A "long-hair," it turns out, is an intellectual. And *World Review* is against the breed. It says they're responsible for most of our troubles.

I don't suppose Americans take Verne Gibson's gibberish seriously, though they do buy his magazine. It's curious that the mass-circulation magazines should be so full these days of gibes against intellectuals. Why is an American with brains suspect?

LAKE PLACID, JANUARY 12

A RELIEF to get away from the office and — we both agreed reluctantly — from the children. We love the youngsters beyond telling, but . . . well, we enjoyed being to ourselves for a few days. I had forgotten how lovely Yvonne looked in a ski costume against the background of the glistening snow, and the green woods and the deep blue winter sky, and how graceful she could be taking the turns on a steep slope. Myself, I am more timid on skis than I used to be — a sure sign of advancing age. We haven't had such fun in ages.

FEBRUARY 1

A CABLE from Steve Burnett. He is flying home next week to face the music. Our Washington office tells me O'Brien is out for blood and that Steve, regardless of his innocence, which no decent person doubts, is in for a rough going-over.

I can't find out what the charges against Steve are. I telephoned O'Brien. He said he would make them public "at the proper time."

"And, by the way, Whitehead," the Senator admonished me, "I should think it would be a very healthy thing for you if you stayed out of this."

FEBRUARY 7

IN THE elevator today I overheard one of the office girls telling another that Mark Robson was going to institute a loyalty oath at F.B.C.; Mark isn't that silly. But that such a rumor could get about, even among the stenographers, indicates a climate I don't much like. I never expected Americans, one of the few peoples too sensible to fall for Communism, to become so jittery about Communists. What would we be like if they formed the largest political party over here, and controlled the bulk of the trade unions, as they do in France?

I know there is the problem of a tiny handful of American Communists who commit espionage for Russia. It is real. But is it not exaggerated, mainly by the professional ex-Communists and the professional witch-hunters? Catching the few culprits is, primarily, it seems to me, the task of the F.B.I. and the various security bodies. You're not going to ferret them out by setting up loyalty oaths. Indeed, Communists would be the first to sign.

I know I ought to say these things in my broadcasts. But I begin to play it safe, like everyone else.

FEBRUARY 10

DISPATCHES from London today tell of a Dr. Fuchs admitting in a signed confession that he passed on secret atomic information to Russia for seven years because of his own personal devotion to Communism. Fuchs says he practiced what he calls "controlled schizophrenia." One part of him was devoted to advancing atomic knowledge for Britain and America. The other part brought him to betray that knowledge to Russia.

This is beyond me.

FEBRUARY 16

THE esteemed City Council of San Diego today decided, on the advice of Admiral William H. Standley, former ambassador to Russia, not to list two of President Roosevelt's Four Freedoms on a Veterans' Memorial Building plaque. The eminent admiral and ambassador contends that "freedom from want" is a "Russian communistic slogan" and "freedom from fear" is a "political slogan."

FEBRUARY 18

STEVE BURNETT telephoned to say he had been detained in Washington, but would arrive tomorrow for a couple of days. I didn't get to see him on his arrival last week. The weather was so bad here that his plane went on to Washington to land. I am anxious to hear what he's up against. So far — wisely — he has managed to stay out of the newspapers.

FEBRUARY 19 (SUNDAY)

STEVE came up on the overnight train so that at least we had a few minutes together at breakfast before I had to leave for the office to write my broadcast. It was a delight to see him and to discover that he had his chin up and was in good spirits. There was so much to talk about concerning his family — his three girls had returned to Berne a few days after I left — and about Switzerland and Europe, that there was no time to go into his difficulties with the O'Brien committee. Steve said he didn't even know what the charges were although the Senator promised to state them sometime this week. Steve, though, had no doubt what they would be: they would be in line with O'Brien's rantings that the State Department was full of Commies. So far as he was concerned, he would knock that one flat, and perhaps O'Brien too — in the process. He said he wanted to spend the day as lazily as he could, playing with Dick and Maria and gossiping with Yvonne. We could settle the world's affairs after I came home from the broadcast in the evening.

[73]

At the office there wasn't much spot news of interest. I decided to do a review of the week and a preview of the ensuing one from notes I had jotted down the past few days. I was just finishing when a copy boy brought me a bulletin from Washington off the ticker.

O'Brien had just made public his charges against Stephen A. Burnett, timing them so he could reach the large audience on Sunday evening radio and capture the big headlines on the Monday morning front pages, news being scarce, as a rule, on Monday morning.

The accusations are ridiculous, but, in the present climate, serious. They made my blood boil. For several minutes I just sat there staring angrily at the outrageous words.

The charges were two: that Burnett was a card-carrying Communist; that he was a "leader in the Soviet conspiracy to turn China over to the Communist hordes and thus betray the best interests of the United States." Hearings would begin a week from tomorrow before the Senate Committee on Security and Americanism, of which O'Brien is the chairman. "Mr. Burnett," O'Brien was quoted as saying, "will be given every opportunity, in our best American traditions, to defend himself."

As soon as I had calmed down, I telephoned home to give Steve the gist of the dispatch. There was only an hour before air time. If he listened to my broadcast, I said, he would get the full story. Steve's reaction was typical of him.

"Now, Raymond, for God's sake, keep your shirt on," he urged.

"I've already taken it off, Steve."

"Well, put it back on. No use you getting involved in my troubles."

I couldn't help it. I shoved my other copy aside (for my broadcast had been practically written) and sat down in a white heat of anger and wrote a defense of an American I have known for a quarter of a century, who was never a Communist or a Communist sympathizer, but who was never a narrow-minded reactionary either, being instead a fine, liberal-minded patriot who had served his country loyally and with deep devotion. There was not enough time to finish my piece, and so I ad-libbed the end, leaving very few minutes, I fear, for the other news of the day.

I remember, when I finished, looking up at Archy Oakes, who, though it is not necessary, always shows up Sunday evenings on behalf of United Tobacco and listens to the broadcast in the control room directly in front of me. His face was white, his mouth wide open, his eyes staring frightenedly at me.

When I got back to the cubicle which is my office the two telephones were clanging madly. The usual cranks were on the line, only there were more of them, and they were more vehement than usual. I phoned down to the switchboard operator and asked her to say I had left. But a moment later one of the phones was ringing again.

"Sorry," said the operator. "But there is a woman on the line who insists on being put through. Says she's a close friend of yours."

"Put her on," I said. I might have known who it was.

"That did it, darling!"

"What did what, Elsie?"

"Made it impossible to keep your name off."

"Off of what?"

" 'Red Airwaves' — that black list I've been trying to keep you clear of. . . ."

I regret — now — at least, my rudeness. I hung up on her.

At home I found Steve Burnett in better spirits than I expected. He was relieved, he said, that at last O'Brien had come out in the open and stated the charges. He would make mince-meat of them — and perhaps of their perpetrator.

"You were wonderful to say what you did about me in your broadcast, Raymond, but . . ."

"I would have been a heel not to — or to have remained silent," I interrupted.

"I appreciate it. But, Raymond, why should you go out of your way to look for trouble?"

"It isn't out of my way, Steve. It's very much in it."

Bob and Barbara Fletcher dropped by after dinner. For a second, when Bob came in, I thought maybe his purpose was to raise hell with me for going off half-cocked on Burnett. After all, what was said over F.B.C. was one of his main responsibilities. This time I did not exactly welcome his perpetual frown.

But he said: "Raymond, I caught your broadcast. It made me proud of you."

"Thanks, Bob." Friendship aside, it was something to have the number two big shot in F.B.C. back of you.

"We'll have some trouble, Raymond," he said, his keen black eyes narrowing into a squint, as if he himself were in pain. "But you can count on at least one executive on the twenty-ninth floor giving you full support. I am sure there will be others."

"And you can count," Barbara broke in, "on at least one housewife writing half a dozen letters under various pseudonyms to F.B.C. praising you for your courage." She had been watching Bob rather closely, I felt, when he first began to talk, though I am sure that, like me, she had no doubt whatsoever of what stand he would take.

"You give me an idea," Yvonne spoke up. Veteran that she was of our troubles and struggles, she had been calm and collected all evening. Deep down, though, I knew, her Gallic temperament, which over the years she had learned to discipline, was raging. "Barbara," she proposed, "let's go up to Raymond's study and type a few letters right now."

I tried to stop them. "It isn't quite cricket, faking letters," I protested.

"You can be sure that's what the other side will do," Bob said. "They're organized to set up a stink at the drop of the bucket. They can produce a thousand letters of protest overnight, and as many telephone calls. In fact, the office tells me our switchboard has been flooded with calls tonight. I know where most of them came from. Trouble is, Raymond, the decent side isn't organized to bring pressure on broadcasters. High time, they were, too."

"High time Yvonne and I were getting to work," Barbara laughed.

After they had left and the three of us men sat alone, I was pleasantly surprised to discover that Bob and Steve were old friends. Apparently Fletcher had done a year out in China when Burnett was stationed there long before the war.

"You've got to realize, Steve," Bob said, after they had rehashed old times, "that most people in this country are completely deluded about China. They've been sold the nonsense that your State Department is responsible for the Communists taking over there. That being so, don't underestimate the power of the O'Brien committee, backed by the Clark press and a lot of other newspapers, not to mention a pack of columnists like Woodruff and their counterparts on the air. The Senator and the other ignoramuses who dominate his committee will try to trip you up on a thousand hidden wires. If I may give you a bit of advice, Steve, prepare your defense well. And don't wait for them to attack. You start attacking — the first minute you get on the stand."

"It seems incredible, Bob," Steve said. He was still, I could see, in sort of a genial daze. "It used to be that in this country a man was considered innocent until proved guilty."

"Things have changed." Bob smiled dolefully. "Now, it's the other way around. In the bulk of the press, anyway, and before most of these Congressional committees."

"I will try to keep it in mind," Steve said. He spoke softly and you could feel some inner glow behind the honest, ascetic face that gave him a great and purified strength. "Living abroad most of the time makes one forget that there are such people in this country."

"And in such high places," I put in. It was a situation that still baffled me though I had been home several months.

"It's the same pack," Bob went on, "that has openly — in the Senate, at least, where a man cannot be sued for what he says — accused General Marshall, and other patriots almost equally great, of treason in favor of the Communists."

"You mean," Steve laughed, "I'm in excellent company?"

"In the very best," Bob said, grinning.

FEBRUARY 20

MARK ROBSON phoned down this morning — a little frostily, I thought — and asked for a copy of yesterday's broadcast.

FEBRUARY 22

I HAVE decided to do a piece on O'Brien next Sunday. No one else on the radio has dared to, so I might as well try. I got in a few licks last Sunday, but my remarks were more a defense of Steve Burnett than an attack on the wily Senator.

A brief stay in Washington yesterday convinced me that the man has become a national menace — and also that he is vulnerable. The State Department, to which I went yesterday morning with Steve, has become a sorry place. Almost everyone is frightened to death of the Senator. And Steve's case has all but wrecked the morale of the foreign service. The atmosphere of suspicion and mistrust which O'Brien has managed to stir up hangs heavy over the whole capital. No one knows where the man will strike next and with what new lie and smear. So far he hasn't turned up a single Communist in government. But he has ruined a lot of decent, loyal public servants.

The principal case against O'Brien, of course, is his unscrupulous methods of pillorying innocent people and the damage he is doing in falsely engendering suspicion and distrust. But some interesting evidence of skulduggery in the Senator's past, which I unearthed yesterday, will be helpful in exposing the witch hunter for the mountebank he is.

FEBRUARY 23

YVONNE indignant over a paragraph in Woodruff's column this morning:

Didn't Stephen A. Burnett, striped-panted diplomat whom the O'Brien committee next week will hear on charges of being a key Communist in the State Department, spend the week end in the New York apartment of Commentator Whitehead? Isn't it a case of birds of a feather flocking . . . etc.?

In the office, where Woodruff's column is practically a Bible, I felt some unfriendly glares today. And though it is Thursday I haven't had a peep out of Archy Oakes all week. He usually phones daily.

FEBRUARY 25

I SPENT most of this Saturday writing tomorrow's broadcast on O'Brien. I thought it politic to tip off Bob Fletcher as to what I was up to. He thought it was an excellent idea. He said he would alert Mark Robson, who was weekending with friends in Washington, to be sure to listen.

FEBRUARY 26 (SUNDAY)

ABOUT an hour before I was scheduled to begin the broadcast this evening, the president of F.B.C. telephoned from Washington.

"What's this story, Raymond, I hear you have on Senator O'Brien?"

I started to tell him.

"Read me what you've written, if you don't mind?"

I read it to him. There was a moment of silence that seemed longer than it was.

"Sorry, Raymond," he said at last. "You can't broadcast that." His voice was flat, the tone imperative and final — not at all like him.

"Why not, Mark?" I asked good-naturedly. I thought perhaps he was pulling my leg.

"I don't care to discuss it on the phone, Raymond. Drop up to the office after lunch tomorrow and I'll talk to you."

I was amazed. I phoned Bob. Barbara said he had just stepped out to the drugstore to buy some cigarettes. I asked her to have him call me.

Archy Oakes happened to be sitting in my cubicle when

Robson's call came through. I had shown him the story on O'Brien and, as I had anticipated, it had made his face turn from its usual potato hue to chalk-white. But he hadn't said anything. Now, as I hung up on Barbara, he got up steam enough to say:

"It's none of my business, Whitehead, but I can't help feeling that Robson is right."

"You think so, do you?"

"I tell you it is dynamite, Whitehead. Dynamite. God!"

"Archy, will you get the hell out of this office, where you've got no business being in the first place!"

Alone, I tried to calm down. I glanced at the big Western Union clock on the wall. There was just forty-two minutes to air time. Not nearly enough time to compose another broadcast. I would have to gather up the stacked sheets of teletype which I had torn off A.P. and U.P. and ad-lib some kind of broadcast of the news.

I set to work sorting them out. The phone rang. Bob's very dejected voice was on the other end.

"I'm sorry, too, Raymond," he said glumly.

"You've heard then?"

"Yeah. The old man phoned me. Don't think, Raymond, I didn't argue."

"I'm sure you did, Bob. But, listen. In the next forty minutes we've got to get on the phone to him again and convince him he's wrong. We ought to have a little freedom, Bob, to say something on F.B.C."

"We ought to," Bob said, and for the first time I was discouraged by the tone of his voice. There was such a frightening resignation in it. "We ought to, brother," he intoned, "but today, apparently, we haven't."

"Listen, Bob . . ." I guess I was grasping for a straw. . . . "Will you phone Mark once more and remind him of what he's doing and . . ."

"It wouldn't do any good, Raymond," Bob cut in, and I caught the despair in his voice, the finality of his judgment.

"Okay, Bob. Thanks for trying anyway," I said.

"We'll raise hell with him tomorrow, Raymond."

Tomorrow would be too late, but the idea seemed to cheer Bob up.

FEBRUARY 27

I FEEL low tonight. It isn't so much that I was suppressed yesterday. What has me down is the sudden discovery of what kind of person Mark Robson really is — and, for that matter, Bob Fletcher.

It happened very quickly in Robson's office starting at 3 o'clock this afternoon. I had hoped that Bob and I could have lunch together to talk things over, but he said he was tied up. He was with Mark when I arrived.

Mark greeted me friendlily enough, but behind his genial grin I felt something I had never sensed there before: hostility. Perhaps it was in a certain coldness in his eyes, or in the rather abrupt manner of his speech. Did Bob Fletcher feel it too? He sat in a chair off to one side staring gloomily out of the window. My first thought was that he had already had a fight with Robson. If that were so, I would soon be battling on his side.

But Bob didn't say much. In fact, Robson did most of the talking.

"I've felt this thing coming to a head for some time," he began, contriving to make me feel at the start like a prisoner in the dock. Until this minute our relationship, when we met, had been based on good-natured banter, on an easy, informal give-and-take, on an equality which assumed that we were both free to speak our minds. Now, I saw, he was speaking to me as a boss to a hireling.

I listened patiently to what he said: that I was abusing my unique position on radio by taking sides, by airing my personal prejudices, by protecting my friends and attacking my enemies, by indulging in propaganda which many listeners quite rightly resented.

"Listeners, or sponsors?" I cut in.

"I just don't like your whole attitude, Raymond. And to be blunt, you'll have to change it. Quickly and radically."

I waited for Bob to spring to my defense, but he still sat off to one side, glaring moodily out the window. It occurred to me that at this minute he hated us both: me for bringing on this clash, Robson for behaving so arbitrarily. So I spoke up for myself, as I was bound to do in the end anyway.

"In the first place, Mark," I said, trying to bring us all back to where I thought we had been, "I'm a little taken aback by your manner. I thought the three of us were good friends enough to talk over our differences like good friends."

I waited a second for him to respond to this, but he said nothing.

"Be that as it may," I went on. "I quite realize that it is pretty difficult to have complete freedom on the air. But I gathered from all you said, and all Bob said, that on F.B.C. at least we were free to give the facts, to state the truth, within certain limits."

"You constantly overstep those limits," Mark said.

"Apparently I didn't quite realize how narrow they were."

At this point Bob looked up, his face furrowed with pain. However, he said nothing.

"Take your last two broadcasts," Robson said. "Your defense of Burnett, which you aired, and the attack on Senator O'Brien, which I wouldn't let you air. I'm not contesting your facts. I'm not disputing their truth. What I am saying is that the radio is not the proper forum in which to expound them. At least, F.B.C. which takes no sides in public controversy, is not, and won't be so long as I'm here."

"Mark, you astound me," I said, trying to smile. "There are at least a dozen commentators, a couple of them on F.B.C., who take sides on every issue. I don't happen to like the side they take. But I like the freedom they have to take it. It is invariably reactionary. It pleases the sponsors. You don't object to those broadcasters, do you?"

He turned away in a gesture of intense annoyance. But I could not quite stop.

"Take Whitney Shuttleworth, whom you and Bob have been trying to lure over here. Three times last week Shuttleworth made snide attacks on Stephen Burnett, making it plain he considered him guilty even before Burnett has had a chance to defend himself. And making it plain too that he considers Senator O'Brien on the right track."

Mark bent forward, planting both elbows on his desk. He was not angry, I saw; he was merely fed up with me.

"I don't care what Shuttleworth says on another network," he said dryly. "I do care a great deal about what is said on this network. And I'll have to ask you to conform to our policies."

I looked around again at Bob. He was stooped in his chair, gazing morosely at the floor.

"Bob, how do you see it?" I asked.

"This is between you and me, Raymond," Robson said sharply.

I looked at Bob. He stirred, glared at Robson and then me, and broke into the melancholy smile he has.

"I think you're both wrong," he said simply. I could have hugged him. He was the only executive on the premises with any guts. ". . . and childish, if I may say so."

At this instant, Mark Robson lost his head and, a moment later, I regret to say, Bob Fletcher lost his guts. It is difficult to write it down. Usually your illusions are not shattered in a flicker of time.

"I don't care what you think, Bob," Mark said frostily. "Perhaps you feel yourself torn between your friendship with Raymond and with me. I respect your feelings. But F.B.C. happens to be a business. And I happen to be running it. And what I say goes. For both of you."

That was when the agonizing moment came. Bob looked up with an expression on his face which I will never forget.

"You're the boss, Mark," he said.

FEBRUARY 28

      I CAN'T get over the way Bob Fletcher looked at the end yesterday. It was unbearably painful to me.

As we broke up, I felt a deep resentment rising in him — and

[83]

quite understandably too; resentment that I had seen him in such an abject state and that I had been the principal cause of it.

In the corridor outside Robson's office he gave me a glance that showed both his hurt and his anger.

"Well, are you satisfied?" he muttered.

"No."

"Was it necessary?"

I did not answer. He knew all right who had convoked whom. He ducked into his office without a further word, and I took the elevator down to mine.

This afternoon I phoned him and suggested we dine some place alone.

"Sorry, Raymond," he said, rather curtly. "I'm tied up."

MARCH 1 ·
   I HAD planned to go down to Washington last night to be present at the opening of Steve Burnett's hearing today before the O'Brien committee, but the mess at the office makes that impossible. Yvonne and I sat up until after midnight discussing what to do. I feel the only honorable course is to resign, since Robson obviously has lost all confidence in me and Bob is doing loyally what the president of F.B.C. tells him to do. More important, would it not be a shabby thing to continue, at a fat fee, to broadcast when you were not permitted even to say anything, however tepid, that would displease the likes of Senator O'Brien or stir up controversy, which in itself is displeasing to the sponsor?

Yvonne argues, on the other hand, that it has not exactly befallen me to reform radio, or anything else in America. I have to take what I find back here, and the only question is, as she rightly puts it, how far you want to compromise yourself to get along.

Yvonne is very much against my resigning — this week, anyway. She strongly advises giving it more thought.

"Wait and see what Mark Robson or Bob Fletcher or the fabulous Mr. Forbes does," she suggested. "Probably in the end you won't have to make a decision. It will be made for you. That will be fate, darling—something we can accept philosophically."

This is not the ideal way out, but I am taking it.

MARCH 2

THE REPORTS in the papers of Steve Burnett's first day on the stand say that he never even got to the end of the first page of his prepared statement. The distinguished Senators kept interrupting him with their questions.

MARCH 3

I LAID aside my troubles tonight and took the family to a basketball game in Madison Square Garden. It was all Greek to Yvonne, and a little beyond Maria, but Dick, who is playing forward on his school team, and I loved it. I had forgotten what an exciting game it could be.

MARCH 5 (SUNDAY)

TO MY astonishment Bob Fletcher, who almost never comes to the office on Sunday, appeared today, summoned me to his office as soon as I had broadcast and told me flatly I could not testify for Steve in Washington, as I am scheduled to do tomorrow.

"Who says I can't?" I asked, scarcely disguising my surprise.

"Mark Robson, if you want to know. And what he says around here goes. Sorry, Raymond."

It was another painful moment for me. It hurts me to see Bob in this predicament. I could see he was as unhappy as I.

"I'm sorry, too, Bob. But I shall have to do it. Even if I hadn't given my word to Steve, I would feel I had to do it. I think you know why. Will you tell Mark?"

"Personally, I wish you wouldn't, Raymond," he said after a pause.

"Personally, Bob?" I did not believe that for a moment. Steve Burnett was an old friend of his too.

The muscles in his face were twitching.

"You heard what I said."

His eyes had turned hostile.

"Yes, I heard, Bob."

There was nothing more to say, and I left.

WASHINGTON, MARCH 6

I CANNOT say that my appearance before the Senate Committee on Security and Americanism today was either brilliant or successful. The eminent solons, lawyers almost all, know their business. They were quite clever in preventing me from saying most of the things I had come to Washington to say.

The very fact that I was there to help Steve, to testify to his patriotism, his loyalty, his record, his character, intelligence, and so on, seemed to rub the Senators the wrong way. They are out for victims, and I was trying to thwart them.

Steve had warned me that for this particular committee there were two kinds of witnesses — "friendly" and "unfriendly." It is very simple. Friendly ones are those who go along with the committee; unfriendly ones are those who don't.

Obviously, the Senators placed me at once in the second category.

As a matter of fact, after I answered the first question and swore I had never been a Communist, the committee lost interest in me. It was as though no one who had not been a Bolshevik could have anything pertinent to say about someone whom the committee was trying to frame as a Red. At any rate, I got what I suppose you would call the ice-cold treatment.

Why had I asked to testify and take the members' valuable time? Answer: because I had known Stephen Burnett since our early days together in the diplomatic service, and could, I thought, help the committee to ascertain the truth about him.

Why had I myself left the diplomatic service? Voluntarily? There was a whole series of such irrelevant questions that had nothing to do, as I ventured to point out, with the charges that had been made in this committee against the accused.

"Accused?" Senator O'Brien roared. "Mr. Whitehead, you come here under a misapprehension. There are no 'accused' before this committee. We are not a court of law. We are an investigating group proceeding under the authority of the Senate."

"You've made serious charges, Senator — contemptible charges. . . ."

There was an uproar at this, and I was admonished not to lightly put myself in contempt of a duly authorized Congressional body.

I tried next to tell them the truth about Burnett, but I might have saved my breath. They were not interested.

"This committee," intoned O'Brien — and as he spoke I could not help wondering how such a shifty little man had ever squirmed into such a high position in the land — "is concerned with Mr. Burnett's part in turning over China to the Communists and thus participating in the Red conspiracy against the United States in favor of atheistic Red Russia."

"Ridiculous, Senator," I managed to cut in.

At that a representative of the Old South (he had reminded me all morning of a popular radio character, Senator Claghorn) leaned forward, his large, fleshy face reddening, his temples throbbing.

"Suh," he bellowed, "I must respectfully ask you to watch your language. I would have you know this committee does not consider itself ridiculous. I resent, suh, your choice of words."

"I said the charges were ridiculous, Senator."

O'Brien, of course, was more shrewd than his colleague.

"Mr. Whitehead," he said calmly but sarcastically. "Will you kindly tell the committee the extent of your experience in China?"

"None."

"What do you know, then, of Mr. Burnett's activities in China?"

"At first hand, nothing. But I have known him intimately in Europe. . . ."

"We're dealing here, Mr. Whitehead, if I may say so, with the China story — with how the Reds in the State Department turned over China to the Communist hordes — and I do not believe you can help us. Any other questions?" He turned, beaming to his Senatorial colleagues.

"Just a minute, Senator —" but he cut me off.

"If there are no further questions, that will be all for the witness."

There were no further questions, and it was all. I was dismissed.

MARCH 8

STEVE made an eloquent closing statement on this last day of his hearing. I do not think he impressed his inquisitors, but his moving words may have a good effect in the country if they are adequately reported in the press and radio.

Speaking calmly but incisively and with a ring of deep sincerity he said:

"I wish to point out that this committee has adopted some very strange tests of loyalty to this country. From your questioning of me it is evident that, in your opinion, an American official was not loyal if he supported the policy and actions of his own country in China. Gentlemen, I supported them and I supported my country. And I make no apologies for having done so. It is becoming clear to me, after a week in your company, that you would have considered me completely loyal — and above suspicion — had I opposed the policy and the actions of my country in China and wholeheartedly supported those of a foreign government — namely that of the inept, corrupt, and far from democratic regime of Chiang Kai-shek in China. I confess, gentlemen, that this peculiar criterion of loyalty to America, which you have done so much to foster in our press and among our people, and which holds that an American who felt more allegiance to the democracy of Roosevelt and Truman and General Marshall, than to the tyranny of Chiang Kai-shek is a traitor to his country and a Communist, to boot, is one which I do not subscribe to. With all due respect for this committee of the Senate, I tell you that it is a contemptible concept."

O'Brien rapped for order, his face twitching with anger not only at Burnett's words but at the applause in the room which greeted them.

"We did not invite you here, sir, in order to hear your views on what constitutes loyalty, but rather to hear your explanations of why you and other responsible officials of the government became so sympathetic to Communism that you participated in the Communist conspiracy to hand over China to Moscow."

This was an opening Steve Burnett was waiting for, and he made the most of it, I thought.

"Senator," he said, "I have been before you now for a whole week. You have prodded from me an incredibly vast amount of trivia about my life, my work, my behavior, my associations and my thoughts. You have sought, hour after hour, day after day, my opinions on every conceivable subject, problem and person here on earth. But you have not produced one iota of evidence in support of the charges you preferred against me: that I am, or was, a Communist, and that I participated in what you call a Communist conspiracy to turn over China to Red Russia. There was, of course, no such conspiracy in the State Department or anywhere else in America. The whole thing is a figment of the Senator's fertile imagination. China was never ours to keep or to give away. We made mistakes in China. But what happened there was, in the end, the result of history. We tried our best within our erring limits, to avert the catastrophe, for the Communist triumph there was a catastrophe — for us as well as the Chinese. We failed. The forces of history were too strong.

"Senator, indict the course of history, if you feel so moved. But I do not think that in the long run you are going to fool the people of America, as you may be fooling them for the passing moment. You are looking for scapegoats for all our failures. Finding scapegoats is easy. Finding the truth is difficult.

"In my own case the truth is very simple. I will restate it, as an answer to your specific charges, before I leave off. I am not, nor have I ever been, a Communist. My views on Communism, on Russia, on China, are on record over the years. Unlike your witnesses against me, former Communists for the most part, I did not ascertain the nature of Communism day before yesterday. I felt its true nature from the start and so expressed myself.

"One last word, if I may. The committee has impugned my loyalty to my country — in other words, my patriotism. It is always difficult and indeed somewhat embarrassing for a patriot — and I consider myself a patriot — to defend his patriotism by words. And I shall not here and now attempt to. I will merely remind you that a man's loyalty to his country can only be judged by his life, by the acts of his life. Mine, because of the nature of my work, are a matter of public record. They may not have been of much importance, but, such as they are, I stand on them. And I defy you, or any other body, to find them unworthy of a decent citizen."

Steve's voice fell away into silence and he sat back in the witness chair, a faint smile not so much of defiance but of inner confidence, lingering on his bony, ascetic face. The spectators, even the newspaper and radio reporters, seemed moved by the simple eloquence and by the burning sincerity of this remarkable man. There was an instant of silence which, to me, seemed an age. I saw O'Brien reach frantically for his gavel, but he was not quite quick enough to squelch the roar of applause which suddenly broke out from all sides of the room. Whatever the committee ultimately found, this spontaneous outburst was an important vindication for Steve, and I felt deeply thankful that it came at a moment when it must have greatly encouraged him. For though he did not show the least signs of it on the witness stand and had not breathed a word of it to me, I knew how immensely hurt he felt that such baseless accusations could be publicly hurled at him by members of the highest legislature in the land.

For the first time during this long final session, he turned his head to gaze about the room, as if surprised at the handclapping. I saw in his face how it pleased him. What matter if Senator O'Brien was hysterically pounding his gavel for order and shouting angrily that he would have the marshals clear the public out if it did not desist from any further demonstration. Burnett watched O'Brien with calm amusement.

NEW YORK, MARCH 9

STEVE thinks he completely cleared himself with the committee, or at least with the majority — for no decent man could hope to clear himself with Senator O'Brien. He was in good spirits coming up on the train from Washington this afternoon. At the State Department this morning everyone congratulated him on the way he had handled himself at the hearings and the secretary wished him Godspeed on his return to his post. Steve will spend the week end with us here and fly back to Berne Monday evening. He was also cheered by a trans-Atlantic phone call with his youngsters, though Marcia is down with the chicken pox, it seems.

MARCH 11

WHILE I labored all day and most of the evening on tomorrow's broadcast, Steve took Dick to a basketball game at the Garden this afternoon and Yvonne to the opera tonight.

As we sat around having a midnight snack just now, Steve said: "All day I've been thinking how much I have missed — missed forever — by being away so long." And turning to me: "Raymond, you old fool, you still don't know how lucky you are."

MARCH 12 (SUNDAY)

WE INVITED half a dozen people over after the broadcast tonight for a farewell dinner to Steve Burnett, but nearly all of them made excuses.

I was disturbed that Bob Fletcher turned us down. He is not only my friend, but Steve's. Bob — for God's sake — can't be afraid! Barbara Fletcher came, though — the more I see of her the more I love her . . . and admire her. She seemed bothered too about Bob. He had been, she said, detained at Robson's country place at Westport. The two of them, she suspected, were hatching something big for the network. But they might have broken it up, she thought, this Sunday evening, especially as it was Bob's last chance to see Steve before he left.

Barbara was not in the least disloyal to Bob. She was merely frank about him, as she is about all people and things.

"Steve," she said, in her quiet, low voice, "you ought to be glad you're not in the radio business. I think Bob was much happier when he was merely broadcasting."

"Well, diplomacy, Barbara, has its pitfalls too," Steve said good-naturedly, almost with a grin.

"You were wonderful down there, Steve," Barbara said. "We were all awfully proud of you. Or, perhaps I should speak for myself. I know I was. And Bob."

"Bob?"

Christopher Chambers perked up. He and a friend of Steve's, the head of the Federal Public Power Committee, named Sidney Goodrich, were the only ones besides Barbara who had come.

"Yes, Christopher — Bob, too," Barbara said, with some emphasis.

"My dear, I'm glad to hear it," Chambers said. So Christopher, I thought, has some doubts too. I hoped, though, for Barbara's sake, he would not pursue them any further. Not this evening, anyway. In the theater, he was merciless with those he thought were not living up to his own high standards of probity. And lately, when no new plays were opening, he had been turning in his column to radio and TV dramas. God help the network shows if he ever really does the job on them he has done on the Broadway theater.

Chambers turned to Burnett. "You've done more for this country this past week than you perhaps realize," he said.

"Have I?" Steve asked innocently. "I can't say I've been aware of it."

"You injected some guts into a lot of wavering people."

Sidney Goodrich spoke up for almost the first time. He was a man of fifty, with a weather-beaten, narrow, bony face and rather deep-set, intent eyes. A Midwestern type, the kind I grew up with as a youngster.

"You certainly put some beans into a lot of discouraged people in Washington," he said. "In all my years there, I've never known such gloom, such defeatism. You were the first, Steve, as I've told you, to stand up to O'Brien and expose him for the charlatan he is."

"He scarcely gave me the opportunity to do that, Sidney," Steve said with a chuckle. "He kept shutting me off."

"Not until you had got in a mouthful," Goodrich said. I recalled now what I had heard of this man with the gaunt look of a Mississippi Valley farmer. As chairman of the Federal Public Power Committee he had fought toughly for public power, especially for the big dams the Federal Government had built in the Tennessee Valley and out West. He was, I suppose, the most hated man in Washington among the private power groups. Almost daily in the papers he was attacked by some private business organization. Shuttleworth, Bert Woodruff and other commentators and columnists were continually holding him up to the public as a menace to the American Way of Life. I could see now, as I looked him over, that he carried a good many scars of battle. He had a battered but unbowed look.

We did not, however, spend the evening wallowing dejectedly in concern over the ills of this blessed country. Steve himself soon steered the conversation to more pleasant topics. It was not at all that he was trying to escape or even ignore or forget the consequences of what had shocked him and hurt him on this brief visit. The truth was that other things interested him also and that he had woven them into a life so rich and varied that really it could never be ruined or even greatly darkened by the Senator O'Briens and their minions in the press and on the radio, or by any temporary aberrations in a country he passionately loved.

"By the way," he said, turning to Christopher Chambers. "I was interested in your column today about our theater being in the doldrums. I regret I haven't had time to see more than two or three Broadway musicals. But I must say I greatly liked them. They're something we're doing, at the moment, anyway, better than anyone else abroad. There's really nothing in Europe that can hold a candle to them."

"I agree with you on that," Christopher said grudgingly.

"What a concession, Christopher!" Barbara laughed.

"And music, Chambers!" Steve fairly bellowed. *"N'est-ce-pas,* Yvonne?"

"It is wonderful in this country," Yvonne said.

"Last night, Chambers," Steve said, "I went to the opera with Yvonne. . . ."

"Where was Raymond?" Chambers said facetiously.

"He doesn't appreciate opera," Yvonne laughed.

"I was working," I said, "on the bloody broadcast."

"They did *Parsifal,* Chambers," Steve resumed. "I've heard it in Berlin, in Munich, in Vienna, even in Wagner's native Bayreuth. But I'm telling you, you have to go to the Met to hear it as I believe Wagner meant it to be heard. It was tremendous!"

"They do it all right," Chambers conceded.

"All right? They do it magnificently. I tell you, Chambers, you have a city here! It's beyond anything else in the world!"

"I like it. It has its points," Chambers grunted. I had never heard him concede so much before.

"By the way — if I may change the subject —" Steve spoke up. "Are the Yankees and the Dodgers going to repeat this year? And give me another nervous breakdown, as they practically did last year, even though I could only listen in on a screeching short-wave receiver there in Berne, when they both cinched their pennants on the very last day — the Yanks, remember, with a 5-3 win over Boston, and Brooklyn with a ten-inning victory — I forget the score — over Philadelphia?

"What's the dope this year?"

What a man!

MARCH 15

THERE was a mimeographed notice on the Bulletin Board at F.B.C. this morning which I never expected to see. The company is instituting a loyalty oath!

MARCH 16

I HAVE thought it over. I am not going to sign. I tried to see Mark Robson, who personally signed the notice, to explain my position; but his secretary said he was tied up. Bob Fletcher says I am making a mountain out of a molehill, and that this is not the time to do that. He agrees with me that the idea of a loyalty oath is silly. He says he argued with Mark all last week end to forget it. (That's why he couldn't join Barbara for the dinner for Steve.) He can't understand what the hell has got into the boss. It's only a temporary aberration, he's sure. In the meantime, he says, why not humor the old boy — and avoid being misunderstood by the sponsors, not to mention the public — and sign?

"It doesn't mean a thing, Raymond."

"Why sign a meaningless thing then, Bob?"

"Why be so stubborn over a trifle?"

We are drifting apart, Bob and I.

MARCH 17

AM I being stubborn, as Bob says?

The whole question of a loyalty oath is a difficult one — at least to me. I am asked by a private individual, the head of a private enterprise, to formally state to him that I am not, and never have been, a member of the Communist party; that I am not, and never have been, a member of any organization, assosociation, movement, group or combination of persons which advocates the overthrow of our constitutional form of government by force, violence or any other unconstitutional means.

Mark Robson knows perfectly well what the answer is in my case. If he has any doubts, he can ask me and I will answer him, as man to man, or, if he prefers, as employee to employer — namely, privately and personally.

Legally, it is none of his business. Until recently in this country a man's political beliefs were his own affair. According to the law they still are. It is not a crime, as E. B. White once remarked, "to believe anything at all in America."

Where will Robson's power as an individual lead, if he gets by with this one? If he, as a private citizen, can bring pressure (the threat of losing my living) on me to declare today that I am not a Communist, can he not tomorrow force me to state whether I am a Democrat, a Republican, an Elk, a Legionnaire or a member of the Society for the Prevention of Cruelty to Animals? It was not so long ago in some industries that mere membership in a union caused a man to lose his job.

And why stop with broadcasters (and teachers and civil servants)? Or, for that matter, with an oath of loyalty only? Why not ask every citizen — businessman, lawyer, doctor, banker, Congressman — to swear, not only that he has never been a Communist or been otherwise disloyal, but that he has never done an unethical thing in his career?

On the other hand, in these uneasy times, after what we have learned of Communist methods of infiltration and learned too where an American Communist's allegiance lies, I am prepared to admit that there is a case for Robson not wanting to have Communists working in a field so important to the public as radio.

But is he going to weed out any Communists at F.B.C. through a loyalty oath? Of course not. The Communists will be the first to sign. No doubt the vast majority, who are not Communists, will, with a few exceptions like myself, sign too. Their life is insecure enough without placing it further in jeopardy by indulging in the luxury of standing up for their civic rights and their law-given freedoms against the head of an industry which gives them their living. I feel a deep sympathy for these folk and do not blame them for conforming. They are the already beaten ones, who have exchanged a good deal of their personal freedom for a secure, if modest, income from the owners and managers of private businesses.

Even so, the morale of these people at F.B.C. has been dealt a sickening blow by Robson's demand for a loyalty oath. They will sign, but they resent that their loyalty to this country has been questioned by the company. Many of them have drifted into my office since yesterday, some resentful, others angry, almost all frightened and all, I feel, hurt by what they consider an affront to their personal dignity.

They have asked me to head a delegation to discuss the matter with Robson.

MARCH 20

AFTER the broadcast yesterday Archy Oakes announced triumphantly that we had been renewed for another thirteen weeks. William McKinley Forbes had phoned him in the control room while I was on the air. The old man must have liked something I said, though I cannot imagine what.

"Did he have anything particular on his mind, Archy?" I asked.

"Only that he was renewing. What more do you want?"

"Well, the last time it came up," I said, "he told me bluntly he didn't like my line. Bad for business, and all that."

"We're selling cigarettes, aren't we?" Archy exclaimed, as if the mere idea excited him and, moreover, exhausted the subject.

Though Yvonne did not agree with me, I felt today that I ought to let Forbes know that I wasn't signing the loyalty oath at F.B.C. and explain why. But I couldn't get through to him on the phone. These business barons are guarded like medieval lords behind their ancient moats.

Maybe, in renewing, Forbes is merely being a good businessman, since my audience rating now tops all other Sunday early evening shows on F.B.C. Maybe a big audience for his commercial about United Tobacco products is more important to Forbes than any ideas of mine he may not like.

And maybe not. Maybe he couldn't get a suitable replacement in time.

Anyhow, I'm contractually employed for another 13 weeks. Yvonne says she doesn't understand the radio life — this living, as she puts it, by brief spurts.

"Maybe some day, Raymond," she said tonight, "we can find something a little permanent in America."

MARCH 21

THE president of F.B.C. finally received us this afternoon. Bob Fletcher was at his side, but scarcely took part in the conversation. To his credit, he seemed depressed by the whole affair and spent most of the time, as on a previous occasion, gazing morosely out of the window at the fog which lay thick over Manhattan's spires.

We got nowhere with Mark Robson. He seemed especially resentful that I should be the spokesman of his intimidated employees. And he made it plain that he was displeased to find F.B.C.'s personnel questioning his judgment, particularly on what he called "the issue of patriotism." Of course, if it had been an issue of business policy we wouldn't have been there. But we denied that patriotism had anything to do with it.

Mark, dapper as always, but a little bristling, I thought, as if he wanted us to take only a few minutes of his valuable time, opened the meeting with a brief speech. He was glad to receive us, he said, but surprised at the reason for our coming.

"As you all know," he said, "we are again faced with a crisis in our national life. The cold war is growing more intense and may soon pass into a warmer kind of war, if not a shooting war. We in radio have important obligations and responsibilities in this crisis. For my part, I am determined to fulfill them; and I know you are.

"Now, one thing we have to do is to make sure that the full

confidence of our listeners — and with TV, I must add our viewers — is not in any way impaired. That is why we have asked you to answer a few simple questions. Your responses, I hardly need say, will be kept strictly confidential, unless, of course, the F.B.I. or some other security agency of the government should ask to peruse them.

"Now I want to emphasize," Mark said, raising his voice, "that we are only requesting you to answer questions which the Federal Government itself asks of every civil servant in the service of the nation."

"There is a difference between public and private . . ." I started to say, but Mark icily cut me off.

"If you don't mind, Mr. Whitehead, I should like to finish my preliminary remarks, which are explanatory of why we have taken this step and which, I assure you, shall be extremely brief. Afterward I shall be more than glad to hear your questions.

"We are engaged, as you know, in a distinctly public business," Mark went on — as if the dullest member of our little delegation did not know that however public radio was, it was carried on for private profit, by private management and that this private aspect was one of the issues involved in the loyalty oath — "and therefore it is only fair, I think, that all of us in radio and TV take the same pledge of loyalty as that taken by public servants, that is, by those who serve the public directly in government. Just as in government we cannot tolerate subversion, no more can we tolerate it in broadcasting.

"In fact, radio is a particularly sensitive organism of our public life. I need not tell you that in the minds of some patriotic citizens and of some patriotic organizations radio is already suspect. We must make ourselves, like Caesar's wife, above suspicion. That is the reason for this loyalty oath, and the only reason. I myself shall take it. I expect you to take it. Any questions? I am at your disposal."

He looked at us, beaming and confident, as if he were the most reasonable man in the world.

I tried to put our case as best I could, striving to express not so much my own personal opinions, which were rather

strong, but those of the dozens of employees who had spoken out of their hearts to me, and which were, God knows, moderate enough.

In summary it was this: that the company's proposal raised the disquieting specter of one private citizen assuming the authority to investigate and pass judgment on the private life of another, or of one private business concern doing so.

"The employees of this company," I said, "feel as loyal to this nation as any other group of citizens. They recognize the Communist danger. But they also recognize that you are not going to catch a single Communist by this loyalty oath, since Communists will be the first to sign it.

"You have said," I continued — and I could see on Mark's face his growing impatience with me — "that you are asking only that we sign the identical oath required of all Federal civil servants. Aside from the difference between public and private employees, between the government and a private employer, there is an even greater difference here. In the government, a suspected or accused person has the right of a hearing. He can appeal the decision of one board to a higher one. Has F.B.C. provided any such elemental safeguards?"

Mark was at first a little taken aback by the question and then resentful of it.

"I don't see what safeguards you need. All we're asking you to do is to sign a statement," he finally replied.

"It would seem only fair," I said, "for F.B.C. employees to have the same protection as the government provides civil servants. The oath, as you emphasize, is identical. We think the safeguards should be too."

"I'm sorry I cannot follow you," Mark said, and moved as if to dismiss us. But I didn't want to be dismissed without a final word.

"We earnestly hope, Mr. Robson, that you will reconsider this matter. We cannot believe that you have any doubts whatsoever as to our loyalty to this country — and indeed to this company. If you have, we welcome your investigation of individual cases, provided, of course, that the suspects are given every fair means of defending themselves."

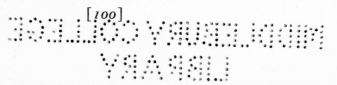

Mark squirmed in his seat, giving me a dark look which left no doubt that at this particular moment he would like to wring my neck.

"One final word, Mr. Robson. We know that you are perfectly aware that practically all of the couple of thousand employees of F.B.C. will sign this loyalty oath if you make them feel that their jobs are in jeopardy should they not sign. But I remind you that it will have no more worth than any other act of allegiance performed under duress. Almost all will sign, but under protest, resentful of what they consider an assault on their personal freedom and civic rights, and an affront to their patriotism and their personal dignity."

I paused. I had a fleeting temptation to ask Bob Fletcher what he thought of the matter, but remembering another time here, I resisted it. He did not seem to be in a mood to talk.

"As for myself," I said, "I will not sign the oath. But I assure you, sir, that I have not asked, and shall not ask, any other employee to follow my example. The others, I am sure, will follow their conscience and their own best judgment."

I might, of course, have saved my breath. Mark, relieved that I was through, smiled pleasantly at us, but it was obvious that having gone so far he was not now going to be put off. I have the impression he thought I was back of this whole *démarche* and that had I minded my own business his employees would have signed without a whimper. His manners, I must say, were conciliatory even at the end though they did not hide his determination to be unyielding.

"We have heard each other out," he said, smiling. "I must confess that some of the things Whitehead said certainly surprised me if, as he claims, he speaks for my fellow workers in F.B.C. But nothing he has said, though I have listened most carefully, has convinced me that I am anything but right, that I am doing anything but my patriotic duty, in going ahead with this loyalty oath. As I said, I shall sign, and I expect everyone else at F.B.C. to sign."

"May I ask, sir," I said, "on behalf of the others, what are to be the consequences, if any, for those who do not sign? Whose principles and conscience, as in my own case, do not permit them to sign?"

"I will be frank with you," Robson said, eying us all. "I myself cannot see that there is any place at F.B.C. for anyone who does not sign. Unless —" he hesitated, looking around at the scowling Fletcher, who had been no help to him at all — nor to us either —"unless there is some compelling reason — and I can't think of any now — to make an exception."

He glared at me, as he finished the sentence.

A heavy fog over the East River tonight and I feel in tune with it. All evening the tugboats have kept up a din with their whistles, and far down the river the big ocean vessels have been chiming in with their melodious foghorns — a melancholy but pleasing sound out of the murky night that brings back in me a nostalgia for the sea and distant shores, where I would be far from the pettinesses of this frantic, ulcered island.

Bob Fletcher stuck his head into my cubicle today and said: "How foolish can you get?"

I started to ask him to come in, but he vanished.

MARCH 26 (SUNDAY)

AFTER the broadcast this evening I half expected to receive a note from Robson notifying me that this was my last broadcast. But none came. Archy Oakes looked worried, but said nothing. The talk at the office today was that all but seven had signed the loyalty oath.

Jim Fiske, one of the news editors, father of a large brood of children, and a very decent chap, probably expressed the feeling of the vast majority today.

"What the hell, Raymond, we're all whores. We'll do anything for money. We have to live, don't we?"

Yvonne off this morning with Barbara to the Fletchers' country place for the rest of this week to help get it ready for spring. It has been so wintery I had not realized that spring was upon us.

What is that line from Shelley — or is it Keats? . . .

O, wind,
If Winter comes, can Spring be far behind?

MARCH 29

THE house lonely without Yvonne. We have now been together uninterruptedly for six months, since last September 1 — the longest such period since our marriage. It has been the best time of all. Fun, too, the last couple of days, having the children all to myself. I know them a lot better now after seeing so much of them the last half year. But that is not to say they are not unpredictable. Last evening, with Yvonne gone, Maria, who is going on thirteen, announced firmly that I was mistaken if I thought her bedtime was 8:30.

"Well, what do you claim it is?" I asked. It was already past 8:30.

"It is not 8:30," she insisted. "It is much later than 8:30."

She was scheming to see some silly show on TV at 9 P.M., I realized later. A few minutes after 9, I came down from my study to catch her, with Dick, absorbed in some God-awful drama in the darkened dining room. I waited until it was over, and then carried her up on my back to her bedroom.

"I thought your mother and I had an understanding with you, Maria, about this TV business."

"What understanding, Papa?"

"That it's limited to the hours between 5 and 7 — and then not while you're having dinner."

But she did not admit knowledge of any such thing.

After I had put the youngsters to bed tonight — Dick kept me up until ten with his expert dope on the coming baseball season in both big leagues — I fell to ruminating on my work. Even if broadcasting were not so unpredictable and insecure, I ought to think about getting back to my writing. Old Henry Wadsworth Prentice has been after me again to do some articles for *U.S.A.* And there is that book which has been turning over in my mind so long — a sort of farewell to Europe — and the notes I have been scribbling since New Year's for a play.

[*103*]

I have held off returning to the discipline of writing because I wanted to give everything I had to the Sunday broadcast. I have really worked at it seven days a week. Apparently some people around F.B.C. think that is excessive — for one show. They point out that other commentators are doing five broadcasts a week.

Most curious of all — and most distressing: apparently one or two persons at F.B.C. who ought to know better, think that by confining myself to one performance a week I am lazy. A hint of Bob Fletcher's to that effect the other day troubled me.

MARCH 30
I MET Dick and Maria at their school this afternoon and took them ice skating at the new artificially frozen pond in Central Park. The season ends tomorrow and there was an unholy mob of shouting, tumbling youngsters getting in their last licks. But we had fun. Afterward I took the two of them over to Rumpelmayer's on Central Park South for a cup of hot chocolate and cakes. Maria especially seemed entranced at being treated like a lady, but I doubt if either she or Dick got as big a kick out of it as did I.

MARCH 31 (FRIDAY)
ELSIE McCABE must be psychic about Yvonne being away. At any rate, she phoned me at the office this afternoon and insisted that I drop by her place for a cocktail. As I had nothing else on, I went.

She has been dieting furiously these past months. She said she was down to 150 pounds — from the 200 in Geneva last summer. Even if, as it looked to me, she's nearer 165 pounds, that's quite an improvement. Physically, she begins to resemble the Elsie of old. But otherwise, I really can't take her any more.

She talked mostly about "Red Airwaves," which, she said, is about ready to go to press.

"What are the charges in my case, by the way?" I asked.

"Two," she snapped.

"Only two?"

"Two main ones, anyway. First, that you were active in some anti-Fascist, anti-Nazi group which was dominated by the Commies. Second, that in your broadcasts you constantly take the party line."

"I wouldn't even know what that was," I broke in.

"Well, specifically, they cite your defense of Stephen Burnett."

"If that makes me a Red, my dear Elsie, I'm guilty. And, of course, I was active in a group in Europe to rescue Italian and German intellectuals from Mussolini and Hitler."

"I'm not denying they've got the goods on you. I'm merely saying . . ."

"For Christ's sake, Elsie!" I had vowed I would keep my temper, but it was of no use — with her.

"I was merely trying to say . . ."

"Well, don't say it!"

I suddenly thought of something that Steve had asked me about.

"By the way, Elsie. Is it true that you testified in secret session before the O'Brien committee against Steve Burnett?"

She eyed me closely for a moment, half shutting her eyes.

"I testified."

"Voluntarily?"

"Of course."

"You bitch!"

"I felt it was my duty," she added, and now she was the cold female I remembered who in the old days would do any dirty job if she thought it helped the Communist cause. Her iciness cooled me too, and calmed me down.

"You knew the truth about Steve — that he not only was never a Communist nor fellow traveler but opposed them in every diplomatic post he had."

"Not in China. He took the party line there. A mere coincidence, no doubt."

"Not true. And you, Elsie, who worked for the party out there for a short time before you broke, know it perhaps better than anyone else. You hated him then because he took an American line, laid down by his own government."

But argument was useless with Elsie. When will I get it into my soft head that her fanaticism burns as fiercely as ever, that it scorches a sense of truth out of her today as it did before? And that it is as senseless to argue with her now, when she is at one extreme, as it was formerly when she was at the other?

I got up to go.

"At least you're going to stay for a drink," she said determinedly.

I suppose that was the least I could do. Anyway, I stayed for it. It seems to be part of the pattern of our rare meetings over here, which I ought to terminate for good. Like the last time, sipping a highball together seemed to mellow her. She joked about her dieting and her beauty treatments. I, relaxing a little, too, congratulated her on their success.

"You're wiping off the years, Elsie."

"From you, Raymond, that's more than a compliment. It gives me hope, darling."

At the door, just before she kissed me good-by, she said: "Are you happy, Raymond? On the whole?"

"Quite."

"At home, I mean."

"Yes."

"How is it possible?"

It is something she will never understand. I smiled, we kissed and I left.

APRIL 3

FOR some time now I have felt that Barbara and Yvonne were jointly troubled about Bob and me. I suspect that is one of the reasons why Barbara invited Yvonne up to the country for all of last week — to talk things over.

They were both on the phone the minute my broadcast was over yesterday, insisting that I drive up for supper and spend the night. Bob, said Barbara, would stay over if I came.

We had a good dinner, the four of us, Bob being quite chipper and full of talk about the farm. He spoke eagerly of building up his dairy herd and of buying some nag in England for improving his breeding of horses. He thinks perhaps Winston Churchill, who has taken up the pastime, will send him one.

It was a relief for me to get away from my troubles at F.B.C. At least, it was at first. But toward the end of dinner I began to feel that Bob was straining a little to keep the conversation away from them. Once when Barbara started to ask me about something I had said in the broadcast, he gave her a rather severe glance, raised his voice and went on with his talk about the horses and cows. Churchill, he said, now that the elections had gone against him, might be slipping over here for a brief rest and, if so, might spend a week end at the farm.

By the time the dessert came I could feel too that Barbara, and even Yvonne, were getting awfully anxious to see that Bob and I hit it off. They kept trying to steer the conversation back to old times. But it wasn't much use. Bob didn't go for it; neither did I.

They insisted on leaving us alone for coffee and a smoke, but well meant as the gesture was, it was pretty futile. I could see Bob resented it. He offered me a cigar — I knew how proud he was of his special stock — and seemed slightly annoyed when I said as good-naturedly as I could that I would stick to my pipe. Bob used to be a pipe-smoker himself.

He sat morosely staring at the candles in the centerpiece and biting his cigar. The silence was enormous, and I kept wondering how I could break it. For a few moments I hoped that now that we were alone — secluded from the office vipers and even from our wives — he might tell me frankly and quietly whether I was through at F.B.C. for not signing the loyalty oath. I was quite in the mood to hear the worst, and hearing it straight from him, with no nonsense, would have afforded me considerable relief. But he said nothing, and I did not try to prompt him. Finally he forced a smile and turned to me.

"Tell me, Raymond, how are the youngsters?"

"Full of beans," I said, and asked him about his.

"You must bring Dick and Maria up here soon for some riding. They were pretty keen about the horses last summer."

"Nutty about them," I said, trying to laugh.

"What do you say, we join the ladies?" he said, getting up. "By the way, Yvonne is looking more beautiful than ever."

"I was just thinking the same about Barbara."

Probably my words sounded as hollow as his. Actually Barbara becomes more attractive each month. She is in some kind of a new bloom, physically, spiritually, and her roots are deep. And she grows closer to Yvonne, who reciprocates her affection.

As we entered the living room both women greeted us warmly, a little as if we had just come in from a long journey. It was half in fun, of course, but I could feel them eying us closely for some clue as to how we had fared alone. Bob put on a jaunty air, and I tried to be as nonchalant as possible. Both of us, I suppose, fear to drag our wives into our troubles, but Yvonne knows the score well enough and I gather Barbara does too, though perhaps not from much that Bob has told her.

Bob poured highballs and then proposed a round of poker. He is a keen and shrewd player with a genuine passion for the game but, as usual, when the four of us play, he contrived to let the women win most of the hands. It was quite a bit of fun. We laughed a lot and for an hour or so, until we broke up, Bob seemed to free himself from the hard shell he has encased himself in until I began to think — and happily — that perhaps my own sizing him up of late had been a little faulty or at least premature. Perhaps one expected too much of friends, especially at the age we had reached when the scramble for the big prizes of career and position and wealth reached its climax and the going became rough and tough and a certain ruthlessness was necessary over the final stretch.

When I came down to breakfast this morning at eight, Bob had already left for town. He had an early appointment, Barbara thought, with Mark Robson.

APRIL 4

ELSIE told me the other day, after we had subsided, that Sidney Goodrich, who has taken such a beating from the business leaders as the courageous head of the Federal Public Power Committee, is resigning to join *World Review* at twice his government salary. I doubt it. What could Goodrich write that Verne Gibson would publish?

APRIL 5

BOB FLETCHER phoned down to my cubicle this afternoon and told me to beat it up to Mark Robson's office immediately.

"And, for Christ's sake, Raymond, be reasonable. I've been working on Mark all day. He's ready to be sensible, if you are."

I hurried up to the twenty-ninth floor and darted into the president's reception room. Apparently the matter was not as urgent as Bob had indicated. Miss Peckwith, one of Mark's secretaries, blond, metallic and cool as a cucumber, asked me to wait.

"It will be a few minutes, Mr. Whitehead, I'm afraid," she said. "Mr. Robson is in conference. But he's expecting you."

I ought to be used to cooling my heels outside of Mark's inner sanctum. I suppose almost everyone has to, except the mighty ones like Forbes or General Clark. It's part of the etiquette in Radio City or along Madison Avenue. It reminds you of rank, of your place, in case you forget, as I tend to do. But I never get accustomed to the waiting, nor take it very graciously.

After fifteen minutes or so, Miss Peckwith ushered me into the big office. Mark Robson, in a dark blue, double-breasted, pin-striped suit (he has them sent over from Saville Row, Bob says), greeted me quite cordially, I must say.

"Sorry to keep you waiting, Raymond," he said. His boyish grin was disarming. You couldn't help but like him at moments like this. He offered me a cigarette from his big silver case, and we sat down at his desk.

"How's the Sunday show going?" he asked pleasantly.

"All right, I guess."

"Have you seen old Forbes lately?"

"No, I haven't."

It occurred to me that I had pretty well lost personal contact with my sponsor, but I didn't want to go into that.

"You've given us a hell of a lot of trouble," Mark said. He was genial enough, as if he were half-jokingly rebuking a pestiferous child.

"I'm sorry if I have," I said, trying to reciprocate, at least, his good feeling.

"And some lousy publicity, Raymond."

I said nothing to that, and he went on, a little more seriously now but kindly enough.

"As Bob probably told you, we've been threshing this loyalty oath thing out. We're not going to fire you for not signing — that is . . ."

"I appreciate that, Mark," I broke in.

". . . that is," he continued, "if you're willing to play the game."

"What game?"

"I mean, if you don't go around crowing about putting something over on us — and . . ."

"Why should you ever think I would do that?"

"Well, I just wanted to be sure. We don't want you rushing off to the newspaper reporters, the radio editors and the columnists."

"It would never enter my head, Mark."

"Bob Fletcher tried to convince me you would be reasonable, and I'm glad to see that you are."

So Bob had really not turned against me; just the opposite.

"I've always tried to be reasonable, Mark," I said, half-joking.

"I can't say that you've always succeeded," he answered. Then his smile began to evaporate.

"I want you to know, Raymond," he said — and now his tone was a little formal as if he were beginning to address a recalcitrant employee — "that we have made an exception in your case because we know you personally and because we're familiar with your record, and we know what the answers to the questionnaire, in your case, are."

"I always told you," I said, "I would be glad to answer the questions personally and privately to you or Bob or any other official of F.B.C."

"I know that," he said, and I could feel that his resentment had not been entirely dissipated. He had still not completely forgiven me for leading the delegation to protest the loyalty oath. Now what lay beneath the surface — something Mark Robson rarely exhibited — began to come out. Probably he had not intended that it should. Perhaps I had provoked it.

"I must say frankly, Raymond," he said — leaning over the table, his eyes flashing a little and his youthful, smooth face set as sternly, I felt, as he could contrive — "that I have been tremendously disappointed by your general attitude since you returned."

He waited for this to sink in, and as I said nothing stifling the obvious question, he went on:

"I didn't expect, or want, you to be a yes-man — about F.B.C., your sponsor, the radio business or about anything else in this country. But I must admit I didn't expect you would be so out of sympathy with what we're trying to do."

"I call the shots as I see them, Mark," I said, a little abashed at my own cliché. "I don't claim I'm always right."

"You're wrong as hell most of the time, it seems to me. You're . . ." he stopped to search for the words . . . "You're so god-damned critical of everything!"

It wasn't that, of course, I was sure. It was the general view I took, the side I was on, which vexed Robson. Actually it had been his side too until fairly recently, until it began to be unpopular and threatened to become, perhaps, unprofitable. No one in Manhattan's jungle had a shrewder sense of business than Mark. I tended to forget that, but I remembered it now and decided that reasoned argument would be a waste of time.

"I quite realize, Raymond," he continued, and now he seemed to unfreeze a little, "that, as Bob Fletcher keeps reminding me, you were away a long time, out of touch with what was really going on here at home, and that, therefore, as you yourself have often said, you have a lot to learn. For that reason, Raymond, I'm staying with you. And I hope you'll stay with me."

I think I know what he meant. He grabbed a file of papers, slapping them down in front of him, indicating the interview was over.

I stood up. "Thanks very much, Mark. I appreciate your decision."

He sprang up and took my hand. "I think we understand each other better," he said, smiling.

"I think we do."

Tonight, thinking it over, I am sure I do.

APRIL 8
　　　　　YVONNE'S breakfast, though not mine, spoiled by an item in Bert Woodruff's column which she espied while we lingered over a second cup of coffee.

> IT WAS ABOUT TIME. The word in radio circles is that Prexy Mark Robson had Commentator Whitehead up to F.B.C.'s twenty-ninth floor for a choice dressing down. Vice-president and general manager Robert Fletcher took part in the spanking. Seems Spieler Whitehead, who chose to spend most of his life abroad, is balking at signing the network's loyalty oath. What's he afraid of — if his record is straight?

And Mark warned *me* about spilling our meeting to the press! Still — I do not get any pleasure in seeing Robson, and especially Bob (who, of course, was not present) become the darlings of a worm like Woodruff.

APRIL 9
　　　　　EASTER SUNDAY, and we took the children to St. Patrick's. It was so crowded we couldn't get in. We got caught up in the Easter parade along Fifth Avenue.

The display of wealth and fashion was impressive — if vulgar.

Pope Pius XII, I noted in my broadcast later, made a rather startling suggestion in his Easter sermon in Rome. He urged a voluntary redistribution of the world's wealth "according to a more equitable criterion of justice and charity."

If anyone in this country asked for that, he would be branded "Communistic." I do not believe the Pope is a Communist.

APRIL 10

TO A youngsters' party at the sumptuous Park Avenue apartment of "Betty and Bob," though Dick, who is fifteen now, declined to come, arguing he was much too old. Betty and Bob Collier, I ought to realize, are among F.B.C.'s better assets. They do a breakfast program from their home every morning, have an enormous following and a dozen well-paying sponsors. As Bob Fletcher puts it facetiously: without Breakfast with Betty and Bob, as the program is known, millions of Americans couldn't start the day properly.

The two of them fascinate me. For one thing, they are killing themselves — though they don't need the money. In their income bracket (Betty reminded me today they grossed a cool quarter of a million last year) most of what they earn goes to the Federal Government anyway — in income tax. It's a curious greed — for money you can't keep. Even without radio both of them would be twice as busy as most hard-working people. Bob Collier, dark, short, slight and as high-strung as a nag at the wire, has a widely syndicated Broadway gossip column in the dailies. He must average at least one piece a week in the slick magazines. He turns out four or five blasts a month for General Clark's papers. He is a frequent guest on other radio programs and he is working up a TV show for the fall. He's always dashing off a book of some kind. And lately he has given in to popular demand as an after-dinner speaker or toastmaster, for which he gets, he was saying today, from $500 to $1000 a shot.

Betty, as brittle a blonde as I've met in this town, but with a

[*113*]

driving power no less intense than her husband's, has a fabulously successful public relations firm she built up herself. She's in nearly all the big, slick women's magazines every month with some kind of cozy article. She also churns out drivel by the yard for General Clark. She's listed as one of Verne Gibson's editors on *World Review*. That alone, she says, brings her $25,000 a year.

But their main job is a half-hour breakfast program from 8 to 8:30 A.M. over our network six weekdays, and a half-hour Sunday show at noon — a back-breaking job in itself. Next fall they plan to televise all seven performances.

In radio, I guess, once you're at the top you can't stop. Not until you're toppled over by a new fad.

"We're making hay while the sun shines," Bob said. Even in private conversation he hops from one shopworn cliché to the next. He had great blotches under his eyes, which kept winking nervously. I wondered when he and Betty got any sleep since despite their furious labors they are constantly written up in the gossip columns as night-club owls. I asked him.

"Haven't had any for years, Raymond," he laughed. "Learned to do without it. Same with Betty. Wouldn't mind having a little in the morning. But they rout us out at 6 A.M. for the bloody breakfast show." He made a grimace that he probably is practicing for TV. "It's a dog's life, Raymond. But it pays."

It's difficult to see how these two ever had time to have a couple of children but, as millions of listeners know, they have them all right. They are called, of course, Betty and Bob, Jr., and sometimes, when you are listening to the program, you get a little confused by the Bobs and the Bettys.

At the party this afternoon I thought Betty and Bob, Jr., who are nine and twelve, respectively, were two spoiled brats. No wonder, the way their parents exploit them on the air. I suppose this is the one thing about the Colliers, who are otherwise harmless, though tiresome, that revolts me — the way they force the two youngsters each morning into the numerous commercials.

Our Maria, though, thinks Bob, Jr., is wonderful. They've struck up quite a friendship.

[*114*]

APRIL 11

SENATOR O'Brien is quoted in a Washington dispatch today as saying that his committee's report on Steve Burnett will be made public "soon." He gives no inkling of its nature. The fact that he hasn't leaked it to the Clark press is encouraging. If it were bad for Steve, I am sure O'Brien would have tipped off the General and the smearing would already have begun. Steve, himself, judging by his letters, is confident the committee will clear him.

APRIL 12

BETTY COLLIER told me the other day that Mark Robson was finally getting his divorce.

"It's going to cost him at least a million berries," she said, her eyes sparkling. Even mention of that much money casts a spell over our breakfast-hour heroine.

"Whatever happens to poor Colette Robson," Betty said, "she won't starve."

She won't have a husband, either, for whom she gave up the stage when she was already a star, and he was struggling to set up the F.B.C. network. Perhaps Betty was not thinking of that. I am fond of Colette Robson, though we have seen little of her. She has a timeless beauty and much grace and intelligence. Like all of us she is growing older, of course. The ballet dancer Mark is going to marry is quite young, they say — twenty-eight, I believe.

APRIL 13

YVONNE and I caught the Betty and Bob program at breakfast this morning. They put on a wonderfully smooth spiel together, chatting amiably about last night's new play, what people wore, who was with whom and tidbits about the players and the playwrights, all of whom they referred to by first names as if they were old personal friends. About halfway through the program, the children appeared and there was fam-

ily chatter about their school, to which they were getting off, Bob
Collier asking his son with true fatherly concern how he was
doing in "mathematics" and Betty chiming in with a similar
question about her daughter's "geography." (I can't imagine
Betty having the faintest notion where *any* place outside of midtown Manhattan is.) Then the children were slipped smoothly
into a commercial.

"My darlings," said Betty. "Did you get your Rice Crackies
this morning?"

"Yes, Mother," they chorused.

"Were they good?"

"Tops, Mother."

That was the cue for Bob Collier to cut in with his deep,
warm, cushy voice.

"You see, folks, there's nothing like Miller's crunchy Rice
Crackies to get the youngsters off on the right foot every morning of the week. Rice Crackies build them up too. And they
taste good. . . ." He hesitated a second. "How about it, son?"

"That's right, Papa. Rice Crackies taste good. And they make
you strong — like Superman!"

Young Betty, aged nine next got into the act on her own
power.

"Mama," said she, with a feigned whine. "When are we going
to have pancakes again for breakfast?"

"Why, darling," said Betty, in a most motherly fashion, "we're
going to have them tomorrow morning, without fail. Golden,
delicious griddle cakes made of Seagraves's ready-mix — like
Mother used to make."

"They're wonderful, Mama. Really wonderful," the little tot
recited.

Finally Bob, Sr., intervened. "Now off to school, children, or
you'll be late. Kiss your mother good-by." One heard the
smacks, as if the sound technicians were at work, and . . .

"Do you want to hear any more?" Yvonne asked impatiently,
her finger already on the dial.

"That will do for one day," I said. "By the way,
Yvonne . . ."

"What?"

"How would you like to do a breakfast program with me? They pay money for it. And I wouldn't have to say anything that would displease the sponsor and the network. Just rave about Crackies and Crunchies."

"God forbid!" She laughed.

APRIL 14

I SUPPOSE the real reason Mark Robson keeps me on is that I am a bit of a commercial asset. Archy Oakes telephoned today to say "our" rating again topped all other F.B.C. Sunday early evening shows. That's about all the advertiser cares about. And if the advertiser is happy, so is F.B.C. Still — William McKinley Forbes has not of late communicated his happiness to me. I wonder why.

Archy didn't know, when I asked him today.

"Don't worry," he chirped.

"I'm not worrying. I just wondered what had happened to the old bastard."

"We're selling his tobacco, ain't we?" Archy said.

APRIL 15

SATURDAY, and I took the youngsters over to Madison Square Garden to see the circus. There's more pageantry and color in it than in my boyhood days in Indiana when I saw it under canvas, but the clowns don't strike me as being as funny now as then. The stuff on the trapeze is still exciting. There were a couple of daredevil acts this afternoon that kept Dick and me glued to our seats, breathless. Maria liked the horses best.

It was fascinating watching the youngsters — they got such a tremendous pleasure and so much pure excitement from the spectacle. Dick, at fifteen, is fast becoming a man. His voice today was almost as deep as mine. He is within an inch of my six feet, though still on the spindly side. And he is eager as hell about life, which pleases me greatly. Of course, he's a little mixed up right now in his adolescence. He gets moody. I suspect the girls trouble him somewhat.

Maria, at thirteen, is just getting into adolescence, and so far it hasn't bothered her. Despite a slight resemblance to me, she is going to be rather pretty: the snub-nosed, sparkling-eyed, vivacious, extrovert type. Apparently she is going to skip the awkward age.

I could not detect today any trace of the French accent they brought over with them less than a year ago. I don't know why this should so please me — am I a Midwest provincial at heart? — but it does.

APRIL 17

A LETTER from Wendell Lewis Philpots in Paris. It was good to hear from him. Underneath his sweet reasonableness and even cheerfulness, I detect a slowly growing desperation about life. He asks how I feel about America now that I've been back so long. What shall I reply? What *do* I think?

His question gives me an idea. For many months now I've been making notes for the "Farewell to Europe" book. Perhaps I had better try to do a book on coming home to America.

APRIL 18

NO WORD from Elsie for some time. I wonder what's happened to that radio black list she used to get so excited about?

You can't fail but follow her doings. She's in the papers nearly every day now as sort of a finger-pointer for Senator O'Brien. The eminent solon has had some more hapless victims from the State Department before his inquisitorial committee and Elsie, according to the newspaper accounts, has put her finger on a surprisingly large number of them, swearing under oath she once knew them as Communists. In the case of three or four whom I happened to know well in Europe I am positive Elsie is lying.

[*118*]

Yesterday at a public hearing of the committee when one Senator finally got up enough guts to ask Elsie for some proof of her charges she answered blandly that the particular persons she was asked about were "known" to be in the party.

" 'Known' by whom?" asked the brave Senator.

"By our top-level officials," said Elsie.

"Did their names ever figure on any of your records?" the Senator persisted.

"Not necessarily. But I can assure you, Senator, these gentlemen accepted party discipline."

"Meaning?" the Senator started to ask.

"Meaning they took the party line."

No proof, in other words; merely the word of a former lady Communist fanatic whom I personally know to be a liar.

Probably Frederick Newman, who also testified, is even a bigger one. I must ask Elsie about him sometime, when she is in a relatively truthful mood. He was, I gather, a bigwig in the Communist party here during Elsie's years in Moscow, and indeed up until the end of the war. He seems now to be what you might call a professional ex-Commy, denouncing not only his former comrades, which is all right with me, but also denouncing as Communists nearly every liberal whom Senator O'Brien hails before his committee, which is vicious. Newman recently started a daily column in the Clark press devoted to exposing alleged Communists and has become so shrill and hysterical that, as Christopher Chambers predicted the other day, Newman will soon be accusing that old flag-waving reactionary, General Clark himself, of having secret ties with the Reds in Moscow.

APRIL 19

A LOVELY, warm, balmy day, and I felt a spring fever coming on. Stayed home all morning, watching the boats go by and the trees on the river coming alive, and daydreaming about having a little place in the country of our own. Yvonne keeps reminding me that all we lack is the money. Perhaps we can find something cheap.

I told Yvonne we must start looking. Perhaps I can hurry up the book. Perhaps it will be a best-seller.

APRIL 20

CHRIS CHAMBERS dropped by for a drink after dinner tonight and his visit bucked me up considerably. He spoke brilliantly, as usual, about the theater, though he thinks it is in a deplorable state in this country at the moment.

"Playwrights and producers, like everyone else, are afraid. They're afraid of getting out of step, of saying something unpopular — something Senator O'Brien won't like. The result is they say nothing of interest, let alone of importance. Everyone is playing it safe. No wonder the theater is dull — and insipid — like in Russia."

"Like radio — and TV," I said.

"Oh, not *that* bad!" he exclaimed impishly. "I don't see how you stand it, Raymond!"

"Probably I won't have to, much longer," I said.

"So I've heard."

So my precarious status was no longer a secret.

"When the blow comes," Chris said, "as it must inevitably come to all, high and low, in radio, why don't you get out in the hinterland for a while and see how the rest of our splendid citizenry lives. We all get suffocated in New York, especially us critics and the writers. That's why we're so lousy."

"You seem to be surviving rather well, Chris," I said. Though he is in his early sixties and his hair snow white, he has an astonishingly youthful air. And his writing is as crisp and lucid and fresh as ever.

"I ought to get away from it too," he said, in a tone that meant he had not the slightest intention of adventuring beyond the Hudson River.

It would be a change for us to go West for a while. But what would I do out there? How earn a living?

AT BREAKFAST, the heartbreaking news stared us in the face from the front-page headlines in the newspapers.

O'BRIEN COMMITTEE HOLDS STEPHEN BURNETT PARTICIPANT IN COMMUNIST CONSPIRACY — CHARGES HE WAS INSTRUMENTAL IN TURNING OVER CHINA TO RUSSIA — CALLS FOR HIS DISMISSAL

I couldn't finish the meal.

The State Department, already jittery from the beating it has taken from O'Brien, announces the suspension of Steve and his recall from Berne pending a new investigation by the Department's Loyalty Board, which had already cleared him. I begin to see Steve spending the rest of his life defending his innocence — an ironic fate for one who has devoted the quarter of a century of his adult life to serving his country.

The Senate committee does not find definitely that Steve was a Communist, though the effect of what it does say is almost as bad. It points out that at least two witnesses, Elsie McCabe and Frederick Newman, testified under oath that Burnett was known as a member in top Communist party circles. But it adds that it does not "necessarily" find this charge proved.

What it does find proved, it claims, is that Burnett participated in "the Communist conspiracy to turn China over to the Soviet Union." He was "influential," it finds, "in bringing about a change in United States policy favorable to the Chinese Communists."

What nonsense!

And it demands his dismissal. The seething Clark press in red headlines, and Bert Woodruff and Frederick Newman in their columns, insist that Burnett be tried for treason!

This is a terrible blow to Steve. At the office this afternoon, as I was scribbling some notes about the case for Sunday's broadcast, a cable from Berne came in. It was typical of Steve.

"I realize the seriousness of my situation, utterly false as the accusations are. If you mention me in Sunday's broadcast, you might say I have just begun to fight. Hope to see you next week if it is not too embarrassing."

Embarrassing! Does he think I will turn my back on him now?

Do I mention him in the broadcast day after tomorrow? That will depend on Mr. Mark Robson and Mr. Robert A. Fletcher. Yvonne admonished me when I left for the office today to keep as cool and collected as possible. It was easy. No one at F.B.C. even mentioned the Burnett case.

APRIL 22

I MUST be catching on and growing up. To the Facts of Life. Today — Saturday — I wrote two broadcasts. If Mark and Bob censor the first I'll substitute the second. Who says I'm not co-operative, that I don't play the game? What a louse!

APRIL 23

A COUPLE of hours before air time, Bob Fletcher appeared at the door of my cubicle. He was scowling. He said Mark Robson had instructed him to have a look at my copy.

"You're bothered, I suppose, at what I may be saying in defense of our friend, Steve Burnett," I said, tossing him my first script. He did not take it at once, but, instead, let it lie on the edge of the table where it had landed.

"Yeah, Steve's in dire trouble, I fear," he said lugubriously, his face darkening.

"He certainly is, Bob. But he's taking it like a man. I had a cable. . . ."

"From Steve?"

"It's in there," I said, pointing to the script on the desk before him.

"God, I wish we could help him."

"We can, Bob!"

"I wish we could."

He took up the script, reluctantly, with a grimace. I put my feet up on my desk, lit my pipe and looked out the window, awaiting the verdict — not that I was filled with any crashing doubts as to what it would be.

I wondered why Bob took so long. Mark Robson had certainly given him his orders. I could feel him lingering over every page. Finally he broke the silence of the little room.

"It's a brilliant piece, Raymond," he began, and there was something desperate in his effort to smile. "But I think you know what I'm going to have to say."

"I think I do," I said.

He glared at me, and I could see the torment in his eyes. But there was a gleam of hostility too that I had come to recognize lately, a resentment that I was again forcing him into a humiliating position. I may be wrong, but I think that is what it was.

"I'm sorry, Raymond, but it just won't go. Mark Robson won't have it."

"Why not?"

"I believe you know. Must I spell it all out again?"

"No. I'll spare you that."

"It's kind of you," he said, and his wonderfully expressive eyes fairly blazed. This was another incident, I could feel, he would not forgive me.

"I'm sorry to have to do this only an hour or so before air time," he said after a while. "Have you anything else you can give?"

I tossed him my second script, but he did not take it.

"Anything in there about Steve Burnett?" he asked.

"Not a word. Every line, Bob, is as safe as a commercial."

He got up to go.

"I don't care for your sarcasm, Raymond."

He turned into the doorway.

"Steve was your friend, too, wasn't he?" I asked. He twirled around as if I had stuck a needle into him.

"That's right."

"Did you ever suspect him of being a Commy?"

"Why, no."

"And of doing the Commies' dirty work?"

"Of course not."

"Well . . . ?"

Again his eyes flashed darkly at me. Then he turned and without a word slid through the doorway and out.

APRIL 25

I DROPPED in on Elsie this afternoon, unannounced. For one thing, I wanted to tell her off for lying about Steve. Unfortunately, Bert Woodruff and Frederick Newman were there. It was difficult to get in a word, and of course I was outnumbered. Woodruff seemed even more soured than the last time I saw him, which was New Year's Eve. Unlike the other two he was never a Communist; just a crank — a demented fool.

I was interested in getting a firsthand look at Newman, now that, along with Elsie, he has become Senator O'Brien's star witness. He has the fanatic's burning, bulging eyes, and the tendency to hysteria as soon as he's crossed. He's glib and he's dogmatic. He tears the conversation away from you by simply bellowing.

When I said flatly, but quietly, that he and Elsie lied when they said they knew my friend, Burnett, as a Communist, Newman's eyes strained at their sockets, the veins in his temples throbbed, and he began to thunder that he had been keeping his eye on me, listening to my broadcasts and that more and more they resembled the party line.

"That's another lie," I said calmly, determined to keep my temper but not to give an inch.

"Anyway, you don't follow an American line," Woodruff said with a sneer.

Elsie, to give her her due, kept out of the argument most of the time, though once she interrupted Newman to say: "The main trouble with Raymond is that, like all so-called liberals, he's confused. That makes him blind to the Communist menace."

[*124*]

"Actually I was aware of it back when you and Newman still worshiped Communism blindly as a religion," I said, not failing to smile.

To remind Newman of his Communist past, I quickly learned, was like waving a red flag before a bull. He glared at me angrily.

"Well, Newman," I said, "you'll be denouncing me next as a Commy — though this is the first time you ever laid eyes on me."

"Maybe I will," he said, still glaring at me with his wild, protruding eyes — like a wounded animal watching his chance to strike back.

APRIL 26

RUMORS at the office of the imminent publication of a sensational radio black list — probably the one Elsie has been so excited about. Despite what she said a few weeks back, I can't think of anything in my unspectacular past that would qualify me for any black list — not even one drawn up by the zaniest crackpot. Elsie didn't bring the subject up yesterday.

APRIL 29

A CABLE from Steve Burnett that he would be arriving tomorrow evening. He is confident he will clear himself, and, since his youngsters are in school in Switzerland, he is leaving them there. I wonder how one's children take all this smearing of the father.

The Senate Executive Expenditures Committee has voted $25,000 for a new kind of investigation — though the poor beaten State Department is again the principal goat. This time an inquiry is to be made into the "homosexuals and other moral perverts working for the Federal Government." That may take the limelight away from Senator O'Brien and his hunt for Bolsheviks in Washington. Apparently the Washington vice squad recently informed the Congress that there were some 300 to 400 homosexuals in the State Department. This the Department denies. It says it got rid of 91 "perverts" between 1947 and 1949.

Perhaps there are a few fairies in the Department who have not yet been weeded out. We had a handful in the foreign service in my time and they were unpleasant characters to have to work with. There was always the risk too that the foreign government they were assigned to, or agents of some other government, could blackmail them into providing secrets they had no business providing. They were very vulnerable to blackmail.

We also had in the service, a few individuals who *acted* like fairies, but probably weren't. At any rate, they were married and had even fathered children. They were a great pain, too — especially "X" in Berlin and "Y" in Paris, with their whiny, falsetto voices, effeminate gestures and the damned poodles they were always walking on the leash.

Was "Y" corrupted in Paris by Gide?

APRIL 30 (SUNDAY)

STEVE arrived shortly after I got home from the broadcast. He looked more gaunt than I have ever seen him.

He thinks it best to fly on to Washington tomorrow, report to the Department, which has suspended him, and put himself immediately at the disposal of the Loyalty Board.

I strove all evening to ease his obvious depression. With his consent I sent off telegrams to half a dozen persons inviting them in for after-dinner coffee and highballs Thursday evening to meet him and to hear, off the record, his side of the case. We discussed who should be invited and settled on Mark and Bob, Shuttleworth, Sidney Goodrich, Verne Gibson and two or three local editors and publishers. Shuttleworth, the Great Voice, has been critical of Steve in his broadcasts, but since the old windbag wields such enormous power with his colossal nation-wide audience and since he is amenable to change if he sees some big battalions swinging to Steve's side, I thought it best to include him in our list. I asked Verne Gibson because it will give Sidney

Goodrich, who is soon joining him as an associate editor at *World Review* and who is an old friend of Steve's, a chance to work on his new boss. Steve seemed as surprised as I was that Goodrich was giving up the Public Power Committee to work for a man of Verne Gibson's hidebound views.

"Who's caving in to whom?" he asked.

"One guess," I laughed.

Not that it's funny.

MAY 1

MAY DAY and spring, which comes later here than in Europe, though we are more southerly, fairly burst out. Even in this city of stone and asphalt and grime, choking from the exhausts of a million sputtering gasoline motors and the raw, black belchings from the myriad chimneys and smokestacks, the air seemed full of the aroma of spring flowers. It was warm and soft. The causeway along the bank of the East River adjacent to the drive was full of strollers, their faces pale from the long winter, but their eyes lit up from a stirring inside. Off-duty crewmen on the tugs and barges, naked to the waist, were stretched out on deck in the sun. Yvonne was as happy and as radiant as a child because her tiny tulip bed had, overnight, broken out in bright red and yellow. At the office, it was just another day. In the bustle of a great radio network spring seemed shut out.

No replies yet to my telegrams.

MAY 2

THE Baldwin Day School is no doubt excellent, full of alert teachers, progressive theories and a fine, democratic spirit — and all that. But I wish to God it would find some means of imparting to Dick and Maria the elements of simple arithmetic, simple grammar, simple spelling and not leave that job to me. The time I've spent with them on the three "R's" would have sufficed to allow me to write the "Coming Home" book — or any other major opus. After two hours this evening

[*127*]

between them, I am firmly convinced that Maria has not yet really learned the multiplication table — no wonder she can't multiply fractions — and that Dick doesn't know an adverb from an adjective. Also, he spells by ear!

On the phone to Steve Burnett in Washington this afternoon I'm afraid I lied a little. I suggested we postpone the Thursday meeting. No one will come. But I couldn't tell him that. I just said everyone was so busy in New York you had to give them more notice. Most of the people we had asked said they were tied up.

Sidney Goodrich had the decency to phone from Washington to say that he was winding up his affairs there and couldn't get up to New York. He said he would see his friend Steve there. When I congratulated him on his new job at *World Review* he sounded slightly embarrassed.

"A man gets in a rut here, Raymond, you know," he said. "There comes a time, you know, when you have to think of your family and the future — when you have to think about getting out of debt."

"Quite right, Sidney." He had paused, and I had to say something.

"You know, for years, Raymond, they've been slandering me as being an enemy of private enterprise. I never was, you know. Thank God, Verne Gibson understands that."

"Well, good luck, Sidney," I said. "And let us know when you are here."

MAY 3

I BUMPED into Bob Fletcher in the elevator this afternoon and practically bludgeoned him into having a drink. He said he had to hurry home to dress for dinner.

We found a relatively quiet corner at the men's bar at the Waldorf. Bob looked so tired and worn I hesitated to say what was in my mind. But we seldom meet alone now. There might not be another chance for some days — or weeks. I put it as diplomatically as I could.

"I want your advice, Bob. I wanted very badly to get you and Mark and a few others like Shuttleworth together to hear Steve Burnett. I don't need to tell you he's completely innocent. None the less, he needs our help."

"I'm sorry, Raymond, I couldn't make it. I'm tied up as hell this week. What about the others?"

"The same, Bob. All tied up."

"Really?" he said, his handsome if weary face a picture of innocence. "That's a damned shame."

"Do you think there's any chance of setting up a meeting later?" I asked.

"Why not, Raymond?"

"Will you come, Bob?"

"I'll do my damndest to."

We lapsed into silence. I felt from his manner, polite though it was, that he would never come. Too much risk. And I began to feel something else. He began to eye me quizzically.

"I see in the papers," he said after a bit, "that Steve is staying with you."

"Don't believe everything you see in Woodruff's column, Bob."

"He isn't staying with you, then?"

"He stayed with us Sunday night — on his arrival. He certainly has a standing invitation, Bob, to put up with us whenever he's in town. At the moment, though, he's in Washington."

Bob seemed relieved at the news.

MAY 4

ELSIE tried several times to get through to me on the phone at the office this afternoon, but I didn't feel like talking to her. As a matter of fact I felt so low I didn't feel like talking to anybody. Mercifully, no one in the office, not even any of the men in the newsroom, who usually drop in to pass the time of day or suggest ideas for the Sunday broadcast, bothered me.

JUST before turning in tonight we caught the midnight news on one of the local stations. As a result I am making this brief, late-hour entry before going to bed.

The announcer read the piece excitedly, talking so fast that at first we were slow to catch on. "Red Airwaves," he said, will be published tomorrow and it will "rock" the radio industry and "shock" the country.

"Isn't that the thing you said Elsie has been ranting to you about?" Yvonne said, raising her voice above the staccato notes of the radio.

"That's it," I said.

The voice from the little box leaped on:

> "Red Airwaves," published by the Committee to Wake Up America, contains the names of 250 actors, writers, directors, composers and commentators prominent in radio who the publication alleges either belonged to Communist or Communist-front organizations or served the party line in what they wrote or said over the air. "We do not specifically accuse those listed," say the publishers, "of being Communists. We do accuse them of aiding and abetting Communism — in many cases perhaps unwittingly. Our only purpose in publishing this booklet is to inform the public, and in particular the networks, the advertising agencies and the great companies which sponsor the bulk of the programs on the air, as to what kind of persons — in 250 cases at least — are today providing America with what it hears on radio!"

Then followed — and here the announcer calmed down, lapsing into a monotonous tone — a "partial list" of those named in the book. There were some very well-known names. Mine was next to the last, almost as if it had been thrown in as an afterthought, or to bring the list up to a full 250, though it might have been because my name started with "W."

The voice went on to the other news of the day and Yvonne turned it off.

"Will you please explain what that's all about?" she asked. She has caught on — fast — to an awful lot over here, but there are a few things that still escape her and this, I could see from her face, was one of them.

"It's a black list," I said. "You know, the thing they had in Germany under Hitler and still have, I suppose, in Russia. Only, this one is private."

"Not important, you mean?"

"I doubt it, Yvonne."

"Nothing to worry about, then," she said, obviously relieved.

"I don't think so, darling."

"But you're not quite sure?"

"I'm never quite sure about anything nowadays."

She hesitated and then rather impetuously said, "Oh, Raymond, did you expect it would be like this?"

"Not exactly, maybe. On the other hand, Yvonne, I didn't expect this country would be predictable. Did you?"

She smiled.

I must ask Bob Fletcher — or someone — tomorrow about that other attempt — it was back in the mid-Thirties, I think — of some self-appointed superpatriot to put over a black list on radio. I remember reading about it in Europe. Over there it was taken as a joke. The thing, I believe, had a name similar to "Red Airwaves" — "Red Network," I think it was called. Among the "Reds" listed as a danger to America — if I am not mistaken — were Ramsay MacDonald, then prime minister of Britain, Freud, Gandhi, Bill Bullitt, Senator Norris and William Allen White. There were hundreds of others, mostly persons who didn't like the Fascists or Nazis. I might even have been on that one, for all I know. I never saw it.

I don't believe it ever got anywhere, though. A little too loony for the climate then.

MAY 6 (SATURDAY)

THE phone jangling all day. And what a day! I must try to figure out where it has left me.

William McKinley Forbes has canceled the sponsorship of my

Sunday broadcast. But Mark Robson is keeping me on, sustaining, for the remaining four Sundays of May. After that the time reverts to United Tobacco. I am going to fight that one, since with my audience rating I am sure I can sell the show to another sponsor. Apparently, despite the unbelievable tempest of this day, I stick at F.B.C.

It being Saturday, with business offices closed for the week end, I was unable to see anyone personally. I tried repeatedly to track down old Forbes after Archy Oakes phoned me the news from his home at Rye. Forbes had got him up in the middle of the night and ordered him, Archy said, to "fire" me — just as if he owned the network. Archy — very decently — spared me until eight A.M. On the phone he sounded as if the tobacco king had hit him over the head with a baseball bat. Probably I haven't sounded so chipper myself today. In fact I've been damned sore all day.

Forbes wasn't at his office, of course. I phoned him at his suite in the Waldorf Towers. A secretary — or perhaps it was the maid — said he was out of town for the week end. Where? She didn't know. I fired telegrams at him to every address I could think of — asking for an immediate interview, today! — but nothing has come of them.

Bob Fletcher has been encouraging. He is up at his country place in Connecticut, and Mark Robson is at his, nearby, but we have been on the phone together several times. Bob doubts that F.B.C. is going to be stampeded by "Red Airwaves," but expects plenty of trouble from the chicken-hearted sponsors. He says Mark Robson's first reaction is to ignore the black list.

Mark himself has behaved quite decently today. I talked to him twice on the phone and though he was not friendly, as he used to be, he was obviously trying to be fair.

"Forbes can cancel, but he can't fire you off the network," he said, when I first reached him. This afternoon he relayed his decision on me through Bob. (As Bob reminded me, Mark had several other decisions to make too; at least thirty-five named in "Red Airwaves" are connected with F.B.C. or with some of its shows.)

While I appreciate Robson keeping me on the Sunday spot for the rest of the month and thus defying the sponsor, I tried to argue with Bob that it was my understanding the time belonged to me as long as I kept it salable.

"Keep your shirt on, Raymond," Bob admonished. "For the time being you continue your broadcast. That's the main thing. Starting Monday we'll begin to thresh matters out."

I gather that Mark and Bob think the storm will blow over. But that there was such a tempest at all today is a shocking thing. The story got blazing headlines on the front pages. The Clark press had a hysterical editorial, encased in red borders, calling on the radio industry to immediately fire all 250 persons named on the "roll of Red dishonor," as it called the black list. The inimitable Bert Woodruff had an "exclusive" tip from United Tobacco that it was getting rid of, at once, the dozen or so persons on its four shows who figured on the "Communist list." "The first to feel Mr. Forbes's sharp ax, I can report this morning, will be Commentator Raymond Whitehead, the pundit for whom America wasn't good enough — all those years he preferred to live abroad and soak up un-American and Communistic doctrines," is the way Woodruff puts it in his column.

The funny thing — if it is funny — is that I have not yet been able to learn what the specific charges against me in "Red Airwaves" are. Yvonne toured the bookstores and newsstands today, but couldn't get a copy. She even went to the office of The Committee to Wake Up America. It was closed.

Probably I could have picked up a copy from Elsie, or at least found out what I'm accused of. But I'm not that defeated — yet.

I wonder if old Forbes knows what the charges are?

MAY 7 (SUNDAY)

I WROTE a brief but, I thought, fair and objective note for the broadcast today explaining why there was no commercial. When I read it over the phone to Fletcher, who is still in the country, he hit the ceiling.

"You mustn't even mention it," he ordered.

"Won't a lot of people wonder, Bob, why — suddenly — there's no commercial?"

"Let them wonder," he snapped.

Later, just before air time, he phoned me to make sure that I had "correctly" understood him.

Tonight one of the young ladies who works Sunday evenings on the telephone switchboard at F.B.C. — I believe she is a student at Columbia — phoned and said there had been about fifty calls following my broadcast. About half of them, she judged from what she overheard, protested against my being allowed to continue to broadcast; the other half praised F.B.C. for the same reason.

MAY 8

THE great Woodruff relates in his column today that "hundreds" of telephone calls swamped F.B.C.'s switchboard last night in a wave of angry protest against my "still being on the air despite the disclosures in 'Red Airwaves' "!

I had not thought of it in all the excitement: loss of the sponsor means loss of $1000 a week. Robson will pay me a sustaining salary of $1000 a month. We won't exactly starve. Yvonne says she will give notice to the maid. We will have to figure out whether we can keep the youngsters in private school — which comes to $2000 a year alone. In any other city, I would have put the kids in public school anyway.

Yvonne and I always said that a thousand a week was too much money for the likes of us. Half of it went in income tax, of course. And we were putting aside nearly half of what was left: for the farm, or for the proverbial rainy day.

MAY 10

THE newspapers say the first edition of "Red Airwaves" sold out over last week end — which explains why Yvonne couldn't find a copy — and that a new edition is being rushed through the presses. Betty Collier on the "Betty and Bob" show this morning said the publishers stood "to make a lot of dough," which impressed her, and, I must admit, impresses me, though perhaps for a different reason.

Defamation is a very old practice, especially in politics or in religious controversy. But this must be one of the first times it has ever been used "to make a lot of dough." I learn that the so-called Committee to Wake Up America is actually a corporation of three or four individuals who have been making their living for years by issuing Red-scare sheets. Several of Elsie's ex-Communists have joined in backing the corporation's publication of "Red Airwaves." But apparently the profits go to the original three or four.

MAY 11

ELSIE sent over a Western Union boy with a copy of the booklet today. She had phoned me this morning at the office and asked me if I had seen it.

"No. I haven't seen it yet, Elsie," I said. "But I've heard about it."

"I'm furious, Raymond — that they put you in, after all. God knows I did everything to keep you out."

"I know, Elsie."

"Not that you deserved it . . . really."

"Right."

"Raymond, my dear . . ."

"Yes, Elsie . . ."

"Will you come by for a drink . . . later? We must talk things over."

I said I couldn't; not today.

The "charges" against me are just about what she said they were. The editors of "Red Airwaves" have come up with three.

Number one: that I was a member of the "Communist dominated" International Committee to Rescue Intellectuals and Artists from Fascism.

Its name sounds a little highfalutin now. No doubt if we had known as much about the suppression of artists and intellectuals in the Soviet Union then as we do now, supposing it was as bad then as now, we should have added to the title of our organization: ". . . and Communism."

The committee, of course, was never dominated by the Communists. There may have been two or three of them on it — all Frenchmen, I think. But the group was actually dominated by a handful of eminent writers and scientists, mostly British and American. I believe most of our money came from American philanthropic foundations. And we did succeed in rescuing two or three hundred excellent men and women from Germany and Italy and settling them in Britain and America, usually in a good university. Five or six of the scientists were Nobel Prize winners and two of them, whom we brought to this country, contributed mightily to the making of the first atom bomb. My own role in the committee was a minor one, though I shall never use that fact to try to excuse myself with the publishers of "Red Airwaves." Since, as a journalist, I could move easily around Germany and Italy without arousing suspicion, my job was to contact numerous victims of Hitler and Mussolini and arrange for their secret departure.

So on the first charge, I must plead guilty.

Number two: that I opposed Franco and Chiang Kai-shek "in their fight against Communism." Well, I have written and said things against them, especially against Franco. Franco is a Fascist butcher. I don't like him. Chiang is, in many ways, a great man and I have often said so. But I have criticized his regime for its corruptness and ineffectualness. Apparently that is today considered in America to be a crime, to be proof you were a Communist.

Of course I never opposed them, or any other dictator, "in their fight against Communism," but merely for the reasons given above. There is a difference. But I am not sure it is discernable in New York and Washington today.

Charge number three is that I have "often" taken the Communist party line, or the "fellow traveler" line. Specifically, that

I have been a staunch defender of men of such "questionable loyalty" as Stephen Burnett.

The only line I have ever taken has been my own — right or wrong. I have, of course, defended Steve Burnett and intend to continue to do so. Anyone who has read or heard what I have written and broadcast about the infamous Nazi-Soviet Pact of August 1939, or of Russia's attack on Finland and its joining Nazi Germany in invading Poland that same year knows how much I follow the party line!

Now, what do I do about these ridiculous accusations, which have already cost me my sponsor?

Before leaving the office I phoned the eminent lawyer, William Rikind, and made an appointment for tomorrow. Rikind is not only eminent, he's a liberal and has a great reputation in this country, I believe, as a staunch defender of civil rights. In my case, he ought to make mincemeat of the publishers of "Red Airwaves." Perhaps he can bring old Forbes around to reason too. Forbes, incidentally, has been unreachable all week. Even little Archy Oakes has made himself invisible. Mark Robson has been "busy," but Bob says he will see me tomorrow.

MAY 12

AFTER breakfast, to the skyscraper office in mid-Manhattan of lawyer Rikind. The place very plush. Rikind, who, at Bob's request, has handled my radio contracts and income tax, was most affable, though I have only seen him three or four times in my life. He's a small but wiry man, of handsome features and graying hair. About sixty, I should guess. And genial. And exceedingly self-confident.

A bit of a Manhattan *bon vivant*, I gather; a first-nighter at the theater, somewhat of a regular at "21" and at some of the more expensive night clubs. And yet inordinately proud of his reputation as a vigilant defender of civil rights and of many a poor devil who got into the clutches of some medieval, intolerant

[*137*]

part of the law — usually in the South. Something of a "name-dropper," though God knows he represents a number of big-name folk in the theater, the movies and radio. And he gets about in Washington too. First-names the President, most of the judges of the Supreme Court, and a host of Congressmen.

To my surprise, he said at once, after I had explained my business, that he would advise against my suing the publishers of "Red Airwaves."

"I know how you feel, Whitehead. I know you're no more a Communist than I am. But I'm not going to take your good money to fight a libel suit. If we were in England, yes. I would bring an action immediately. But in this country, Whitehead, you almost never win a libel suit, no matter how good your case may be."

"You mean there's no redress at all?" I asked. I admit I was taken aback.

He thought a moment, throwing his handsome head back and gazing at the ceiling.

"I'll tell you what I suggest, Whitehead," he said breezily. "I'll get hold of these crackpots next week. From all I hear they're not bad fellows at heart — just a little cracked on Communism, like everyone else nowadays. I'll set up a lunch at '21.' We'll talk things over, man to man. And we'll make them withdraw their charges against you. How does that suit you?"

His face brightened as if the problem were already solved and could be as good as forgotten — just leave it to William Rikind.

"In the first place," I said, "I do not care to lunch with the gentlemen. In the second place, suppose they do withdraw their charges. The book is already out. Ten thousand copies have been sold. Nearly every one of them reposes in the right-hand desk drawer of some radio or advertising executive. Who is going to remember a retraction? If you're on the list, you're out."

Rikind was disappointed in me, I could see.

"Well, sue then," he said, frowning. "But it's throwing your money away. Personally, Whitehead, I won't take it."

"Is there anything I can do about my sponsor, who bowed out the very week end 'Red Airwaves' came out?" I asked. Rikind had certainly doused me with cold water.

"Has he offered to pay you until the end of your cycle?" he asked rather sharply.

"Yes, but . . ."

"Then there is nothing actionable, Whitehead."

"There's more to it than just the money, isn't there?" I persisted.

"Ah, Whitehead. Money . . . money . . ." he said, as if the thought made him sad. "It talks . . . It talks, you know. Especially in radio." His eyes lit up. "Why, Whitehead, do you know how much old Forbes pays out annually to F.B.C. alone? Three million bucks! What chance have we against three million bucks, I ask you, Whitehead?"

The question answered itself. As soon as I could, I left.

MAY 13

I WAS still somewhat naïve, I guess, when I arrived toward the end of the day at Mark's office up on the twenty-ninth floor. Bob Fletcher was already there, as morose as I have ever seen him. Mark was by no means dapper, as he usually is. I could feel him, as I entered, screwing up his face into its most serious vein. "They're putting on an act," I thought. "I must not take it too seriously." Probably it happened every day in Mark's inner sanctum.

"Mark, I appreciate your keeping me on in the Sunday spot," I said at once.

"I'm glad you appreciate something around here," Mark snapped.

"I realize how difficult it was," I said, trying to ignore his irritation.

Robson thrust on his glasses and looked at a sheaf of notes. "As we told you, you'll continue Sunday evenings for the rest of this month — sustaining."

He had hesitated and then practically hissed the last word as if it were almost too unpleasant to pronounce. I could see how, with him, it might be. "Sustaining" meant no sponsor, no revenue; in fact, an expense.

"And after this merry month of May?" I asked, as cheerfully as I could.

"The time reverts to Forbes, to United Tobacco," Bob Fletcher cut in to answer. He was stating an obvious, unalterable fact, I realize now, but yesterday it seemed to me as if he were suddenly interceding in order to remind both Robson and me, in case we had any doubts, where he stood, which was squarely and loyally by the side of the president of F.B.C.

"I was hoping, Bob, that since I have built up that Sunday spot from scratch it sort of belonged to me and that we could sell it to another sponsor."

"It belongs to United Tobacco," Mark said. "They have a contract for it."

"Didn't they perhaps forfeit their right to it when they threw me off?"

Robson glared at me as if I were crazy.

"No, they didn't," he said.

"I know we could sell it to someone else," I persisted. I was not quite so wise yesterday as I am today. "After all we have worked up the highest Sunday early evening audience rating on the network."

"Is that true?" Robson turned to Fletcher. I was surprised he didn't know it, but encouraged that he would now learn. Ordinarily in radio a top rating was all that mattered. Archy Oakes had reminded me of it many times.

Bob Fletcher hesitated. He scowled at me as if I had been unfair to bring the matter up at such a moment. I couldn't help smiling back.

"It's true," Bob finally conceded.

"What are the figures?" Mark asked, still not quite believing.

"Between fourteen and fifteen, isn't it, Raymond?" Bob asked.

"That's right," I said, smothering a temptation to take advantage of my little triumph.

"Humph . . ." Mark grunted.

"A show with a rating like that is not too hard to sell, is it, Mark?" I asked, rather confidently.

That was when he hit back hard.

"It is, Raymond, when your name is in 'Red Airwaves.'" He hesitated a second to let that sink in. "In fact, it's impossible, eh Bob?"

My good friend agreed.

"But let's not go into 'Red Airwaves,'" Mark said. "It has given me enough headaches the last ten days."

"Isn't that the whole point of this discussion, Mark?" I said quickly. "This phoney black list and what we're going to do about it?"

I was presumptuous all right — if not downright dumb, as I realize today. Where did I get the "we" stuff?

"I'll tell you, Raymond, what we're going to do about you," Robson said sternly, making clear the discussion was over. "Despite the pressure — and I don't think you have the faintest idea of how tough it has been and how it's still building up — and despite all the other trouble you've given us — on the loyalty oath, for one thing — we're going to keep you on, sustaining. That's Bob's recommendation and I concur in it."

I mumbled a word of appreciation. I was confused. Both men were trying to do at least something for me. Once again Bob was standing up for me — to a certain extent. Perhaps I was unreasonable to expect more.

"You finish out this month on the Sunday spot," Mark added. "After that we'll see. We'll try to find time on some other day. On Saturday, perhaps."

Sunday was the only logical day for a weekly show of my kind. Saturday afternoon and evening was a time for sports followed by jazz. But I said nothing.

MAY 14 (SUNDAY)

THE shock of my life this evening. When I left F.B.C. after my broadcast pickets were milling around on the sidewalk in front of the lobby. I couldn't make out their signs,

[*141*]

but there was no doubt that the demonstration was against me — and against F.B.C. for allowing me to broadcast this fine spring day. The men — they reminded me of rowdy storm troopers in Berlin just before Hitler came to power — chanted slogans: Whitehead, go back to Russia . . . back to Russia . . . back to Russia . . . and F.B.C. is un-American . . . un-American . . . un-American. . . .

One trooper in the mob — he wore a soiled, shabby raincoat despite the balmy evening — suddenly recognized me as I made my way down the sidewalk. He started shouting. There was a crescendo of boos that rose to an ugly roar.

I had difficulty in hiding my feelings from Yvonne and the youngsters at dinner tonight.

"One of your best broadcasts, I thought," Yvonne said, as we sat down at the table.

"Pop, you were wonderful," young Dick chimed in.

Had they heard what had happened? I wondered, and as a consequence were they just trying to cheer me up — and make me forget?

Later this evening the young student-telephonist on the F.B.C. switchboard Sunday evenings phoned.

"They're swamping us with calls tonight," she said. "I thought you ought to know. I'm sure it's all organized, Mr. Whitehead."

"What makes you think that?" I asked.

"Everyone says the same thing. It's like they were reciting a piece someone taught them."

Yvonne, I am sure, was quite aware of the state of my nerves all evening, but she strove bravely not to show it. We played some Haydn and Beethoven chamber music records until bedtime.

MAY 15

ALL this Monday morning at the office I could feel the tension at F.B.C. building up. Not that anyone came into my cubicle to talk things over. But I was aware of many persons passing by, quickening their step as if my office were a

[*142*]

contagious ward. Occasionally there was a furtive glance. About noon a copy boy brought in a sealed envelope from Jim Fiske, one of the news editors.

Confidential! And for Christ's sake, tear this up after reading, deposit it in can, and flush!

They're panicking up on the twenty-ninth floor. A thousand angry letters demanding your head, they claim. (Actually, I can tell you the number is about half that.) Last night there were some 370 telephone calls, but Robson has raised the figure in his mind to a convenient 1000 — to match the letters.

The Committee to Wake Up America has really organized this one, Raymond. It has the Clark press screeching, as you may have noticed. And it has thrown the fear of God into floor twenty-nine.

I wish I could really help. Most of us in this outfit do. But remember what I told you once during the loyalty-oath trouble? Good luck!

J.F.

(Now into the can with this treasonable note!)

I phoned up to Bob Fletcher, thinking to ask him out to lunch. I could find out from him what was happening. His secretary said he was "in conference." I asked to be called back. But when no call had come by 1:30, I went out alone. The first two or three drugstore counters I tried were all full. Finally I found one, ill-ventilated and smelling of greasy soup, down toward Forty-second Street. In the stench I gobbled down my sandwich and tasteless coffee, elbowing my neighbors to right and left, and being elbowed from both sides in return. They were mostly shopgirls or stenographers at the crowded counter. Their chatter somehow soothed me.

I had not been back from lunch long before Bob phoned down and asked me to come up at once. There was a darkness in his face that is difficult to describe: it was in the furrowed eyebrows, the glare in the eyes, the sunken cheeks, the tightly pressed lips, the sallow color of the skin. He looked up as I sat down at the side of his shiny, big desk and tried desperately, I thought, to crack at least the hint of a smile.

"There's been a bloody hurricane up here, Raymond."

"So I hear, Bob. But rather artificially contrived, wasn't it?"

"Possibly. But the result is the same."

"There is a difference, isn't there, between the real thing and the ersatz?"

"Listen, my friend," he said, and there was no mistaking his impatience. "You may have heard that our switchboards were swamped last night because of you. At least a thousand calls. And this morning the postman staggered in with his load — at least a thousand letters raising hell with us about you."

"My figures on the mail and the calls are less than half of yours, Bob. But that's not important now. What is important, it seems to me, is that this uproar was instigated and organized by some people taking advantage of 'Red Airwaves.'"

Bob eyed me carefully. "Can you prove that, Raymond?"

"If there was time, I could."

"That's the rub, my friend. Mark Robson has already made up his mind."

"To what?"

"You're off the air."

"Completely?"

"Completely."

"For good?"

"Not necessarily, Raymond. But at least until the storm blows over."

Now that he had gotten it off his chest, he seemed relieved. The twitching in his face stopped and it began to lighten.

"Where does this leave me, Bob?" I asked after a while. It was getting to be a familiar question.

"Oh, I forgot something, Raymond," he said, almost joyously. "Your salary continues, of course — your sustaining salary, that is."

"I get paid for doing nothing?"

"You'll get paid, I said."

"For being a good boy. For keeping my mouth shut. For playing the game so as not to further embarrass F.B.C. — is that it?"

"That's not the way I see it, Raymond," he said, quite earnestly.

I hesitated for a moment, I admit, and then I said it. "You have my resignation, Bob. Here and now."

"I won't have it. I won't accept it," he said, and now he was being quite facetious, I thought.

"I resign. I have the right to resign, haven't I?"

He sat back, rather relaxed now, almost smiling.

"Listen, Raymond," he said. "We're still friends, I hope, despite what has happened. Let me talk to you a moment as a friend."

It was incredible, outrageous even — but I didn't have the guts to say so. He went on.

"You're tired, Raymond. Overwrought. You've been through a nasty business. It must have seemed like an ugly nightmare. What you need is a rest. A change. A vacation."

He paused — for breath or at least to swallow.

"It's spring. School will be out in a couple of weeks. Why don't you take the summer off, pack Yvonne and the kids into the car and set off across the country? It's a wonderful country, my friend, and you've been away from it a long time. It would do you a world of good and I'm sure Yvonne and the youngsters would enjoy it too. Comes the fall, come back — and I'm sure we will find a spot for you."

"Thanks very much for the suggestion, Bob, but . . ."

"I won't take no for an answer, Raymond." Bob was becoming positively jaunty, as though he had done me an enormous favor and solved all my problems — and his too.

I got up to go. "I'll put it in writing," I said, "— the resignation."

"I won't read it," he laughed.

He put his arm on my shoulder as I walked toward the door. "Listen, what are you all doing this week end? Will you come up to the farm? The orchard should really be blossoming."

"Thanks. But I think I'll be looking for a new job."

"A silly thing to be doing this particular week end, Raymond.

Wait till the storm blows over, I say. Then if you want to leave us, all right. I hope you won't."

There was no use saying any more. Besides, I had got to the doorway and shaken his arm from my shoulder.

"So long, Bob," I said, and went out.

MAY 16

YVONNE has taken it all wonderfully, which bucks me up. We walked up and down the river in the warm bright sun for an hour after lunch discussing what to do.

MAY 17

YOUNG Richard came bursting into my study on his return from school this afternoon.

"Pop, is it true you're a Communist?"

For a moment I was stunned, then hurt, then angered by Dick's question. It must come to many a father in this country these days.

"No, it isn't true, Dick," I said. "Where did you ever get such an idea?"

I knew all right where he got it.

"That's what they were saying in school — that you were a Communist."

"Who was saying it, son?"

He hesitated. "Well, Mark Fletcher, for one."

That's an irony that hurts a little. One of Bob's youngsters, of all the hundreds of brats in school. It had never occurred to me before — Bob must have named the boy after his boss.

"Mark Fletcher says you were fired from the radio because you are a Communist."

"He did? Why, the little liar!"

"Did anything happen, Pop — like they say at school?"

I saw that I had to do some explaining at once. I did it — truthfully — and as comprehensively as you can to a fifteen-year-old.

It was hard. He had many questions and there was much he did not seem to understand.

MAY 19

A NOTE by the post from Jim Fiske. He says Mark Robson has hired the publishers of "Red Airwaves" to investigate the "loyalty" of all F.B.C. employees and of the entire personnel of all F.B.C. shows. I did not know it, but Jim says this is an old racket. You attack a big company for harboring alleged Communist subversives among its employees and then offer, for a fat fee, to ferret them out by a thorough "loyalty" investigation.

MAY 20

WILLIAM McKINLEY FORBES has a statement in the newspapers this morning denying that United Tobacco fired me from the Sunday show because my name was in "Red Airwaves." He has never even seen the publication, he says.

United Tobacco decided last fall to experiment with the sponsorship of a Sunday-evening news commentary. It did so in the belief that an informed America is a better America. Since the birth of radio, United Tobacco has been one of the principal backers of pure entertainment on the air. Its various shows on all the networks — musical comedy and straight drama — have enjoyed great prestige with the American people. United Tobacco has also, as is well known, sponsored various sporting events of nation-wide interest.

The company's experiment with news commentary has been given a full trial of eight months and is now being abandoned. By its very nature, news commentary is bound to be controversial. We do not dispute that such controversy is a useful and necessary part of radio and belongs to our democratic American way of life. But we do not think that it is compatible with the principles of advertising. Controversy over a commentator and what he says is bound to antagonize a number of customers. Frankly, it affects the acceptance of our products and harms our public relations.

For that reason, and for that reason alone, United Tobacco is dropping the sponsorship of Raymond Whitehead and his commentary on the news. This in no way implies any judgment — one way or the other — of Mr. Whitehead's views. William McKinley Forbes, President of United Tobacco, wishes to state most emphatically that the decision of the company has nothing whatsoever to do with any alleged black list, private or public. Mr. Forbes wishes to state that he has not, in fact, seen any black list, private or public. He does not believe in black lists, feeling that they are better left to the totalitarian dictatorships.

Beginning in June, the period on F.B.C. formerly occupied by Mr. Whitehead will again be sponsored by United Tobacco with a new show of pure entertainment to be called Music From Hollywood.

Well, I'll be damned!

MAY 21 (SUNDAY)

THE first Sunday since we came home last fall that I have not broadcast. I felt restless. After breakfast, Yvonne suggested that we all pile into the car and head out into the country, which pleased Dick and Maria greatly and no doubt was good for me.

I had not remembered that May was so lovely here. The air was soft and warm, but not hot, not humid, and the countryside was pink with apple blossoms, and wonderfully green and alive too with the leafing of the trees, above all the maples and the elms. We drove leisurely up the Saw Mill River Parkway, thence, at Hawthorne Circle, onto the Taconic highway, crossing the Hudson at Bear Mountain and continuing on up to the Catskills. It is a glorious, changing landscape, of thickly wooded hills, sloping green pastures, fantastic outcroppings of rock, neat white-frame homes and solid red barns — and always the majestic river and sometimes, in the distance, a mountain.

Yvonne looked as lovely and fresh as the day in a trim white suit, which set off her shiny, coal-black hair. All day long she kept her keen French eyes on the farmhouses we passed, as if to store them up in her memory when we start looking for a place.

I guess we shall not be buying a farm now; just looking. We picnicked by a stream above Woodstock. You could see several fairly high mountains to the northwest and we argued whether we should buy a place in the mountains or by the sea. Maria was all for the sea "because you can go swimming every day."

"And, Papa," she argued, "we could have a big boat, a boat for the ocean, all to ourselves!"

Maria is perky and pretty and there lingers with her the last vestiges of the miracle of a child's voice and accent.

MAY 23

I STILL haven't sent in my resignation yet. William Rikind, my legal mentor, insists that I see him first — day after tomorrow.

MAY 24

YVONNE all for buying a farm now, and spending the summer on it.

"How do we pay for it?" say I.

"Go into debt," says she. "Everyone else in America does."

MAY 25

BILL RIKIND very much against my resigning from F.B.C. Apparently he thinks I'm a bit off my nut.

"Don't be a fool, I beg of you," he said. "You've got a three-year sustaining contract. Let F.B.C. pay you a thousand a month until it runs out. That comes to quite a little dough, my friend."

"For doing nothing," I reminded him.

"Why not? It's in the contract."

MAY 28 (SUNDAY)

YVONNE is inclined to agree with Rikind — that I should not resign. Her true feelings about Mark Robson begin to come out.

"If he can do this to you," she said today, "why not make him pay?"

"But that isn't the question," I argued. "Let's be fair to Mark. He hasn't objected to paying me."

"It is difficult for me to be fair to a swine," Yvonne said. Her acid tone was quite out of character. "Of course he doesn't object to paying you. It is his obligation. He has to do it, no?"

"Yes. But as I said, that isn't the question."

"What is the question then?"

I could see Yvonne was a little annoyed with me.

"The question is," I tried to explain, "shall I take F.B.C.'s money — Robson's dough, if you want to put it that way — for doing nothing, nothing but keeping my mouth shut so as to spare him embarrassment for having knuckled down to a phoney private black list?"

Yvonne looked at me quizzically. I could feel she thought I was being rather naïve. My false pride, perhaps?

"Did it ever occur to you, Raymond," she said, "that you can shout to the housetops about whatever you please — and still collect your F.B.C. salary for another couple of years?"

"First, I'm going to look for a broadcast on another network," I said. "I think it will be easy, Yvonne, after the high rating I had on the Sunday show."

"You think the other broadcasting companies aren't paying any attention to 'Red Airwaves'?"

"I don't think they will in my case — because it's so absurd, so god-damned ridiculous. The charges, I mean. If I get another broadcast the question of taking a salary from F.B.C. becomes academic, doesn't it?"

"Naturally." Yvonne thought for a moment. "Will you promise me this much, then? Not to resign until you get another broadcast?"

"It's something to consider," I conceded.

After lunch we persuaded Dick to take Maria for a romp through Central Park. It was another perfect week end for the country, but we had not gone. While the youngsters were away, we took a stroll along the East River below the house. Of late we have snatched at moments like these to be alone, even from the children. (There is so little privacy for a man and woman with children.) Yvonne, I soon saw, was still burning with indignation at what we were going through. Suddenly she stopped, planted one foot on the railing on the river side of the walk and turned to me.

"Did you suspect," she began, "that Mark Robson was such a contemptible coward?"

"Frankly, no."

"Neither did I."

"I suppose it's that." It wasn't that I had any doubts. There were other factors though.

"You haven't any reservations, have you?" Yvonne asked sharply. I sensed her Gallic temperament beginning to boil again. ". . . The way he caved in on you at the first sign of trouble!"

"No. But I was just thinking. It's more than cowardice. It's his greed too — for money, for power. And coupled with that, his terrible fear — I suppose many businessmen have it — that all that he has built up will collapse — if he isn't careful. Probably Mark is continually haunted with fears beneath that smooth, jaunty exterior. One of them was that because of me he might lose the United Tobacco account. Have you any idea, Yvonne, how it feels to lose — suddenly — three million dollars?"

"I doubt if it is half as painful to Mark as you losing your job is to you. You, Raymond, are left with nothing. He would still be taking in a few millions, wouldn't he?"

"Yes, but he would worry himself sick over them. There would be the fear that the big sponsors and the big ad agencies might get the impression that F.B.C. is crammed with liberals, with long-hairs, that it is getting out of line with business views. Once that feeling seeps down along Madison Avenue, Mark is in for it — or thinks he is. To give the louse his due, I am sure Mark Robson personally is against black lists. But 'Red Airwaves' has caught on. It has suddenly become a sort of Bible among radio and ad men. Do you think Mark is going to buck it — and risk losing good customers?"

"He would if he had principles," Yvonne said. "Wasn't it Mark who was always talking about principles?"

"He and Bob Fletcher. High principles too, Yvonne. On the other hand Bob never ceased reminding me that F.B.C., like all other concerns, was not in business for its health. I sometimes wonder if Bob really believed I thought it was."

Mention of Bob obviously disturbed Yvonne. Thoughts of Mark Robson had merely brought on anger and resentment. Now her face darkened and I could see she was deeply troubled. We resumed our walk down the river and for a minute or two, neither of us spoke. I recalled how concerned she and Barbara had been a few weeks back about Bob and me falling out. Down the river the high oblong pile of the new United Nations Secretariat glistened in the afternoon sun. At Forty-ninth Street, a small dock juts into the water. We sat down on a weather-beaten plank. It was a clear day and far downstream you could see the outline of the Williamsburg Bridge, gracefully spanning the water.

"What about Bob?" Yvonne said, quietly.

"What about him?"

She took my hand and put it in hers. "I suppose we have to face it. Bob hasn't any courage either, has he?"

"He has stuck by Mark — and the company."

"Against you."

"Yes."

She paused and I was sure she was searching for an excuse, for at least some mitigating circumstance, that would stave off a final and heartbreaking reckoning. I had sought one myself for months.

"Did he have to?"

"Stick by Mark and dear old F.B.C.? He didn't have to, Yvonne. I mean, Bob is a free man, with a free man's choices. On the other hand, what he has done is not surprising, is it? Certainly I think I understand it."

"You understand it?" Yvonne looked at me, puzzled.

"I think so," I said. "I remember something Bob told me when we first came back — I think it was on that fantastic Labor Day week end at his place — remember?"

"I remember the week end."

"Mark Robson had just made him vice-president and general manager of the whole network, but he was not as happy as you might expect. 'I'm deep in this thing,' he kept saying gloomily."

"What did he mean by that?" Yvonne's skepticism was not to be dented by obscurities.

"This, I think. Bob is wedded to his job — and to the position it gives him in business, in advertising, in politics, and in the smart, influential world of New York and the Connecticut week-end countryside. It's a marriage that by now, I should say, is beyond the possibility of being dissolved. Not that Bob would ever want to give it up. It has its comforts, its luxuries — the show place in the country, the horses, the sleek convertible, the custom-built station wagon, the lush apartment on Park Avenue. It has its spices of life — the gala parties, the first nights on Broadway, the flights to Florida and Hollywood, the hobnobbing with the rich and the great and the notorious. Probably it is even pleasing to have the spotlight on you in the gossip columns and the radio columns. But, above all, Bob's position gives him power. He largely determines what millions of Americans hear — and now with television, what they see — over the air: their entertainment, their music, their sports, their information. Think of the power right there, Yvonne! And take politics. Radio and TV have become the politicians' chief platform in this country. It is not surprising then that the carpet is out for Bob whenever he goes to Washington. It is rolled out for him from the White House, the State Department, the Pentagon, and every last office of every last Senator and Congressman up on Capitol Hill.

"You think Bob is going to give up all that for the sake of a few old battered, vague principles that nobody in radio or advertising gives a damn about? I said a moment ago, Yvonne, that as a free man he has his choices. Actually, of course, he is not very free any longer. And his choices are limited. In fact, to two. For if he does give up this life, having got this far, where does he go in America? Into oblivion. Where else?"

Yvonne did not immediately speak up. But the puzzlement in her deep, black eyes was subsiding. She turned to gaze down the river. Even on Sunday the stream was dotted with barges, moving up and down and across the river, pushed or pulled by the tiny, snorting tugs. In a way, I envied the men working them. They had an interesting, useful job to do and were doing it, utterly unconcerned with the matters that weighed on my life and me and on how few others in this teeming city.

"Bob is wedded to Barbara, too," Yvonne said, breaking the silence.

"And that is very important to him."

"She has certainly contributed to his success."

I agreed. I was thinking of her charm and intelligence and of the tact she showed to others. And of her influence as a decent, civilized human being on Bob.

"Do you know, Raymond, that she's worried about him?"

"I didn't know it, exactly. But I suspected it."

"She's afraid for him."

"It's probably too late," I said.

"She wanted us to come to the farm for the week end, you know," Yvonne said.

"I suppose we have to face that one too, Yvonne. How can we go there now?"

"We can't. But it hurts to say so. I love Barbara."

"So do I."

We had come, I realized, to the point of a problem whose resolution would hurt. Personal friendships were among the few decent experiences one had. But there were obstacles they could not get over; blows they could not survive. In the clash with a man's, or a couple's, self-interest, they were inevitably destroyed.

"Barbara will stick by Bob," I said. "He and his position are her life too."

"I realize that," Yvonne said. I have rarely seen her eyes, usually so dancing with joy, so still and sad.

"And we must not try in the slightest way to come between them."

"I agree," Yvonne said. It was a mere whisper.

"In a more civilized society it would be absurd for two persons such as you and Barbara to break off a friendship because of a falling out of the husbands. But here — where career is all, or almost all . . . Still, if you want to try to keep it, darling, you have my blessings."

"I shan't try," Yvonne said, trying to smile through her tears. "If only for her sake and for what I truly feel for her."

All evening, especially after the children went to bed, we were depressed. Not even the playing of some gay new recordings of Italian opera — one done by Toscanini — budged us from the depths.

MAY 29

A BLUE Monday. I did nothing. Cross with the children too.

MAY 30

SNAPPED out of it. It must have been the weather yesterday. The chilly rain. Today was different; the air as light as a feather, the sky a deep blue. I phoned some friends at two of the other networks and asked them to make appointments for me to see their bigwigs for a job. They all advised me to wait a little.

JUNE 3

I THINK I will have to beard the bigwigs on the other networks by simply barging in on them. All my attempts this past week to arrange interviews through my friends or their secretaries failed. I'm confident that if I can get in to see them, I can convince them.

Steve Burnett coming up tomorrow from Washington.

JUNE 4 (SUNDAY)

STEVE, who returned to Washington tonight, looks worn though he tried not to show it and, in fact, spoke little about his latest ordeal. But it is doing something to him, being put through the wringer again. Fortunately the Loyalty

Board hearings are private so he is escaping the wear and tear — and the humiliation — of being made to perform in public under the glare of the camera lights and the sharp eyes of the reporters.

Since he was cleared once by the same Loyalty Board it takes an immense effort of concentration, he says, to go over the same ground — the same questions and charges and prying — as before, and not be caught napping or in any traps. He feels that two or three members of the board are frightened to death of Senator O'Brien. Three members constitute a majority and the board's decision is by majority vote.

He is still puzzled that Elsie McCabe and Frederick Newman should continue to swear that he was known to them as a Communist. Elsie knows better, he says, and Newman probably never heard of him until he came under O'Brien's fire. He mentioned the effect of the investigations on his work at the Berne Legation — the embarrassment of his relations with the Swiss officials, not to mention those with the Americans in the legation itself.

JUNE 5

STEVE asked me yesterday whether I had seen Sidney Goodrich. They are old friends. Steve said Goodrich came to see him the other day in Washington, just after he had stepped down from his job as chairman of the Federal Public Power Committee. Steve said Goodrich acted like a man who had received some mysterious blow in the head that had permanently stunned him.

JUNE 6

COLETTE ROBSON dropped by to see us this evening. She was very flattering; she said she missed me on the air.

She is going to Las Vegas for the divorce. She may be getting a million from Mark, as Betty Collier says, but she is not happy. It is not, I judge, that she bears much love for Mark. But her pride has been wounded. She resents being discarded, like an old suit.

Colette is probably forty-five. There is an eternal bloom in her finely chiseled face. The nose still tilts a little upward; the eyes are unusually far apart and lively and gay, and blue as the sky; the mouth is both wistful and sensuous. She is full of physical vitality and her mind is young and she speaks with a voice unlike any other I have ever heard, pitched unusually low, and resonant and rich like the tone from an old cello.

One wonders why any man, even Mark, should want to give up a woman like that. I kept pondering the problem after Colette had gone.

She gave up the stage to marry Mark rather early in a career that had already made her a star. That must have been about fifteen years ago, when she was thirty. Bob Fletcher told me once that Mark was very insistent that she retire from the theater. So she gave the best years of her life to him. Is she now unreasonable to resent being cast off when she has reached a certain age?

Dora Faye, whom Mark is going to marry, is a talented young American ballerina. Off stage I find her not so pretty and not so vivacious and certainly not so interesting as she is on stage. That is true, I believe, of most dancers and probably of most actresses, though not of Colette.

Barbara Fletcher told us recently that Robson was tremendously impressed that Dora Faye was divorcing Lord Kingsbury to marry him. He proudly introduces her around town as Lady Kingsbury instead of by her stage name. (I believe her real name is Schmidt — she comes from a Milwaukee German family; her father works in a brewery there.)

But who is Lord Kingsbury? A joke. Known in London as a silly cipher. Barbara confides that Mark is paying him a tidy sum too.

JUNE 8

I WENT to the office today to fetch my mail. No one has displaced me from my cubicle. I suppose that is because I'm still on the payroll.

I felt a little lonely, I must say. Then Jim Fiske came in. He carefully shut the door behind him.

"I'm really sorry, Raymond," he said, after I had greeted him.

"It's tough to be off the air, Jim," I said. "But I'm still on the payroll, you know," I added as jocularly as I could.

Fiske gave me an uneasy glance. "You haven't heard the latest, I guess."

"Is there something new?"

"It's top secret, Raymond. They decided on the twenty-ninth floor yesterday to fire every single person whose name is in 'Red Airwaves.' That goes not only for F.B.C. personnel, but for anyone appearing on a network broadcast."

I shouldn't have been surprised, but I was.

"You're absolutely sure, Jim?" I asked.

"They're not going to announce it," he said. "On the contrary, Bob Fletcher has been ordered to deny it if the reporters come snooping around. You don't think Robson, Fletcher and the rest of them have the courage of their convictions, do you?"

"Well, I would have thought . . ." I started to say.

"Nevertheless, it's a fact, Raymond. Everyone who is on the list is out. With full severance pay, of course. Fletcher, I'm told, insisted on that."

"Bob did, eh?"

"Yeah. What do you think of the guy, anyway? In the newsroom we used to think he was a pretty decent guy. But lately!—"

"Well, thanks for tipping me off, Jim," I said.

He got up to go.

"I'm damned sorry," he said. He really looked sorry and saddened. "This country gets more like Russia every day."

"We've got a long way to go, Jim."

"If the rest of us had any guts, we would strike — or do something. Threaten to quit, at least. Hell, Raymond, we're just like the yes-men in Russia. Afraid to speak out for fear we'll lose our living."

"But not your life, remember, Jim."

"Hell, that makes us the bigger cowards, Raymond. I can

understand a guy in Moscow keeping his trap shut — if to open it means he gets snuffed out. You want at least to live, however miserably. But we keep our mouths shut — in order to cling to a comfortable, well-paying job. At least I do."

In the end, I was trying to comfort him, instead of the other way around. His doubts, his misgivings, bucked me up, in fact, after he had gone, and I took to mulling over what he had said. As long as the hired help in this country questions what is being put over on them nowadays in the name of patriotism and anti-Communism, there is hope.

JUNE 11 (SUNDAY)

OUT to Ebbets Field today with Dick to see the Dodgers take on the St. Louis Cardinals. It was a taut game that kept our nerves on edge until the final out, Brooklyn winning 2 to 1. Afterward I felt as if I had been through the wash. Yet it was immense fun. Dick loved it. And so did 25,000 other fans. I kept envying them. They're not rich or powerful. Most of them, I suppose, have mediocre jobs and live in drab houses and have little learning and no appreciation of art. Yet, as human beings, they have a capacity for happiness. Baseball fascinates them, and the fortunes of the Dodger team, which is a profit-making business, touch them deeply and give color and a sense of identification and excitement to their lives. I doubt if seven persons among the 25,000 rooters there this afternoon have ever heard of "Red Airwaves" or would give a damn about it one way or the other if they had, or — what is more important — feel that their freedoms in America are in the slightest way being trampled upon. Are they not to be envied by the likes of me?

JUNE 12

RIDING home in the subway yesterday Dick inquired casually what we were going to do this summer. School is out this Friday.

Yvonne and I discussed it this evening. We had planned to

take a cottage out on Long Island near Montauk. We wonder now if we can afford it. We had an eye on a modest little place on the sea, but it comes to a thousand dollars for the season. It seems a crime to keep the kids cooped up in New York City all summer.

JUNE 13

GOT down to work on the book today. From now on I must labor on it each morning and as many afternoons and evenings as possible — just as if I were working on a regular, salaried job. I had that discipline once in Europe. It is very necessary when you are on your own.

JUNE 14

BOB FLETCHER phoned this afternoon, his voice and manner warm and friendly as in the old days. He asked me to drop by his office tomorrow at my convenience.
"Any time will do, Raymond," he said. "Just suit yourself."

JUNE 15

TO BE honest, I suppose it was more painful for Bob than for me. There were moments when I felt more sorry for him than for myself.

He had a martyred look when I arrived. His brow was knit, his dark eyes watery, his mouth sagging. As usual he began by forcing a smile through his gloom.

"Raymond," he said, and his voice was slow and melodious, "I know you will not want me to beat around the bush."

He paused, but as I said nothing, he quickly resumed.

"Believe me, my friend, what I am about to say hurts me more than it does you. I might explain, Raymond, that I have had nothing to do with certain decisions reached by Mark Robson and the Board of Directors. In fact I fought against them to the very last, especially the one concerning you. I . . ."

"Bob, you *are* beating around the bush," I said.

"Sorry, Raymond. I just wanted you to know where I stood personally, though I am sure you had no doubts. And since we are old friends, have been through a lot together, and all that, I'm going to play square and tell you exactly what has happened, though I must ask you to treat it in strictest confidence."

"Well, what did happen?" I said.

"A hell of a lot, my friend. The Board has decided, Raymond, that everyone connected with F.B.C. — regular employees or performers on the air — whose name is in 'Red Airwaves' must go. Raymond, you'll never know how I argued against it, in your case and two or three others. But as you can guess, I was overruled.

"Now, I'm telling you all this, Raymond," he went on, "in the strictest confidence. I . . . ."

"In the strictest confidence!" I cut in. "You mean you fire us because we're black-listed by a bunch of crackpots and then say we can't explain to the public, if we wish!"

"We'll deny it, if you do," he said, and a smile of triumph flashed over his handsome face. "I merely told you, Raymond, because we're old friends, I wanted you to know the truth, and I knew I could trust you."

"Bob, you're kidding yourself. If I'm fired, I'm going to tell anybody who's interested, if anybody is, why."

"I didn't say you were fired, Raymond. In your case I have Mark's express permission to allow you to resign — with full severance pay, of course."

"I tried to resign, Bob, remember? You wouldn't hear of it. But I'm not going to resign now. You've got to fire me and take the consequences."

It was incredible, but Bob seemed actually hurt by my response. It was as if he felt he had fought valiantly in my behalf and deserved my gratitude. Instead, I was unappreciative, even defiant. But his wounded expression soon changed to one of impatience and then resentment.

"Very well," he finally said in a grim tone, tightening his lips. "If you insist, Raymond, we shall have to discharge you. But

[*161*]

remember, we'll deny that it has anything to do with 'Red Airwaves.' And you won't be able to prove that it has."

"But you just said so yourself, Bob."

"That was in confidence."

I couldn't suppress a laugh; or a last word.

"Bob, do you have to do Mark's dirty work?"

"I do my job, Raymond, as I see it."

"I would like to have a last word with him," I said, "since I dislike talking behind a man's back."

"He won't see you, Raymond." There was no mistaking the finality in Bob's voice.

"He isn't God."

"No, but he runs this shop."

"You don't think you could arrange it, Bob?"

"It's out of the question."

The boycott was getting awfully complete. No one would see me.

I got up to go. Bob grasped my hand warmly.

"I wish you luck, Raymond."

"Thanks."

"There's no hurry about evacuating your office."

"I'll be out of it today," I said.

"Shall I have the check sent to your house?"

"Where else, Robert?"

I was getting slightly annoyed, I guess, at his untimely solicitude.

"I hope there will be no ill-feeling between us personally, Raymond," I heard Bob say.

I had turned and was walking out the door.

JUNE 16

I CONFESS I didn't sleep so well last night — a rare experience for me. I was aware of keeping Yvonne up, but she did not let on. I tossed in my bed most of the night trying to figure out what to do.

I TOOK a bus down Madison Avenue to see Archy Oakes. He kept me waiting nearly half an hour in the thickly carpeted, oak-paneled reception room, which was presided over by one of the coldest, snippiest, blond receptionists I have ever encountered — even in this town. I made the mistake of tangling with her at the outset.

"Have you an appointment with Mr. Oakes?" she demanded.

"I believe I have," I said.

"For what time?"

"For ten o'clock, I believe."

She shifted her haughty glance from me to her wrist watch. "It is five past ten now." Finally she condescended to lift up the white-ivory telephone receiver.

"Mr. Whitehead to see Mr. Oakes," she intoned, listened a moment, put the receiver back and turned again to me.

"Mr. Oakes is in conference. May I help you?"

"No, you mayn't," I said — rather gruffly, I fear.

She did not bat an eye. "Will you please take a seat then," she said, dismissing me from her presence.

I whiled away the time thumbing through Mr. Luce's publications — *Time, Life, Fortune* — which were stacked about the place. Twenty minutes or so passed; they seemed much longer. I got up.

"Will you be so kind as to give Oakes a buzz and see if he is free now?" I asked.

"Mr. Oakes will let us know when he is free," she said. I retreated from her iciness to my seat.

Archy, when I at last got in to see him, was scarcely recognizable. For a few minutes it was difficult to realize that this was the meek little busybody I had suffered on my program for nearly a year. Though the features were the same — the fleshy, smooth, common face and the beady eyes under the egglike bald dome — he no longer reminded me of a gnome. Indeed he fairly bristled with an air of importance. In entering his office I had noticed that his title "vice-president" no longer had the "assist-

ant" tacked onto it. I hastened to congratulate him on his pro-
motion in Dunsany & Dunne. It suddenly occurred to me that
he had achieved one of his burning lifetime ambitions. To become a full-fledged vice-president, a v.p., in the weird world of
radio and advertising was to hit the high plateau. You gained
admittance into a select circle. At last you were *somebody*,
looked up to in the office by all who were not v.p.'s, given a
little respect by those who were, and recognized as cutting a
certain figure as you strode up Madison Avenue or hurried over
to Radio City. Sponsors were easier to talk to and so were the
network executives when you became a vice-president.

Archy accepted my congratulations with mock humility.

"It just increases my work," he smiled.

"And your pay too, I hope," I said.

"Well, it didn't reduce it any."

I noticed as we talked, a growing self-assurance which had
been completely lacking in him before. I must say I liked him
the more for it. His toadiness during the time of my broadcasts
at F.B.C. had not attracted me.

"What can I do for you, Raymond?" Archy said, sitting back
and lighting a cigar. I took out my pipe and filled it.

"I'd like a show on another network," I said, determined to
come to the point at once. "I thought maybe you would like to
find me a nice, well-paying, liberal-minded sponsor."

"Easier said than done, my friend," Archy opined, sitting
back and blowing his cigar smoke toward the ceiling.

"I realize there are certain difficulties."

"There certainly are," he said, rather emphatically.

"On the other hand," I said quickly, "we had a good commercial rating on our Sunday show."

"We certainly did," Archy said proudly, as if it had been as
much his achievement as mine.

"With that kind of a rating we ought to be able to find another sponsor, don't you think?"

"We ought to," Archy said, but there was something uneasy
in his glance.

"Will you see what you can do, Archy?"

"I'll certainly look around, Raymond. You can count on that."

There was no conviction in his voice. He started to tap a pencil on his desk.

"I won't keep you any longer," I said.

"Oh, you're not keeping me. I enjoyed talking with you, Raymond." He beamed at me through a cloud of cigar smoke. "By the way," he said, "have you seen Senator O'Brien lately?"

"No, I haven't."

"You know what he's up to?"

"What?"

"He's got us worried, Raymond. He's threatening to investigate radio next."

"The hell he is! Looking for Communists, eh?"

"Of course, you realize there's no place in a sensitive field like radio for Communists."

"I agree," I said.

"Or those suspected of being Communists."

"Well, that's different, Archy."

But I saw he did not see the difference. No one in radio did, apparently.

JUNE 21

DICK seemed very restless about the house today. I realize this is no place for a strapping fifteen-year-old boy to spend the summer. Yvonne and I discussed bundling him off to a camp. But it's expensive. We have decided not to take the summer cottage out near Montauk. Chris Chambers has invited us to spend August at what he calls his "little shack" up in Cornwall, Connecticut. Until then we will have to confine ourselves to driving the youngsters out to the beaches — Jones Beach seems like a nice place — and to exploring Central Park and the Bronx Zoo. Unless I get a job.

I went to see old Henry Wadsworth Prentice, the editor-publisher of *U.S.A.*, for which I wrote a number of pieces when I was in Europe. He was quite courteous and not unfriendly, though I detected a slight pique in his attitude toward me —

probably due to the fact that I did not bother to see him when I was riding high on the radio this past year. I could not blame him. He held out some prospect of my doing articles for him again, but he did not commit himself.

JUNE 22

WHEN do I get on with my book? I have really not got down to hard work on it. I let the tiniest distraction take me off it. This morning, for instance. Dick was in a bad temper. He said he was going to get a job. I told him he was too young. He stamped out of the house. He didn't come home until supper. All afternoon Yvonne and I were a little uneasy. I found it hard to concentrate at this typewriter.

LATER. Chris Chambers and Bill Rikind dropped by this evening for a drink and gave me what, I suppose, is good advice. That is, to forget radio for the time being, and write my book. Chris, an author himself of a dozen books about the theater, came up with a timely suggestion. Make my publisher advance me at least $2500 on the book. This had not occurred to me.

"If he won't do it, come to my publisher. I know he will advance you that much, if not more. Then you can stop worrying."

"I'm not worrying, Chris," I said.

"Good. But you aren't working." His youthful blue eyes were full of good humor, but he was also serious, I could see.

I mentioned to Rikind that Archy Oakes was looking for a sponsor for me.

"Forget it, Raymond," he said, to my surprise.

"What do you mean, forget it?" I demanded, raising my voice.

"I think Chris will bear me out — from his own contacts with the radio and advertising gentry. . . ."

"I keep clear of the hucksters," Chris interjected with a twinkle in his eyes.

"I can't," Rikind laughed. "Some of them are my best clients. And I've been talking with them — not about you personally, Raymond, but about that 'Red Airwaves' black list. The situation is this, my friend: None of them like it. None of them will defend it. But they are all afraid of it. And they'll all knuckle down to it."

"Archy Oakes didn't give me that impression," I answered. "In fact, he didn't even mention 'Red Airwaves.'"

"Of course he didn't," Rikind said spiritedly. "That's the point I'm trying to make. It's bad 'public relations,' as they say, to even mention the black list. The smart thing to do, as one of the top executives of a big advertising firm put it to me only yesterday, is to give some *other* excuse. Say you're making a change in the programming. Or want another type of performer. Or a different kind of a show. Above all, never give the real reason. That's only plain business sense.

"Nevertheless," Rikind went on, "the real reason is the black list. And that's what you've got to get through your head, Raymond. You're on it. It's a monstrous injustice, I know. But that doesn't erase your name."

"I'll get it erased," I said heatedly. "I'll sue."

"Not through me."

"There are other lawyers."

I soon subsided, we had some more drinks, and Chris Chambers turned the talk to other things.

I hate to admit it. But I suppose they're right.

JUNE 23

STEVE BURNETT blew in today. He looked battered but not beaten. He said he finished his hearings with the Loyalty Board late yesterday afternoon, packed his things and caught the overnight train from Washington. He's flying on to Switzerland tomorrow. His children get out of school in Berne next week and he is going to take them to Gstaad up in the mountains for the summer. Since he is still under the humiliation of a suspension and cannot return to work at the legation until he is again cleared, he plans to spend the first part of the summer, at least, with his youngsters mountain climbing.

I didn't have the heart to ask him what he would do if he were not cleared. (He has no doubt at all that he will be.) What could a man in Steve's position do? How even earn a living? If he is held to be of doubtful loyalty to his country no other government agency or department would hire him. No businessman is going to take such a man. No university would dare to. Where does he turn?

We didn't talk about these things. In the afternoon we drove out to Forest Hills and played some tennis — a mixed doubles between Steve and Yvonne on one side and Dick and me on the other. Yvonne and I were terrible, but we all had much fun. Tonight we went over to Central Park to hear a band concert and sip a few beers.

JUNE 24

I DROVE Steve out to Idlewild practically at the crack of dawn to catch his plane. A rather soothing mist hung over the city, but before I got back to Manhattan, a hot summer's sun was beginning to burn it out. From the Queensborough Bridge the skyscrapers of midtown were emerging gracefully from the mist — an unforgettable sight. I am really coming to love this enigmatic, mysterious city. There is something very great about it.

Most of the day I puttered around at my desk, finding excuses not to get down to the book. I started a file of my crank mail. I must have two or three hundred crackpot letters that have come in since it was announced that I had left F.B.C. Most of them are written in a lunatic's handwriting — huge, sprawling, printed letters. Quite a few say: "Go back to Moscow — where you belong!" A dozen or so are vilely anti-Semitic — as if I were a Jew. About thirty of them inclose clippings from the newspaper columns of Bert Woodruff and Frederick Newman celebrating my exit from radio.

Against that, of course, are the thousand or so letters I've received from people all over the country expressing their regret — or sometimes their indignation — at my being thrown off the air. These expressions of ordinary Americans have a quiet dignity about them. They help to take the edge off of what has happened.

Restless. The hot, humid air charged with electricity. The house unbearably warm. Tomorrow we shall go out to Jones Beach for the day, though I dread the crowd.

JUNE 25 (SUNDAY)

WE DID not drive out to Jones Beach. There's a war on!

North Korea has invaded South Korea! Yet — Communist duplicity! — the North Korean government calls it a "counterattack." That is the identical word, the same lie, that Hitler and the German High Command used to describe their flagrant, inexcusable attack on Poland on September 1, 1939. The Communists have learned quite a few tricks from the Nazis. You do not make amphibious landings far behind the enemy's lines the very first day you are attacked.

JUNE 27

TRUMAN may be just the ordinary, run-of-the-mill type of American, but he has courage and, I think, an extraordinary intuition for great decisions.

At noon today he announced that he had ordered United States air and sea forces to give the South Korean troops cover and support.

Then late tonight the U. N. Security Council made *its* decision. For the first time in its history, it invoked military sanctions. It recommended, 7 to 1, that "members of the U.N. furnish such assistance to the Republic of South Korea as may be necessary to repel the armed attack and to restore peace and security to the area." Yugoslavia, which one day may find itself in South Korea's shoes, cast the one negative vote.

For one who had sat through so many weary, frustrating, cowardly sessions of the old League of Nations Council in Geneva, the meeting out at Lake Success today made one proud of the human race and proved that we do make progress after all.

[*169*]

President Truman made a remarkable statement in announcing our military aid to South Korea. He sees clearly that Communist tactics in the world struggle have entered a new decisive phase. As he put it: "The attack on Korea makes it plain beyond all doubt that Communism has passed beyond the use of subversion to conquer independent nations and will now use armed invasion and war. It is the point that Nazism and Fascism reached in the last half of the Thirties when Hitler sent his armies into Austria and Czechoslovakia and Mussolini attacked Ethiopia and Albania."

JUNE 30

THE President today made another fateful decision. He authorized General MacArthur to send American *ground* troops from Japan to Korea. Apparently they are badly needed. Dispatches say that the South Korean army has virtually ceased to exist. That means: if we don't stop the Communist invaders no one else will.

So we're in a war — whatever else it may be called in Washington or at the U.N. — so soon!

JULY 1

I SWALLOWED my pride today and phoned Bob Fletcher, suggesting that we let bygones be bygones and that F.B.C. send me to South Korea as a war correspondent. He was courteous and not unfriendly. He thanked me for my offer and said he would let me know.

JULY 2 (SUNDAY)

RESTLESS all day. I drove the family out to Jones Beach, as I had promised, but I spent most of my time on the sands hovering over a portable radio set listening to the news from Korea. It gets worse and worse.

Much to the disgust of Maria and Dick (the boy is becoming quite a problem) we left early. I tried to explain to them that we wanted to avoid the late traffic jam. In reality I was becoming so jumpy I couldn't bear remaining at the beach any longer. I felt sure Bob Fletcher was trying to reach me.

No word from Bob all evening. His office said he might be week-ending at Mark Robson's in the country. I phoned there, but did not succeed in getting through to either of them.

JULY 3

I AM getting into a state. Both Yvonne and the youngsters seemed fed up with me today. I was furious all morning that neither Bob Fletcher nor Mark Robson would accept my phone calls. I toyed with the idea of simply going to F.B.C. and pushing past their secretaries into their offices. Yvonne dissuaded me.

I phoned Henry Wadsworth Prentice at *U.S.A.* He said he would certainly consider sending me to Korea and was happy to know I was available. But I could not pin him down.

Christopher Chambers had invited us up to his place in Cornwall, Connecticut, over the Fourth. After lunch, however, I informed Yvonne and the children that I could not drive them up today and that they would have to take the train. I said I would drive up tomorrow to fetch them home. Herding them to Grand Central Station, resentful as they were, was quite painful. Not even Yvonne seems to understand what I am going through.

I drove myself hard the rest of the afternoon. I called the other networks and let them know I was available. I phoned the Pentagon in Washington, told the press officer I would be applying for credentials for Korea and asked him what "shots" were required. Then I hurried off to my doctor and took the first ones — for cholera, plague and typhoid.

At loose ends tonight.

JULY 4

IN MY desperation last night I went to see Elsie McCabe to ask if she would use her influence with Verne Gibson to get him to send me to Korea for *World Review*. That's how low I've sunk.

Despite what has happened recently she seemed glad to see

[*171*]

me. It must have been ten P.M. when I got up nerve enough to phone her, so I was not surprised when, arriving a half hour later, I found her attired in black silk pajamas and a lightweight dressing gown to match.

I told her at once why I had come.

"Raymond," she answered, in a voice that was surprisingly low and calm, "you know that I'm always glad to see you. And I'm particularly glad to see that at long last you have awakened to the Communist danger."

For a moment the last part of that remark threatened to blow up our meeting then and there. However, I kept my temper. We had battled too long over that point to leave much left of it.

"What concerns me at the moment," I said, "is that the Soviet Union undoubtedly gave the green light to the North Koreans to begin their aggression. And I want very much to go to Korea to see if the Russians get away with it."

"I call that an awakening, Raymond," she said, with a somewhat triumphant smile.

I could see, though, that she was still puzzled at what I had proposed and also by my sudden nocturnal appearance out of the blue. She had poured large whiskey-sodas before we sat down and now she got up from the lounge where we were sitting to pour a second round.

I began to feel better. I even began to feel relaxed with Elsie —something that had not happened since a good many years. She had turned off most of the lamps to make the room as cool as possible. We lay back in the large overstuffed sofa. I felt comfortable and soothed, scarcely noticing when she slipped her arm around me and nestled her shoulders close to mine.

"Now that after all these years," she said softly, "we've resolved our political war, let's be friends, darling."

"Why not, my dear?"

She moved her head slightly and kissed me, leaving her arm coiled nicely around my neck. I did not object. For a long time we were like that in the silence, breaking it only for another drink. It was a little like the times long ago in Geneva except that we were no longer young and that different, separated lives had left a gulf. It would never be really bridgeable, I knew, nor did I wish it to be. Something, though, inevitably had remained between us and at this moment of anguish, of frustration, it seemed good and comforting.

After a while she stirred. Her face was close to mine, blurred and beautiful.

"Does Yvonne know you are here?" she asked, her voice no more than a whisper.

"No."

"Is she at home? Waiting?"

"She's in the country."

"You can stay the night then, darling."

That broke the spell, and I was sorry. I tried as best I could not to hurt her. I made all sorts of excuses. But they did not much help. First, she argued. Then she insisted.

"I won't let you go! Not this time!" she cried, clutching me. I was surprised at the tempestuousness of her passion, but the more it rose the deader I felt inside. I could not explain this to her. Finally I got up, stumbled through the half-darkened room and made my way out.

All this holiday I have slumped in this stifling, sultry living room listening to the Korean news over the radio and waiting for someone — Fletcher or Prentice or whoever — to call and say I can go to Korea for them. I telephoned Yvonne that I could not drive up to Cornwall today and that she and the children would have to take the train back tomorrow morning. She was obviously annoyed.

"Are you feeling all right, dear?" she asked.

"I'm feeling fine," I insisted.

Actually I've been feeling the full impact of the inoculations all day.

JULY 5

TO GRAND CENTRAL STATION at noon to welcome my family back and I was happy to see them, though Dick was missing. Yvonne says he may get a job as counselor in a summer camp in Cornwall — something Chris Chambers, with whom he is staying, is fixing up. It will be just the thing for the boy.

Exciting news from Korea on the radio when we got back to the house. For the first time since World War II, American troops have gone into action. The first U.S. war correspondents have already arrived at the front.

JULY 9 (SUNDAY)
                I HAD a heart-to-heart talk last night with Yvonne, who always keeps both of her petite French feet firmly planted on the ground. She reminded me that it was not up to me to fight the Korean War. She suggested I relax a little.

So I relaxed today by driving her and Maria up to Cornwall to see Dick, who is a counselor in a camp not far from Chris Chambers's place. We had lunch together at Chris's and in the afternoon took a long walk through a magnificent pine forest nearby. I feel much better. Dick very happy about his job, and I think he has got over his resentment of me.

JULY 10
                I THOUGHT the columnists had forgotten me. But the inimitable Bert Woodruff was back on the scent this morning:

> Ex-Commentator Raymond Whitehead knocking at the doors of all the networks and most of the mags . . . claims he wants to cover the war in Korea. The chump! Doesn't he know whom we're fighting over there? Does he think the radio chains — or even the mags — have forgotten "Red Airwaves"? . . . You haven't got a chance, mister!

JULY 13
                MULLING over the news today an idea suddenly hit me. If by the end of this month the United States has committed most of its limited military strength in Korea, as

seems inevitable, the Russian Red Army will be able to occupy Western Europe without any appreciable opposition and without any fear that we can intervene effectively.

Such a move would certainly plunge us into World War III. The place for me to go, then, is not Korea but Europe, which would be the main battlefield. It won't be necessary to get an assignment there in advance. If the Red Army marches, touching off the Big War, there will be plenty of opportunities for employment.

JULY 14

I BROACHED my idea to Yvonne. She agreed it was a good one. I lost no time in calling the New York office of the State Department and asking for a passport. My old one has expired.

JULY 15

YVONNE proposed today that she and the children come to Europe with me. While I am in Vienna and Berlin trying to find out whether the Red Army is going to march, she and the youngsters would camp out with her parents in Versailles. Behind her suggestion, I felt, was a growing feeling that it might be best for us to return to Europe for good, though she did not say so. My troubles here have been all the more shocking to her because they have been beyond the comprehension of her logical Gallic mind.

I admit it is a temptation to go back to Europe, where we had so many years of happiness and fruitful work. It would be a relief to get away from the hysteria and the intolerance here. But this is my country. I belong here. And however rough the going, I am going to stay — unless a big war should keep me away. If the peace holds after all, I shall return before the summer is up.

Yvonne was so touchingly eager about her project that I hesitated to throw cold water on it. I think I convinced her, though, that it would be wise to drop it. For one thing, if war did come in Europe, France would be no place for her and the children to be. France would be quickly overrun — in a few weeks, at the most — by the Russian armies. That was the main consideration. If war did not come, I would be back by the first of September. Also there was the question of finances. Our treasury is getting low. We could scarcely afford taking the whole family over.

JULY 18

I WENT around personally to the State Department office here today to see about my passport. There is something fishy about the delay. Getting no satisfaction here, I have decided to go to Washington tomorrow.

WASHINGTON, JULY 19

I FOUND out at the State Department today why my passport has been held up. Senator O'Brien has intervened!

Apparently one of his stooges in the Department tipped him off about my application. He thereupon asked the Passport Division to hold it up pending "certain investigations" of his Security Committee. What those are I can't possibly imagine and I couldn't find out today. I phoned the Senator, but couldn't reach him. I went over to his office, but he was either not in or wouldn't see me.

Washington boils in the humid heat. It seethes with uneasiness and suspicion. Uneasiness at Russia's design, suspicion of anyone frowned upon by Senator O'Brien. Suspicion that they're Communists.

Yet withal the reaction against Communist aggression in Korea has on the whole been healthy. Had London or Paris been equally alive to the Facts of Life in the late Thirties when Hitler and Mussolini were launching their aggressions, history probably would have turned out differently. The aggressors would have been stopped in their tracks and there would have been no world war.

BEFORE my train left Washington at noon, I went over to the Senate Office Building and lay in wait for O'Brien, catching him as he was leaving his office.

First, he was cagey about my complaint that he was trying to hold up my passport.

"You're not trying to run away from anything, are you, Whitehead?"

"I can't imagine what it would be, Senator. Can you?"

"I'm just asking."

We walked down the corridor toward the Senate. O'Brien became positively friendly, taking my arm and pushing his face, which somehow reminds one of a rat, very close to mine.

"I always remember that day at your house in Geneva," he said. "You spiked the drinks, remember?"

"No, that was just good old-fashioned Scotch, Senator."

"You gave me a report on that fellow Burnett, I remember."

"I remember defending him," I said.

"Yeah, I've often wondered why you did."

"I tried to do it again before your committee, but you squelched me," I reminded him. The reminder seemed to please him.

"You were pretty irrelevant, Whitehead," he said, smiling. We came to the end of the corridor and stopped.

"Well, Senator . . ." I started to say.

"What do you want to go to Europe for?" he interrupted me.

"To see if the Russians march."

"Hum." It took him a moment to digest that. "You'll be in touch with our embassies?"

"Yes. And with our Intelligence, I hope."

He pursed his thin lips.

"I see no harm in that. Just so you don't get lost."

"Lost? I know my way around over there. Lived there most of my life, Senator."

"I know you did. Well, good luck, Whitehead," he said abruptly, giving me a damp hand to shake.

[*177*]

O'Brien has his troubles too. This evening, after I had returned, I caught a Washington commentator on one of the networks describing a tumultuous session of the Senate that began shortly after I parted from the Senator. O'Brien was denounced as a "perjurer" and a "fraud" and not a single solon rose to defend him. The evening papers carry a story that O'Brien "neglected" to pay any income tax last year.

JULY 21

YVONNE tells me of a telephone message from Verne Gibson to come to cocktails next Monday. It came while I was in Washington. Perhaps I can yet prevail upon him to send me to Korea for *World Review*.

JULY 24 (MONDAY)

A DELIGHTFUL week end at Chris Chambers's place in the Connecticut hills. It was a relief to escape the humid heat of New York and a relief too to spend two whole days in which politics and Korea were not mentioned. Chris slyly suggested we forget it all for a couple of days.

I found Dick so tanned I scarcely recognized him at first. This being on his own for the first time in his life is doing wonders for him, bringing him out, giving him some self-confidence and self-reliance. I liked him immensely. Maria was also something to watch. She tried mightily to act a couple of years beyond thirteen and apparently succeeded, for the youngsters in the neighborhood, who were a little cool at first, took her up in a big way, I thought. She will have plenty of company during August when she and Yvonne will be staying with Chris. Yvonne suggested to our host that perhaps she had better not come since I would not be able to make it, but he refused to listen.

"You'll be perfectly safe," he assured her, his gay, blue eyes twinkling. "The house will be full of people, mostly actors, male and female, who don't know what else to do in August. It will be nice to have at least one beautiful woman. . . ."

"But you'll have several actresses," Yvonne protested.

"That's my point, my dear Yvonne. Now please don't let a jealous husband upset your plans."

Among all the people that came and went over the week end, Yvonne did seem to me to stand out. I have rarely seen her looking lovelier. The thought of being away from her at least a month kept rising to plague and depress me.

Off now to Verne Gibson's party.

JULY 25

THE Korean War a month old and we continue to take a licking. Defeating Communist military power abroad is to be no lark. Interesting that many of those who shouted loudest for exterminating the Communists from the face of the earth are now protesting violently against what they term "Mr. Truman's war."

Gibson's cocktail party at the Somerset Club turned out to be a celebration to launch Sidney Goodrich as associate editor of *World Review* and to call attention to the first of a series of articles he has begun writing for the great magazine.

I was not prepared, I must say, for Gibson's announcement to the ladies and gentlemen of the press and radio, of the subject of Goodrich's pieces. They are to be published, he said, under the title: "I Believe in Big Business — It's the American Way." They will ultimately, Gibson explained, be expanded into a book. The first article, in the August issue of *World Review* out today, is subtitled: "Big Business and Your Security in a Free World."

Verne Gibson, beaming with pride, finished his announcement amid general applause. Then there were cries of "Author! Author! Speech!" emanating, I saw, from a claque led by the two Clark columnists, Bert Woodruff and Frederick Newman, and by Whitney Shuttleworth.

Sidney Goodrich clambered up on the dais. The doughty old warrior for public power looked benign and harmless. The fire that possessed the man for so long, and that carried him through to triumph in many a rough battle in Washington, had gone out.

Sidney looked a little sheepish at first, I thought, speaking his opening words hesitantly and scarcely looking up at the audience, most of whose members would not have listened to him a year ago. He told a little joke at the expense of the "Washington bureaucrats" which brought howls of laughter, though it seemed in curious taste coming from one who had been a member of that bureaucracy — and a good one — most of his adult life.

He hesitated while the laughter subsided, and then flashed an ingratiating smile. "I suppose," he said, "that many of you wonder why I launch my journalistic career with a series of articles on 'Big Business.' It is not so strange as you may think. Public power in the United States is big business — one of the biggest. And I had considerable experience in it. In the course of that experience I came into — shall I say? — rather close contact with other big businesses run by private enterprise. We had some epic battles." (Laughter.) "And during them I gained a good deal of knowledge of and — I want to emphasize — a good deal of respect for, my opponents. I learned that they had their place in our industrial society and that the government, which was my master, didn't always appreciate it." (Applause and cheers.)

"Big government, though I have my doubts and even fears about it, is probably here to stay. Its counterpart in our free society must be big business. Where did we turn during the last war when we suddenly needed tens of thousands of planes, tanks and big guns? To big business. Without it we could not have won the war. Without it today we will not be able to prosecute the Korean War and defeat Communism. That's why I have entitled my first article: 'Big Business and Your Security in a Free World.' I hope you will read it — and the ones to follow. Thank you."

It was a clever little speech and there was no doubt that Sidney Goodrich endeared himself to his listeners. All is now forgiven him. He will certainly not frighten away any of Verne

Gibson's big advertisers. On the contrary. If he keeps this up, he will attract some.

The drinking and the devouring of the *canapés* now began in earnest. There was quite a jam around Goodrich and I stood off to one side with my highball to observe the melee. Mark Robson, Bob Fletcher and William McKinley Forbes strode forward to pump Sidney's hand and pat him approvingly on the back. Then I saw Senator O'Brien elbowing his way forward. His train from Washington must have been late.

"Hello, Whitehead," he greeted me breezily as he pushed by. "Thought you had gone to Europe. Been a hitch, or something?"

"No," I said. "I hope to get off this week, Senator, now that you . . ."

He cut me off. "Don't bring me into it, Whitehead. Didn't I wish you good luck?"

Elsie McCabe was another late arrival, but she did not see me. Neither did Mark and Bob as they brushed by on their way out. I finished my drink and left.

JULY 26

THE State Department phoned from Washington this morning and said I could pick up my passport here tomorrow. I hurried down to Pan-American and booked through to Vienna. There had been so many cancellations due to fears of the Korean War spreading to Europe that I had no trouble getting a seat on the plane for day after tomorrow.

Yvonne had lunch with Barbara Fletcher today. Whatever passed between them seems to have depressed her. I did not question Yvonne, and she said little about it. She did volunteer that Barbara had invited her out to the farm while I am gone, but that she had declined. She will go out to Chris Chambers's this week end for a month.

JULY 27

I RAN into Bob Fletcher on my way to fetch my passport this morning. He was hurrying away from Radio City.

"Raymond," he cried out, "how nice to see you! What are you up to anyway?"

"I'm off to Europe, Bob."

"Really? When?"

"Tomorrow."

"It sounds interesting, Raymond. I wish you loads of luck." He wrung my hand and went on his way.

BERLIN, AUGUST 12

THE Red Army is not going to march. There will be no Third World War just now. Of that I am fairly certain after a fortnight in Vienna, Western Germany and here.

Our military intelligence says flatly there is no evidence that the Soviet Army is being reinforced or that it is building up its supplies. Our generals are absolutely certain that the Russians have decided not to risk a big war despite our being tied down in Korea, though the Red Army could occupy the rest of this continent within a few weeks without much trouble if the Kremlin wished it.

Impossible to describe the relief I feel.

AUGUST 14

ONE other thing strikes me after a few days in Western Germany and here: our example in giving the West Germans and the West Berliners freedom and democratic rights and in generously helping them to rebuild from the ruins — in contrast to the savage tyranny of Communism and the plundering of the Russians in Eastern Germany — has done more to defeat Communism and destroy illusions about the Soviet Union and to enhance our own good name than a thousand Senator O'Briens could ever do.

Off by plane tomorrow for Geneva, Switzerland, and then on by train to Gstaad to while away a few days with Steve Burnett and his youngsters in the mountains.

STEVE BURNETT was on the station platform when the train rolled in, and I saw instantly from his taut, grave face that it had happened. But he did not say so at once. He tried to smile, he took my hand eagerly, and clasped my arm warmly as we walked to the restaurant at the far end of the station. We had a couple of hours for lunch, he explained, before the train for Gstaad left. His face was twitching as we sat down and there was a vacant stare in his eyes such as I had never seen in all the years I had known him. I suggested a strong drink and when the waiter came we ordered double-whiskies, something I rarely drink in Switzerland where a vermouth cassis is my usual cocktail.

"I certainly need it," Steve said after the waiter had brought the drinks and we had ordered lunch. He swallowed half the big glass in one gulp.

"I too," I said. "I'm weary from gadding about."

"You must tell me about it, Raymond. Are we going to have the big war?"

"I don't think so, Steve. But first, your news. Tell me about yourself."

He gulped down the rest of his drink and leaned forward, forcing a smile so sad, so pained, that it hurt to see it.

"The legation telephoned the news over from Berne late last night," he began, haltingly. "Uh . . . The Loyalty Board's findings, that is. It was a 3 to 2 vote against me, Raymond."

He stopped as if there were not breath or strength of mind to say more. "Three to two — a close vote," he finally mumbled. "Better . . . uh . . . than a unanimous vote, I suppose."

"What did they vote exactly, Steve?"

"The worst charge possible, short of treason," he answered heatedly. Now some color mounted in his bony face, which had been ashen. It was the first sign of a man struggling to get back on his feet after a deadly blow.

"The majority didn't have the guts to charge me with disloyalty," he went on. "It merely decided that, as the phrase goes, there was 'reasonable doubt' as to my loyalty to the United States Government."

The very utterance of the words, grotesque and monstrous in their meaning to him — and to me — struck us dumb. He lowered his head and I could see the veins swelling in both temples. Then he looked up suddenly.

"What could be worse, I ask you?"

There was no quest for pity in his tortured face — just despair and shock.

"It's a despicable crime, Steve," I said. "It's an outrageous, contemptible thing they've done. And somehow it has got to be undone — that's what we've got to start thinking about."

The food had arrived and the presence of the waiter, piling the heaping plates on the table, interrupted us. Steve ordered another round of whiskies, but I suggested instead a bottle of Neuchâtel wine. The day was still young and there was too much to talk about and perhaps to decide, to get into an alcoholic haze so early. For one thing, we would have to call the legation at Berne and get the complete text of the finding. Last night Steve had been given merely the decision itself.

Neither of us had much stomach for the food. But the light, yellow wine tasted good.

"How are the youngsters, Steve?"

"Fine. Full of beans. And brown as Indians." For a moment he seemed relieved to get his mind off his troubles. "They're rather keen about going back to New York in the fall and being in an American school again."

I tended to forget how valiant Steve had been in trying to raise the three girls himself. Eleanor, his wife, whom he rarely mentioned, as if the bare pronouncement of the name was too painful to endure, had died toward the end of the war when he was still in Chungking. He had not been able to get back from China to Washington in time for the funeral — a failure that I suspect he broods over to this day. He had not seen her for nearly two years, and he would never know fully how she was those last days, exactly how she looked and what her sufferings had been, for letters told so little. This weighed on him. She had been ill since her last childbirth toward the end of 1942, and had slowly wasted away — this vital and lovely woman — despite half a dozen operations to save her.

Eleanor's sister, the wife of a prospering Washington lawyer, had taken the children in when Steve went back to his post in China. But after the war, when he returned for an assignment at the State Department, Steve insisted on taking them over himself. He rented a small house in Georgetown, acquired a personable Swiss lady named Albert as housekeeper and governess — she was with him until recently, I think — put the two eldest girls in school and the youngest in kindergarten and worked harder than most parents at bringing the youngsters up. When he was sent to Switzerland he took the children and the Swiss housekeeper with him, enrolling the girls in school in Berne and sending them back to America summers to stay with his sister-in-law, whose family had a vacation place in the Adirondacks near Lake Placid. Like me, he wanted his children to sprout American roots. I had not seen Irita, Marcia and Marguerite for more than a year. They would be now about eight, eleven and fifteen, respectively. Irita and Marcia, as I remembered, were blond little bundles of fire: Marguerite was dark and contemplative, like her mother.

Steve must have been reading my thoughts. "I haven't told the children yet," he said. "I started to at breakfast this morning, but there was not much time before the train left. Somehow I couldn't shake a coherent account out of myself. And they didn't seem to catch on to what I was trying to say. But I'll have to tell them this evening. It will be in the newspapers and probably on the radio. And I'll have to face everyone else in the hotel — a lot of retired European diplomats, mostly, who will immediately act as if I were contaminating the place."

"On the contrary, Steve," I said. "They'll probably wonder how a fellow of your intelligence and probity stuck it out so long. So far as I can see over here our O'Brienism and our hysteria over loyalty has almost convinced the Europeans that Washington has surrendered to the lunatics."

After a while our train was called, but we did not catch it. We had another bottle of Neuchâtel, and then I suggested that we spend the evening here at Montreux. There was a comfortable old hotel down on the lake. We could rent a boat and go sailing, do a little swimming off it, have a pleasant dinner on the terrace by the water and in the evening see if the legation had yet received the text of the Loyalty Board's findings. If so, we could then ponder it in a more relaxed mood than would be possible at Gstaad. We could push up into the mountains on the morning train. Steve agreed.

It was a lazy, Alpine summer afternoon. There wasn't much wind and we couldn't sail very far, but we had a good swim off the boat which greatly revived Steve (the water was cold; it comes from melting snows on the mountaintops) and afterward a leisurely dinner on the terrace overlooking the lake and the mountains.

About ten P.M. the legation came through on the telephone with the text, which Steve patiently wrote down. It is unbelievable! It is a horror! It is also so confused and confusing that, as I quickly pointed out to Steve, who at first was quite stunned, it gives the Secretary of State and the President good grounds for refusing to heed the board's recommendation that Burnett be dismissed from the foreign service because of "reasonable doubt" as to his loyalty.

We sat up most of the night discussing it. The first flaw in the decision, I pointed out, is the opening part which contains the amazing statement that while the board did not expressly accept or reject the testimony of Elsie McCabe and Frederick Newman that Burnett was a Communist and under Communist discipline, or the findings of the O'Brien committee that Burnett participated in a Communist conspiracy to turn China over to the Communists and to influence United States policy to that end, the board *nevertheless took these factors into consideration.*

"What the hell does that mean?" I exclaimed.

"Nothing — or everything," Steve said quietly. The shock had been dissipated now and I could feel that his mind, usually so cool and analytical, was beginning to function more normally.

"Well, at least it gives you something tangible on which to base an appeal to the secretary," I said.

"The first ray of hope," he said, and this time a slight smile curved over his mouth without effort. Even the glassy stare in his eyes seemed to be diminishing.

We found what we thought might be other grounds for appeal. In fact, the findings were full of holes, I thought. There was the old asinine charge, which the sluggish-minded O'Brien had made much of, that Steve, in his reports from China to the Department, had "praised" the Communists and "criticized" the Nationalists of Chiang Kai-shek. I was surprised the Loyalty Board retained that one as part of the evidence which made Steve's loyalty doubtful. What this amounted to was that Burnett had often pointed out the weakness and corruption of the Nationalists and their reticence during the war to fight the Japanese, and he had constantly warned Washington of the growing power of the Communists. This act of reporting factually and honestly had been twisted around by the primitive witch-hunters in Washington and taken by the Loyalty Board to signify that Burnett had been pro-Communist and anti-Chiang and thus disloyal to the American Government.

"Was there ever anything so ridiculous?" I declaimed.

"Well, there's that final charge that I associated with Communists," Steve said.

"Guilt by association!" This was, I fully realized, becoming a new American credo though it did violence to our American traditions. The Loyalty Board had included it as one of the reasons for its decision.

"In Chungking," Steve said, "part of my job at the embassy was seeing the official representatives of the Chinese Communists, including the Commy foreign minister, who was in and out during most of the war. I tried to explain that to Senator O'Brien, but he held it against me, you'll remember. And, of course, over here I knew you, Raymond, and you're suspect, you know."

The more we talked it over the better we felt.

Then shortly after midnight the minister called from Berne.

[187]

He had just had a cable from the Department, he was sorry to say, which ordered Burnett home immediately.

That does not look so good.

GSTAAD, AUGUST 20 (SUNDAY)

THIS morning I saw Steve and his charming daughters off on the train to Berne. Stephen will close down his house there, pack his furniture for shipment home and then get off for the States.

He remarked yesterday that probably this would be the last time he would ever be shipping his household goods home from a foreign post. On the whole, though, he has regained his composure and his self-confidence. He is not going to be a professional or an ostentatious martyr. He will continue to fight for his good name. He is sure he will win in the end. But he is intelligent enough, and realistic, to realize that, given the present climate at home, it may take some time and that meanwhile he will be in disgrace — considered guilty by many Americans of the incredible charges against him. They have hurt him to the quick. But he has the inner courage to endure his wounds without complaint and — what is splendid — without much bitterness.

"The country went through the same shameful business at least twice before," he mused yesterday while we were on a final, long walk up a mountain back of the town. "The passage of the Alien and Sedition laws in the early days of the republic loosed what Jefferson himself called a 'ferocious terror.' Hundreds of decent persons were denounced as traitors for speaking out against it. Many were jailed. Then there was the period after the First World War when we again lost our heads. Fortunately it was short-lived. The present hysteria, Raymond, will pass too. Only it will last longer because of Russian truculence, Communist tactics and our fears and nightmares, which arise partly out of both."

Stephen was already beginning to take the long view. We spent a good bit of time with the three girls, hiking and swimming and playing tennis. They took their father's news with fine grace. Their confidence in him is touching; whatever he does is right.

I go down to Montreux this evening and from there to Paris for a few days. It will be a good place to collect my thoughts. Now that there is to be no war to cover, I must go home and get a job. Perhaps the ban on me in radio and — as it looked — in the press will be forgotten. Yvonne writes that our bank account is getting low. Nothing has come in all summer. I must really finish that book this fall.

PARIS, AUGUST 23

THE magic, incomparable city does wonders for me, making me feel as if I could conquer the world.

Yesterday I went out to Versailles to pay my respects to Yvonne's parents. They live in a world I never knew, but no doubt it is as good and rich as mine, if not more so. Somehow it reminds me of the world of Proust and of the impressionist painters — their scenes of the countryside at the turn of the century or thereabouts. The old Senator, though he has retired from politics, talks it at the drop of a hat, pulling at his magnificent beard and gesticulating with all the energy of a Gallic youth. The mother, gentle and yet discerning, sits and embroiders the while.

I had to fib a little. They insisted on putting me up while I am here, though they chided me for not bringing Yvonne and the children. I said I was leaving in two days and that I had a number of interviews to do in Paris meantime, which would keep me frightfully busy.

I want to be alone for a few days, and roam the streets and ruminate.

AUGUST 27 (SUNDAY)

A RATHER sad but memorable afternoon with Wendell Philpots and Wanda. We drove out to a restaurant on the slopes of St. Cloud for lunch, sitting on the terrace most of the afternoon reminiscing. At sixty-six, Wendell is a little stooped and his hair has turned quite white, but his mind is as keen as ever and in his spirit is a dignity and a nobility I have seen in few other Americans. He has taken his great defeat gracefully.

He does not complain. I gather from what little he said on the subject that he ekes out a living writing feature stories for a few provincial papers at home, in England and in Australia. He still spends his afternoons studying and working at the Bibliothèque Nationale, France's greatest library. I imagine the home he returns to in the evening is a pretty shabby place — judging by the location in a poor quarter back of the Pantheon.

Wanda, I felt, did not want me to see it. She insisted on their picking me up today at my hotel. She has aged considerably, though to me she is still beautiful. She looked very tired. She is weary, I judge, of selling hats.

"Take us back to America with you, Raymond," she pleaded, and not entirely in fun.

"I'm too old to go back," Wendell laughed. But behind his chuckle I felt an aching.

We had much good talk. I tried to convince him that he should come home, that we needed him there more than ever.

He smiled sadly: "I shall come home to die, Raymond."

AUGUST 28

QUITE a few Americans have come back to Europe to die. I have run into a dozen of them here. They are rather a forlorn lot. Men mostly for whom the period between the wars over here comprised the golden years and who, through some failure of adjustment, could neither find a niche at home when the last war forced them back nor their old places in Europe when they returned after the war. Many of them used to have important, interesting and even well-paying posts over here. Most were correspondents, some were writers, a few were in business or in the diplomatic service. For various reasons they did not regain their former positions after the war. Some perhaps were a little old. Most, I think, lost their old fire. There was a curious deterioration of mind, spirit, personality. They exist today on various odd jobs, and pine for the past. One passion remains: for this city, for a way of life they say they never found in the land where they were born.

AUGUST 29

YVONNE tried to get through to me on the trans-Atlantic telephone tonight. But there were sunspots or something. The connection never was made. I'll try to reach her tomorrow.

AUGUST 30

ABOUT nine this morning I proceeded, as usual, from my hotel, to the Ronde Point where I bought two or three French morning papers and the *New York Herald Tribune* and then strolled up the Champs Elysées to the terrace of a *café* to read them and have my breakfast. There wasn't much in the Parisian press, which I first glanced at. A murder story, which was rather tame for Paris. Editorials on the front page against German rearmament. A pompous piece by a renowned editor, member of the Academy, about America's "cultural lag." And of course stories from Korea about how we had smashed every Communist attempt to break through the Pusan perimeter.

I sipped my coffee, nibbled my croissant, and turned idly to the *Tribune* for the latest news from home.

The headline stunned me. For a moment I must have blacked out. I felt myself clutching the table to keep from toppling over. It took a minute or two to regain control of myself and to focus my twitching eyes on the headline again.

O'BRIEN NAMES WHITEHEAD
AS SOVIET AGENT
Senator Says Commentator Has Fled
Demands Extradition. Believes
He May Be in Moscow —

The story, date-lined Washington, must have broken late. The dispatch was brief. The headline told all.

I read it over and over and over. My throat felt parched, and I gulped down a glass of water. Then shock gave way to anger. I was half-conscious of muttering a few unprintable oaths against Senator O'Brien. The effrontery of the man! The lies!

He was quoted as saying that I had skipped to Europe although he had warned the State Department not to grant me a passport. Probably I had fled to Moscow. But wherever I was, he demanded my immediate extradition. He would prove I was a Soviet agent.

I remembered that there was a cable office a few blocks up the Champs Elysées and also a branch of one of the airlines. I paid for my breakfast and hurried up the broad avenue. A partial morning mist still hung over it; I could just barely make out the outline of the Arc de Triomphe at the top of the hill. I suddenly remembered a sunny, clear day long before the war when I had seen a French biplane fly *through* the arch. And another day, also sunny and warm — and glorious! — when one of our divisions had paraded down the majestic avenue from the Arc at the time we liberated Paris. I had come into town with a bunch of ruffians from the Resistance with whom I had been operating on an assignment from our intelligence in Switzerland.

At the cable office I scratched out a hasty message to the Senator:

HON. O'BRIEN, SENATE, WASHINGTON, D.C. — AS YOU WELL KNOW I DID NOT FLEE AND I AM NOT IN HIDING. HAVE KEPT IN CLOSEST TOUCH WITH OUR EMBASSIES, LEGATIONS AND MILITARY INTELLIGENCE ESTABLISHMENTS. YOUR CHARGE IS A CONTEMPTIBLE LIE. DEMAND IMMEDIATE HEARING BEFORE YOUR COMMITTEE. RETURNING ON FIRST AVAILABLE PLANE. ADDRESS, HOTEL LINCOLN, PARIS.

At the airlines office further up the street, I got a place, after considerable argument, on a plane day after tomorrow. From the office I phoned one of the American press associations and suggested that if the correspondents were interested, I would be glad to see them at my hotel at noon.

When I got back to the hotel, I found a telephone call waiting from New York. Yvonne and our good lawyer friend, Bill Rikind, were on the line.

"I tried to phone you last night, darling," Yvonne said. "But we had no luck. I suppose you've heard the news by now."

"Just read it in the *Tribune*, darling. Did you ever hear of anything more preposterous in . . ."

"Of course it's preposterous, Raymond," Yvonne cut in. "Utterly ridiculous. Everyone here is saying so. In fact, Bill Rikind, who is here with me and is going to talk to you in a moment, thinks that this time we will really make O'Brien eat his words — and that will be the end of him."

"I hope so, Yvonne."

"I just wanted you to know, Raymond," she said, "so you wouldn't worry."

"I'm not worrying, Yvonne. But I'm pretty sore still."

"Probably not half as much as I am, my dear," she said.

"How are you, darling? And the youngsters?" I asked.

"We're all fine. When are you coming home?"

"On a plane day after tomorrow. I'll cable arrival time later."

"We'll meet you."

"Oh, Yvonne. I dined with the folks."

"How are they?"

"*Père et Mère* both fine," I said. "Your father is in great form. He ought to be back in the Senate."

"Give them my love, Raymond."

Yvonne put Bill Rikind on the line.

"Raymond," he said cheerfully, "there's not a thing in the world to worry about. This time, I think, the Senator has really stumbled."

"Can't we sue the bastard, Bill?"

"We'll challenge him to say it in public. Then we'll sue him for a million dollars, Raymond!"

Rikind rolled the figure on his tongue as if he could already taste the heap of greenbacks.

"Didn't O'Brien make that charge in public?" I asked. "It sure is public as hell in the papers, isn't it?"

"He said it in the Senate, Raymond. You can't sue a guy for

what he says in the Senate, you know. That's why, with your permission, Raymond, I'd like to challenge him to repeat the charge in public."

"Please do," I said.

"One more thing, Raymond. Have the reporters caught up with you yet?"

"They're coming over at noon." I looked at my watch. "In just an hour."

"Be careful what you say. In fact, say as little as possible, if you don't mind."

"Well, I intend to tell them the truth, Bill. That the charge is a contemptible lie. That I did not skip out, and that I'm not in hiding. That's what I just cabled O'Brien, by the way."

"You cabled him? Already?" I could feel his lawyer's uneasiness.

"Yes. I'll give you the text, so far as I remember."

"You didn't make a copy, Raymond?" Really, he was getting awfully fussy, I thought. Why were lawyers usually so scared of the press? I dictated to him the text, as I recalled it, and jotted it down myself.

"Just give the reporters that, Raymond. Nothing more, please. We don't want to spoil our case."

"All right, William. And will you demand that the committee hear me first thing next week?"

"Not next week, Raymond. I'll need time to prepare the case."

"My case is prepared, Bill. I'll be ready Monday."

"Monday is Labor Day."

"Well, Tuesday then."

"It's awfully soon, Raymond. Remember, man, this may be a frame-up. And I may need a few days to get my teeth into it. You'll have to be patient, Raymond."

"Patient! In the face of such an outrage! . . Uh, what did you say about a 'frame-up'?" I had not thought of that.

"What else could it be, Raymond? That's why I may need some time — a week or two."

A frame-up? Not just another wild O'Brien charge, but a trap? Perhaps Rikind was right.

[*194*]

"Okay, Bill. You do what you think is best. See you Saturday. Will you put Yvonne on the line for a second?"

It had occurred to me that though it was eleven A.M. here, it was only six A.M. in New York. She must have been up all night. But she did not want to speak of it. All that she would say was that they had heard the news on the radio after dinner last night and that Christopher Chambers had driven her back to the city from Connecticut and that they had had a long talk with Rikind.

"Get some sleep, honey," I admonished.

"Don't worry about me, darling. I . . ."

At that point we were disconnected.

AUGUST 31

A DOZEN American correspondents arrived promptly at noon yesterday. I read them my cable to O'Brien and explained that on the advice of my lawyer I could not at this time say any more. This must have been the first time in my life that I, who have interviewed thousands of people in my career, was myself interviewed. It all seemed a little absurd and unnatural. And, of course, after we had had an *apéritif* in the corner of the deserted hotel bar and talked shop for a while, I weakened and spoke frankly. All of them, except the Clark press representative, seemed like decent fellows and were obviously sympathetic. After all, I had nothing to hide.

Late in the afternoon several reporters from the French press besieged me and I came down to the bar for a second interview. Perhaps they were interested in me because I was the son-in-law of a well-known former French Senator. Feeling guilty of bad manners, and wishing to save him from embarrassment when he read the papers, I had gone out to dine with Yvonne's parents last evening, but was unable to shed much light on my predicament. The old man kept complaining he couldn't follow me.

"*C'est une blague, mon fils,*" he roared, fingering his luxuriant beard. "*C'est une Chinoiserie. C'est absolument ridicule, je te dis.*"

I had no more luck with the Parisian newsmen. They didn't get it. France had had some unsavory characters: Laval, who was a Senator, for example. But O'Brienism was something the French had happily escaped — at least, since the dim days of the Dreyfus case. They couldn't understand it.

This evening a quiet dinner with Wendell and Wanda at Pierre's. The headlines had shocked them and left them bewildered. Such things had not been possible in the America Wendell knew.

"What kind of country has it become, anyway?" Wendell asked. His thick brows were furrowed, his fine, clear eyes apprehensive.

"An interesting country, Wendell. Anything — no matter how wacky, can happen."

NEW YORK, SEPTEMBER 2

AS I walked down the steps from the plane flash bulbs exploded and the photographers yelled at me (as they do to far more important persons). In the hangar a dozen reporters crowded around. After some argument they agreed to wait until I was through customs and passport formalities.

As I emerged into the public waiting room, Yvonne and the children fell upon me, Maria dancing up and down with joy and excitement, Dick smiling proudly, and Yvonne, I could see, hiding her emotions and restraining herself, her fine face bright with color, her eyes large as walnuts and warm and eager, and yet under control. I embraced them all. I even hugged old Bill Rikind when he came up, the flash bulbs popping all the while.

Rikind took me aside for a moment as the reporters gathered around, explaining that he had scheduled a full-dress press conference in the afternoon and suggesting that for the moment I merely reiterate what I had said in Paris about the O'Brien charges, which I proceeded to do.

At last I was free, and Yvonne drove us home. But there was no opportunity to rest. The telephone rang incessantly. And

Yvonne had much to tell me before Rikind arrived at 11 to help work out a statement for the press conference at three P.M.

Yvonne, I soon saw, had not had time to worry much. She had been too busy helping to organize my defense. With one of Rikind's assistants she had started to comb through hundreds of broadcasts, scores of articles, my two books and my diary notes to show where I had always stood on the subject of Soviet Russia and Communism. At Rikind's request she had begun to prepare a detailed biography of my life.

"Was that necessary?" I asked.

Yvonne, of course, had cheered me up enormously, but in the back of my mind as she talked a feeling began to form, like a dark cloud, that she took the whole thing awfully seriously — more so than it warranted.

"After all," I said, "I am considered innocent until proved guilty. And it's up to O'Brien to prove me guilty. It isn't up to me to prove I'm innocent."

Yvonne gave me a patient glance, but I could see that my attitude troubled her.

"Raymond," she said, "I know the whole thing sounds crazy. But it is also, believe me, very serious. My dear, it seems you *do* have to prove your innocence in this country. Bill Rikind has made that very clear, and so has everybody else who is trying to be helpful.

"For one thing," she explained — and I thought for a second how much this French-born woman had learned about America in so short a time — "you've got to have, it seems, a lily-white record — that is, spotless so far as any Communist taint is concerned. That is the reason for the biographical sketch. Rikind said he had to know *everything*, right down to whether you had ever given a dollar to some group that later turned out to be faintly suspect as being Red or Pink or even Liberal. So I put down everything I knew, darling, including . . ." She hesitated.

"Including what?"

"What I remembered of Elsie McCabe."

"Where does Elsie come in?" I said, scarcely concealing my annoyance, I'm afraid.

Yvonne smiled sadly. "She denounced you, in a secret session of the O'Brien committee, as a Communist and a Soviet agent, that's all."

"What!" For a moment my brain could not find a further word.

"She and Frederick Newman," Yvonne said simply. "Rikind found out."

"Newman scarcely knows me. I only met him the other day."

"Well, he claims to have known you, or about you — as a Communist."

"Good God, Yvonne! Why do they lie?"

"That's something Rikind is trying to find out," Yvonne said. She was very cool and collected.

Bill Rikind came in shortly after eleven, and we set to work in my study drafting a brief statement to the press. Below, the East River tide flowed placidly on this warm September morning and now and then a string of barges floated by. Many of them had little shanties aft — a pleasant, tranquil spot, perhaps, to while away a life, it occurred to me. No great troubles. You did your job, and in return were allowed to live peacefully, decently, unmolested.

Rikind questioned me closely. At first I somewhat resented his attitude until I began to see that the lawyer, usually so urbane and genial and friendly, was only trying to prepare our case carefully and thoroughly. It is possible, of course, that he had a doubt or two since he has not known me long and since most of my life was spent abroad, beyond the sphere in which he has moved. But why, I thought, should he act as if maybe, possibly, O'Brien had something on me?

"Raymond," he said. "I want you to refresh your memory and be very frank. It is of the utmost importance, to me at least, to know a number of things. First, were you ever affiliated in any way with any Communist or front organization — with any outfit that is on the attorney general's subversive list?"

"Not that I know of," I said, a little sullenly.

"You're absolutely sure, Raymond?"

"Yes, I'm sure, Bill. And if it's any comfort to you, I will add that I have never been a Communist, et cetera."

"This is no time, Raymond, I assure you, to become exasperating. I know you're not a Communist. I was asking about something else." I saw I had got his dander up.

"Well, I answered you," I said.

He smiled and turned to gaze out the window.

"I'm not trying to hide anything," I said.

"I know you're not," he answered, turning back from the window. He eyed me with a quizzical gleam in his eye.

"Tell me, Raymond," he began softly. "What about this Elsie McCabe woman?"

"What about her?"

"Did you ever know her?"

"I certainly did."

"Tell me about it." He spoke the words gently.

"I'll tell you, Bill. There's nothing to hide."

I told him the story as fully and concisely as I could. When I had finished he had but one question.

"Why do you suppose, Raymond, that she has testified as she has?"

"I haven't the slightest idea, Bill. I wish I had."

"You sure?" He hesitated. "Is she still in love with you?"

I laughed. "I don't think so, Bill."

After lunch we typed off a short statement for the reporters, who were due at three P.M. More of them came than we anticipated and to my surprise not only the photographers showed up again but a newsreel crew and a television team. Our living room could scarcely hold them. To complicate matters the newsreel and TV men wrangled about the kind of lighting that should be set up. Finally Rikind arranged for pictures to be taken after the newspapermen were through. I would repeat my statement for the benefit of the cameras.

I read my brief piece, reiterating that the charges of Senator O'Brien, as stated in the press — and those were all I had to go on — were ridiculous and, of course, untrue; that I had no idea what had prompted them in the mind of O'Brien, but was trying to find out; that I was wiring the Senator to ask for the details of the charges, and also had demanded an immediate hear-

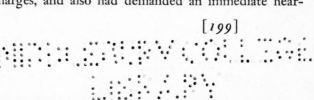

ing before his committee; and that I would swear before the committee that the charges were false and that I had never been and was not now a Communist, fellow traveler or sympathizer with Communism or the Soviet Union — but just the opposite, as the record of my past broadcasts and articles and books would prove.

The questions were friendly, except for one from the reporter from the Clark press, a sneering little man whom Rikind had warned me about — a former Communist who had now become one of General Clark's experts on the Red Danger.

"You have denied the principal charge," he began, "that you were a Soviet agent."

"Denied it and called it ridiculous," I replied rather sharply. "I might add, for the sake of emphasis, that it is an outrageous lie and I am sure O'Brien knows it."

But that did not satisfy the little man.

"Just a minute, Mr. Whitehead, I haven't finished with my question," he spoke up, as I turned to one of the other reporters who seemed about to ask something.

"All right, go ahead," I said as cordially as I could.

"If you were, as Senator O'Brien says flatly, a Soviet agent," he resumed, a sneer breaking over his face, "you wouldn't admit it, would you? You would deny it, wouldn't you?"

Laughter broke over the room, giving me an instant to recover my composure and to soften my answer.

"Since I was not a Soviet agent, and since there is no more ground to think I was than, say, to think Senator O'Brien was," I said, looking the little ex-Communist in the face, "I wouldn't know."

SEPTEMBER 3 (SUNDAY)
ONE can only admire the way Bill Rikind has thrown himself into this affair in my defense. He may be a little dapper in his light moments, but when something arouses him, as my case apparently has, he sheds the petty pretensions and transforms himself into a fighting man of formidable power,

burning with a pure flame, utterly concentrated, and yet all the time cool and shrewd in his judgments, patient with detail, and passionate for thoroughness in preparing for the battle.

He fumes sometimes at what he calls my naïveté.

"You must get through your thick head," he exclaimed today, "what the climate of this country is. It has changed, Raymond, since you left in your youth. Look here, this will indicate what I mean."

He tossed me a clipping which he had torn out from the morning newspaper. I glanced through it. It was from the land of the make-believe. The hysteria had reached even there. A big Hollywood studio, the report said, was dropping plans to film the life of Hiawatha, hero of the Longfellow poem that had seemed so touching when we read it in our youth. Reason: fear that a motion picture of Hiawatha's peace efforts might be regarded as Red propaganda.

"You see what I mean?" Rikind grinned.

SEPTEMBER 5

LABOR DAY yesterday, and we drove up to the Cornwall hills to spend it with Chris Chambers. It was impossible not to remember the Labor Day week end at the Fletchers' just a year ago, which had marked this particular exile's return, and how fabulous the world that revolved about Bob's acres that day seemed and how bright the hope in my own swelling breast.

But no one spoke of it. We played tennis, swam, roamed the woods and, in the evening, gazed up at the stars, musing about the more trifling aspects of this particular pin point in the universe.

SEPTEMBER 7

NO WORD from O'Brien as to when his Senate committee will hear me. There was a dispatch from Washington in the morning newspapers which puzzles us. It says the O'Brien committee is trying to get a summary of the F.B.I. file on me, preparatory to my hearing. I was surprised to hear that in this free, democratic land there is a secret-police file on any private citizen other than those wanted for a crime or suspected of plotting to overthrow the government by force.

Bill Rikind, when I phoned him, said it was nothing to worry about, that there was an F.B.I. file on everyone of any prominence.

I have had some experience with this sort of thing in Nazi Germany and Soviet Russia, but I was unaware we emulated them in this republic. My education continues.

SEPTEMBER 8

CONFERRED with Rikind all afternoon about our strategy before the O'Brien committee. Actually, there was not much to go on. I reiterated to Rikind that I had no idea why the know-nothing Senator had brought his charges. But Bill said that didn't get me out of trouble. Between now and my appearance in Washington, he explained, we must try to find out what O'Brien's line would be, and the nature of his lies and of his traps. In the meantime, revolting as the idea was, we must prepare a detailed defense of my innocence: the story of my private life (so boring, really, to the public) and a complete record of what I have written and broadcast about Russia, Communism, my own country and — Rikind insisted — about Mickey Mouse.

"One more thing, Raymond," Rikind said as he got up to go.

"What's that, Bill?"

"Be careful of what you say over your phone here."

"Why? Not that I would be liable to express any dangerous or subversive thoughts."

"It may be tapped," he said, pointing to the phone in the corner.

"For God's sake, Bill, we're not living in the Soviet Union."

"No, but even in America these days we have to be careful."

"Besides," I said. "Wire tapping is against the law in this country, isn't it? Even for the F.B.I."

"It certainly is, if it is not authorized by the person speaking. The Supreme Court has upheld the law against it time and again. Nevertheless, my dear Raymond, we know that the F.B.I. goes on tapping wires. Therefore, I say: be careful."

SEPTEMBER 10 (SUNDAY)

WE SENT Dick and Maria up to Chris Chambers's for the week end. I want to keep them out of my troubles, though I feel that the boy, perhaps too sensitive for his years, is already deeply disturbed by all the publicity. Yvonne and I worked all week end on my "defense."

"You know," Yvonne said, when we paused for a drink this afternoon, "O'Brien sometimes reminds me of a Senator we had in France: Laval. Remember how Laval used to attack Papa in the Senate and in the gutter press?"

"And your father was a conservative, at that."

"Yes, like most of the so-called 'Radical-Socialists' in France. But he couldn't stomach Fascism. So Laval called him a Communist. Remember?"

"Yes. And I remember what happened to Laval. The French strung him up after the war."

"No." Yvonne corrected me. "They shot him — as a convicted traitor."

We were exhausted by our week-end labors. Not that Yvonne showed it. Since my return a very fierce flame has been burning in her. It is wonderful to observe and to feel. It has driven her night and day to compile an immense dossier for the hearings. It has kept up the spirits of this household, especially mine. And curiously, it has given a new bloom to her handsome, passionate countenance, adding color to her cheeks and kindling the fire in her wonderful black eyes.

When we got up, I took her in my arms and held her and tried to say something of what I felt, but the words, "darling," "beautiful," "love," and all the others that came to me sounded painfully inadequate. Come what may, in Washington or elsewhere, Yvonne's presence is nearly all that matters in my life.

[203]

She drew away and started to adjust her hair, so black and lustrous this day. "Darling," she said, "what time does the children's train get in? I must fix up a bit of supper first."

"No, they will eat on the train," I said. "And you and I, my dear, are going to dine at Grand Central while we wait for them. It's September, Yvonne — if the month has an 'r' in it, you can eat oysters. We'll feast tonight on oysters, darling. Grand Central is famous for them."

SEPTEMBER 11

MARIA announced solemnly at dinner tonight that she is going to be an actress — a famous one.

She has absorbed more at Chris's than I suspected.

"I will be famous," she insisted, "like Katharine Cornell, like Helen Hayes."

"What about like Garbo?" I asked.

"She is in the movies, isn't she? Chris says I should go on the stage, on Broadway!"

SEPTEMBER 12

A NOTE from Steve Burnett from Berne. He has finished crating up his household belongings and plans to motor up through France, give the girls a week in Paris and a week in London and sail for home at the end of the month.

He asks whether I can get the girls into the Baldwin Day School.

SEPTEMBER 13

TONIGHT Bill Rikind, Yvonne and I put the finishing touches to the opening statement I hope to make at my hearing before the O'Brien Senate committee. It bares my life and opinions, my associations and my work, my judgment of events and men — good and bad, right and wrong. It is humiliating to have to do this. But I have now accepted my lawyer's judgment that it is necessary to prove my innocence.

After we had finished the statement we drew up a sharp telegram to the Senate committee asking again that I be heard forthwith.

SEPTEMBER 14

I ARGUED most of the morning with the nice headmistress of Baldwin Day School before she would admit Steve Burnett's youngsters. At first I thought her reluctance was due to Steve (not to mention me) being under fire in Washington. After all, everyone else in this town is afraid to be caught out of step with the petty patriots. But it wasn't that at all. The school already is overcrowded. And there are hundreds of insistent parents, many of them with big bankrolls, demanding that our harassed principal take in their offspring. There just wasn't room this semester for Steve's girls. But the good headmistress is going to make room. And I believe from my long talk with her that the chief reason is that she appreciates Steve's position (and mine) and wants to demonstrate that Baldwin School is not in sympathy with, and not afraid of, witch-hunters.

The lady, who is rather charming once you penetrate her schoolmarm's severity, had a good word for Dick and Maria. They are doing all right, she said. Altogether an encouraging morning.

SEPTEMBER 17 (SUNDAY)

AT THE U.N., which I visited yesterday, officials were talking of the imminent end of the Korean War. Some of my friends there, both American and foreign, think that when peace comes the hysteria in America about Reds and Russia will subside.

SEPTEMBER 18

A SOMEWHAT blue Monday. For the first time Bill Rikind mentioned the price in dollars of defending yourself against the witch-hunters. He says he himself won't take a cent — though I shall certainly contrive to pay him some kind of fee. What he was thinking of, he said, was our expenses. I had not thought of them, but Bill says they will be burdensome. Already, he says, we have spent a couple of thousand dollars in telegrams and long-distance calls (most of them in connection with getting witnesses and depositions). His own law firm, he explained, is going to considerable expense to pay investigators, whose trips to Washington and elsewhere come to a tidy sum. Then when the hearings begin we must buy a daily transcript of the proceedings. The typing and mimeographing of my initial statement, of subsequent rebuttals and general press releases will come to at least a thousand dollars. And so on.

This piece of news somewhat depressed me, and I must have shown it. Rikind tried to cheer me up by suggesting that I let him discreetly organize a "Raymond Whitehead Defense Fund" to help us defray expenses. The idea appalled me.

"Not on your life, Bill. I'll raise the money somehow."

"It would be easy for me to do, Raymond," he smiled. "One of the nice things about New York, you know, is that there are a lot of decent persons in this city who are always willing to help out on such occasions."

"I appreciate it, Bill. But I really couldn't stand it."

I said I would dash out some articles on my European trip and sell them to the "slick" magazines for a lot of money.

"Do you think they would buy them — at this particular moment?" Rikind asked. He put on a smile, but it was not difficult to see behind it. He was calling me down to earth, as gently as possible. "For the moment, then, until the hearings are over," he said, "I will advance you a little. Believe me, it will be a privilege."

"Thanks. But it won't be necessary, Bill."

It was hurt pride, of course. I really didn't know where we stood, whether, in fact, we had a bean left. I had not had time since my return to talk to Yvonne about our finances.

Late tonight we did discuss them, after the children were asleep and out of earshot. Yvonne has always kept our family books, looked after our budget, paid the bills and consequently done all the worrying about such things — an old French family custom, she claims.

"Not counting the expenses of your hearing, we have enough to hold out, on the present scale," she said, "until Christmas or New Year's. After that, we'll have to pinch the pennies, until we get some income again."

"Take the kids out of private school for one thing, I suppose," I said.

"The public schools may not be so bad as we think, Raymond."

"Maybe not. But we won't have to resort to them, Yvonne. Once I've exposed O'Brien for the faker he is, everything will be all right. No need to worry."

"I'm not worrying, darling," she said, a bright wide smile breaking over her fine face.

SEPTEMBER 19

WE'RE not worrying, say we. But how are we going to raise the money for the expenses of my defense in Washington without resorting to charity, which I will never do? Yvonne and I dodged that little question last night.

SEPTEMBER 20

IT SUDDENLY occurred to me that Rikind and I, in the excitement of preparing my "defense," had overlooked a rather important matter: challenging Senator O'Brien to repeat his charges against me in public, where he is without Senatorial immunity, so we can sue for libel and slander.

"It's all my fault, Raymond. I'm sorry and I apologize for my negligence," Rikind said when I phoned him. "I'll get a wire off to the old boy this very minute. Not that I think there's a ghost of a chance he'll accept the challenge. But we'll put him on the spot. At the very least, maybe it will provoke him to hurry up with the hearing."

SEPTEMBER 21

BY OVERWHELMING majorities, both houses of Congress yesterday passed the Internal Security Bill to register all Communists and to intern them during emergencies. The vote in the House: 312 to 20; in the Senate: 51 to 7.

SEPTEMBER 23

THE President yesterday vetoed the Internal Security Bill, but the House overrode the veto within an hour and today the Senate followed suit.

In vain did the President contend that the measure was "dangerous," that it would make a "mockery of the Bill of Rights" and help, rather than hinder, Communists. Mr. Truman thought the bill was bred in "internal hysteria" and made seven major objections to it, including one that "it puts the government in the thought-control business" and another that it gives the government "vast powers to harass all of our citizens in the exercise of their right of free speech."

No doubt, as Senator Lucas, Democratic majority leader, who voted for the measure said: the American people wanted an anti-Communist bill on the statute books.

SEPTEMBER 24 (SUNDAY)

A DAY of waiting. Bill Rikind, who is weekending in Washington, phoned to say the word there is that O'Brien will give us our hearing this week. No word, says Bill, about our challenge to the Senator to repeat his charges in public.

SEPTEMBER 25

THE newspapers say tonight that Senator O'Brien has ordered my hearing to begin Thursday, September 28, though neither Rikind nor I have had any direct communication from him.

WASHINGTON, SEPTEMBER 27

YVONNE, Rikind and I came down on the afternoon train. Tonight Bill received a sharp letter from O'Brien warning him that, as my lawyer, he is not permitted under committee rules to intervene in any way during the hearings which start tomorrow unless specifically asked to do so by the chairman. That leaves me pretty much on my own. Rikind and I debated whether to object to the televising of the hearings while I am on the stand, he being rather against the idea. I am inclined to accept it. I am not so sure I shall completely clear myself with a committee as loaded as this one is with men nearly as bad as O'Brien. But with a television audience I can surely establish my innocence with the public.

To bed early tonight. Yvonne seems very cool and collected and, what is more, confident. I feel a little high-strung myself, but relieved that the waiting is over.

SEPTEMBER 28

IT TOOK a bit of time to get started. The preliminaries seemed unbearably long. But later I realized this had certain advantages. Undoubtedly I was at a high pitch of nervousness when I arrived at the packed committee room. The delays lowered the pitch and enabled me to take hold of myself. As the day wore on, as the inquisitors warmed up to their quarry, I certainly needed all the self-control I could muster.

Even as we entered the crowded committee room, Yvonne, Rikind and I, the photographers' flash bulbs started going off in our faces, and I was soon aware of the blinding glare of the big lights that were being turned on for the newsreel and television cameras. I tried to smile confidently, and obligingly posed with Yvonne, who I imagine looked quite photogenic, for special shots which the photographers raucously demanded. I had made up my mind that if this was the way the game was played here when you were on the spot then I would play it as skillfully as I could.

As I elbowed my way down slowly to the witness chair in the

tow of a kindly, gray-haired deputy marshal, I caught a momentary glance at Senator O'Brien. He was standing behind a long committee table, and while ostensibly chatting with his Senatorial colleagues had, I noticed, one eye on me and he was frowning — as though he resented my stealing the limelight from him for even a passing moment.

I finally got to my chair before a small table. Bill Rikind was allowed a seat at my right and Yvonne one just behind us. We faced the committee, whose members now began to take their places behind the long table. I recognized most of the Senators from my previous appearance before the committee on behalf of Steve Burnett. All except O'Brien appeared, at first glance, to be, if not exactly friendly, at least not hostile. In fact, they seemed to be enjoying themselves, judging by their good-natured banter with one another as they sat down.

Suddenly O'Brien's stentorian voice rang out:

"The committee will come to order!"

The buzz of voices in the great room faded rapidly away. Only a couple of photographers seemed a little slow in responding. They exploded their flash bulbs. Senator O'Brien rapped sternly for order.

"That will be enough of that for the time being," he snapped, frowning at the photographers to whom a moment before he had been all smiles — when they were snapping him. Then he looked sternly at me.

"Will the witness please rise . . ."

I got up.

". . . and be sworn.

"Do you solemnly swear the testimony you give before this Committee on Security and Americanism of the United States Senate will be the truth, the whole truth, and nothing but the truth, so help you God?"

"I do."

As I stood there, my right hand raised, listening to O'Brien intone the oath, it struck me as somewhat ludicrous that the man who made the outrageous charges against me was to preside over what was supposed to be a fair hearing. But apparently none of the Senators shared my feeling. By the luck of seniority and politics this particular committee, with one exception, Bill Rikind had explained to me, consisted of gentlemen, who though they came from both parties, could be grouped ideologically around Senator O'Brien: Reynolds from the Deep South, Kleinschmidt from the Midwest and Breen from the West Coast.

"They represent the extreme right wing of both parties," Rikind had said. And he had gone on to warn me that these primitives, as he called them, who now held my fate in their hands, were not out in the current hearings to expose Communists, but to pin the Communist label on anyone who had ideas which differed from theirs, especially from O'Brien's. No doubt Bill was exaggerating. Some Communists had been unearthed by the various investigating committees of the Congress; some Communist espionage, going a long way back, had been uncovered. But a lot of innocent Americans had been destroyed in the process, and it was this, no doubt, which my lawyer wished to emphasize to me.

Senator Jones, from one of the Carolinas, was the exception, Rikind explained. Lately he had been gaining some national prominence for his liberal views on a good many issues in the Senate, including O'Brienism. How far he would go, however, remained a question. There was always his native South to consider.

"No matter how open-minded or even liberal Jones may be personally," Rikind said, "he is too sound a politician to ever forget that he represents not Senator Reynolds's old, unreconstructed South, to be sure, but a South which, however changing — and it is changing — remains fundamentally conservative."

O'Brien now opened the hearings.

"Before we hear the witness I would like to make it clear that when this committee began its current proceedings, its members were quite aware — the chairman above all — that the committee would be unmercifully attacked by all the Communists, fellow travelers and Pinkos in the land. That, of course, has happened, and I cannot say that we have been taken by surprise. . . ."

How typical of O'Brien's technique, I thought — lumping together all who dared to oppose his witch-hunting, as Communists. I had not seen what the *Daily Worker* had said of the committee, but I had seen — and been encouraged by — what some of the great newspapers and church bodies and educators and others who were not Communists or even "Pinkos" had said. They had been scorching in their denunciation of the committee, and especially of its chairman.

"I cannot say," O'Brien went on, obviously pleased at his sarcasm, "that this committee has been in the least frightened by all the lies hurled against it by the Commies and their allies in this country. We are used to such criticism. . . ."

At this point, to my surprise, Rikind, who was sitting at my right, sprang up.

"May I interrupt?"

"No, you may not," O'Brien snapped. "You have no right to interrupt. It is completely out of order."

"I merely wanted to inquire, Mr. Chairman, as counsel for the witness, whether you wish to imply by what you have just said that a committee — any committee — of the elected representatives of the people considers itself above criticism."

"I am asking the gentleman to sit down," O'Brien thundered. "Otherwise I shall have to ask a marshal to remove him from the room."

I sort of pulled Bill Rikind down. I could not help feeling amused that it was my lawyer, not myself, who was losing his temper first at the very outset of this ordeal.

"As I was saying," O'Brien resumed, "this committee will not be deterred from its duty by the criticism it has received, and continues to receive, from the Commies."

"Not all the criticism has come from the Commies — by any means, Mr. Chairman," Rikind blurted out, half rising.

"That uncalled-for remark will be stricken from the record," O'Brien said curtly.

I felt Rikind jumping up again.

"Mr. Chairman," he said, "I meant no disrespect to this committee. But as counsel for this witness I believe I have the right at the outset of this hearing, to be identified, and then to be advised by the chair as to my rights and privileges."

"You were violating your rights and privileges, of which I shall advise you in a moment," O'Brien said.

"I am sorry. . . ."

"Who are you? Please identify yourself," O'Brien said.

"I am William Rikind, attorney at law, of 486 Madison Avenue, New York City. I represent the witness here."

"I will now instruct witness's counsel as to his rights," O'Brien began. "This is not a court of law. It is an investigatory body operating under rules established by the U. S. Senate. As counsel for the witness, you will be allowed to remain here, subject to the following conditions. You are not permitted to testify. You are not permitted to ask questions, or to interrupt our proceedings in any way. And I want it clearly understood you are not allowed to suggest answers to questions — no prompting of the witness. Is that clear?"

"Yes, sir. Is that all?"

"No, it is not. When the witness wants your advice, as to his rights or regarding his answers, he may consult you."

"May I object to questions?"

"Certainly not."

I had been fumbling the pages of my statement wondering when I would ever get to it. Perhaps Bill Rikind noticed.

"Can the witness proceed with a brief opening statement, as I believe is customary in these — ?" he asked.

"Just a minute," O'Brien interrupted. "I have a question about that statement to put to the witness. Have you released it to the press?"

"Yes, sir," I said.

"You realize that is a discourtesy to this committee?"

"No, sir. I don't."

"And that in your intemperate and groundless criticism of this committee and your personal attack on its chairman, you may be in contempt of this committee of the U. S. Senate?"

"I am not so aware, sir. I do not consider this committee above criticism. It has made serious charges against me."

"The committee makes no charges against anybody," O'Brien retorted.

"You, sir, have. You have made the gravest accusations that could possibly be lodged against an American citizen — that I am an agent of a foreign power, the Soviet Union."

"We will come to that in due time," O'Brien said, smiling.

There was a hasty consultation among the committee members.

"This committee," said O'Brien, "has just consulted. It could decide that this unjustified attack upon it by the witness in his statement had no place in the record of these hearings since it was handed to the press before it was read here. We are mindful, however, of our glorious American tradition of free speech. And in that spirit, despite the incredible insults the statement contains, directed against a legally constituted committee of the U. S. Senate, which is only trying to do its duty, we have decided to let the witness proceed with the reading of his prepared statement."

O'Brien scowled at me, but behind the grimace, I felt, he was wondering if he had duly impressed me with his power. He hadn't; but perhaps he did not know.

"You may proceed, sir," he said.

A feeling of relief came over me. At last my moment had come. I began as calmly and as slowly as I could. Because of the public-address system, it was scarcely necessary to raise one's voice to be well heard.

"Gentlemen. I welcome this opportunity to appear before you to refute the outrageous lies with which your distinguished chairman has attempted to blacken my . . ."

"Just a minute! Stop right there!" O'Brien shouted, color rising in the temples of his face, which usually has the color of paste. "Clerk! Strike the second part of the sentence — beginning with 'outrageous lies' out of the record. As to the first part, I have a question."

Rikind was on his feet. "May I respectfully request that the witness be allowed to proceed, uninterrupted, to the end of his statement. Otherwise . . ."

"Will the counsel please be seated?" O'Brien cut in. "As I tried to explain to you, sir, you have no right to intervene in these hearings. You are completely out of order. Sit down!"

Rikind sat.

"I want to ask the witness," O'Brien resumed, "what he means by the words: he 'welcomes this opportunity to appear here'?"

"I mean just what I say. I am glad of the chance to appear here and defend myself against the dastardly accusations . . ."

"Just a minute," O'Brien said, and now he was smiling and coy. "Are you trying to tell this committee you appear here voluntarily?"

"That is right, sir. Of my own volition."

"You know that we tried to subpoena you all over the globe."

"No, I don't."

"You skipped the country!" O'Brien roared triumphantly, glancing around the jammed room to watch the effect of his little bombshell. There was considerable murmuring, and it did not sound friendly to my ears. Now was the moment, the first moment I realized, to hold my temper and score my first point as quietly and as modestly as possible.

"Senator," I said, "I am surprised to hear that statement from you. The truth happens to be, and no one knows it so well as you, that I did not skip the country."

"Why do you say the chairman knows that so well, if it is as you say?" It was Senator Jones — from one of the Carolinas. His voice was soft. It had a friendly, tolerant tone. I studied his face. It was lean and keen, the eyes rather kindly, reflective and highly intelligent.

"Well, Senator," I said, speaking as softly as I could, "before I left the States I had a little trouble getting a passport. And —"

"Why was that?"

"Because of Senator O'Brien. He asked the State Department to hold it up."

"I don't know what the witness is talking about," O'Brien broke in.

"So I went to the Senator — the date was last July 19 — caught him as he was leaving his office and explained the purpose of my trip to Europe. After some questions on his part and assurances on mine that I was not running away from anything, as he had suspected, and that I would be in daily touch with our embassies and military establishments abroad, the Senator said he saw no objection to my going, and in fact I got my passport a few days later. So the statement that I skipped is false."

Jones glanced at his colleague for an answer.

"I simply don't remember any such conversation with the witness," he said, smilingly. "I suggest he is making this up as he goes along."

But the question was not pursued further. I was allowed to proceed with my second sentence.

"Senator O'Brien has charged that I am, or have been, a Soviet agent — in other words, that I am disloyal to my country and in fact a traitor to it. This is the gravest accusation that can be made against an American citizen. I now solemnly swear to you, on the oath I have just taken, that the charge is a foul and contemptible lie."

I paused, grateful after all that had gone before that I had been allowed to complete three whole, connected sentences.

Senator Kleinschmidt, a plump, smooth-faced individual from one of the Midwestern states — a small-town mortician, I believe — spoke up.

"When and where were these alleged charges you speak of made?"

"On the floor of the Senate, sir, on August 29, last — by Senator O'Brien. In that place, they were, of course, privileged. I have asked the Senator to repeat them in a public place so that I might have recourse to the courts. He has not seen fit to do so."

O'Brien cleared his voice. "I can assure the witness that I shall repeat them here — to his face — if he ever gets done with his interminable statement."

"Here they would be privileged, would they not?" I asked.

"I'll repeat them any place you like," O'Brien said.

"I make note of that, sir."

There was a momentary murmur throughout the room. Obviously no one believed that the Senator would dare risk a libel suit. Had he not often complained in his frequent press conferences, when the questions got hot on this subject, that the "Commies" were trying to trick him into libel suits so they could ruin him financially? "An old Commy trick," he had always said.

But O'Brien did not like the murmurs. He pounded his gavel.

"I must warn the spectators and the members of the press that I will not tolerate any demonstration in this room either against or for the witness." Then looking at me, he said: "The witness may continue with his statement."

But I was not to continue immediately. At that moment a gentleman I had hardly noticed arose to intervine. He was the committee's counsel, a pudgy, bespectacled, middle-aged fellow by the name of David Green, whom Rikind had briefed me on. Green, like some others attached to the staffs of the various Congressional investigating committees, was, Rikind said, a former Communist whose principal object in life seemed to be to live down his past. He had performed brilliantly, Bill said, for the O'Brien committee, being a cross-examiner of the first rank. I must be on my guard, Bill said, when David Green started throwing questions.

He spoke with a rather low but hollow voice, and there was a gleam in his small eyes.

"Mr. Chairman, I would like, if I may, to pose a question before the witness proceeds further with his prepared statement."

"Go ahead, Mr. Green."

"Mr. Whitehead, in view of what you said a moment ago, I wonder whether you would not like to reconsider."

"Reconsider what?" I asked, wondering what he was driving at. He paused for a moment, eying me as if he were about to spring a trap. Then in a flat voice:

"Is it not a fact, Mr. Whitehead — and remember you are testifying here under oath, which means you are subject to perjury action if you do not tell the truth — is it not a fact, sir, that you were a Soviet agent?"

He stopped to let the evil words sink in with their full effect, but I quickly broke the silence.

"It is not only not a fact, not a truth, but, as I said and now repeat as solemnly as I can — a dirty, contemptible lie!"

Unruffled by the swell of voices in the room, he continued in a low, untroubled voice:

"Is it your sworn testimony to this committee that you are not, and never have been, a Communist?"

"I'm coming to that in my statement, if you will kindly allow me to proceed. I would like to answer that completely and fully."

"Never mind the statement. Just answer the question."

"I said I was coming to that. . . ."

"Mr. Chairman." Green turned to O'Brien. "Will you please instruct the witness to answer the question?"

"Surely you can answer that 'Yes' or 'No,' Mr. Whitehead?" O'Brien obliged.

"I will answer it 'No,' naturally, that I am not and never have been a Communist. But I want to make it stronger than that. If I may proceed with . . ."

"You may proceed with your statement when I am finished with one or two questions," Green said icily.

This was the moment, it seemed to me, to clear up a matter of some importance, if I were to get even a semblance of a "fair" hearing.

"Mr. Chairman," I said. "You spoke a moment ago of our glorious traditions of free speech. On that, at least, we can agree."

"Do you have a question? You are here to answer questions, not to ask them," O'Brien cut in.

"Before I answer any more, Senator, I want to know whether I am to be allowed to answer them in my own way, in my own words. If you are going to try to direct me as to how I may answer questions — and cut me off before I have given the kind of answer I deem necessary and adequate, then I tell you frankly, sir, these hearings will be a farce!"

"That last sentence, which was completely uncalled-for, will be stricken," O'Brien said sharply.

"So you believe, suh, these hearings are a farce? Why did you ask to be heard then?" Senator Reynolds, a large, puffing, red-faced man from one of the cotton states, cut in angrily.

"I did not say these hearings were a farce, sir. I said they would be if I were not allowed my rights of free speech to answer your questions in my own way."

"Your choice of words, suh, is most unfortunate. I want you to try to remember that this body, a part of the highest elected assembly in the republic, is not a farce, and that we, its members, are not fools."

"I have never said so, sir, nor do I think so," I said, realizing, though, the futility of tangling with this curious old relic of a South I do not believe exists any more. Reynolds's Southern colleague, Jones, served to remind you of that. He now spoke up.

"Do I understand that the witness would like to elaborate on his answer to the question of whether he is a Communist or not?"

"Precisely, Senator. I have been accused by the chairman of this committee, and also by at least two witnesses whom you have already heard in executive session, of being not only a Soviet agent but a member of the Communist party. I think I have at least the right to refute that charge in my own words so as to make it as categorical as possible. That is why I would like to read from my statement on that charge."

"I see no reason why the witness should not be allowed to do this, Mr. Chairman."

"Very well," O'Brien said.

There was a hush in the room. It was not broken by me. I saw O'Brien glance at his watch. Before I could begin he was saying something.

"Gentlemen, it is now two minutes to twelve. I think this is a good place for a break. The committee will stand adjourned until two P.M."

I looked at my papers, already mussed from perspiring, clawing fingers. I had read, at this first hearing, just two paragraphs, half a page of a fourteen-page manuscript. At this rate . . .

We had a somewhat gloomy lunch in the crowded restaurant over at the Union Station. I had never seen Rikind, who usually bubbles over with self-confidence, so biffed. He was still boiling from the going-over O'Brien had given him.

"At this rate," he fumed, "it will take you a week to get through your brief statement. Then another week of cross-examination. By the way, Raymond, watch that fellow Green. He's a mean questioner. Worse than O'Brien . . . I'm a fine one to advise. I didn't do so well, myself, this morning. . . ." He buried his teeth in a sandwich.

Yvonne tried to cheer us up. "I think you both did all right, considering what happened. Why not talk up to them? I think it's the best tactics in the long run. Just so you don't lose your tempers."

"As I did this morning!" Rikind moaned.

"You did all right, Bill," I said. "You really stood up to them."

Yvonne went out and bought the papers. From the size of the headlines you would have thought Washington was in the throes of another crisis.

WHITEHEAD HITS BACK AT O'BRIEN
DENIES HE'S A SOVIET AGENT OR COMMUNIST
SCORCHES SENATE COMMITTEE

A good part of the front pages was given over to my statement and to pictures of the opening of the hearing.

"I hope O'Brien doesn't see these over the luncheon recess," Rikind said. "He will, of course. And he'll be furious at your capturing the headlines."

"I would feel better if my statement had actually been made," I said.

"Well, it wasn't your fault. You tried to give it," Rikind said, his nose buried in the paper.

We had almost shoved the Korean War off the front page.

The hearing reconvened promptly at two P.M. Chairman O'Brien got right down to business. He began by squelching again my irrepressible lawyer. Rikind had bobbed up to plead —

very respectfully, I thought — that I be allowed to finish my statement without further interruptions. O'Brien threatened to throw him out for defying the orderly procedure of the committee. Then the chairman turned to me.

"Mr. Witness. You gave this statement to the press. It is already in the early editions of the afternoon papers. Yet, you have read to us only a few pages."

"A few paragraphs, not pages, sir. In fact, just two paragraphs," I corrected him.

"That makes it even worse than I thought," O'Brien said, trying to look both pained and stern. "Do you now think it is fair to this committee for you to have given material to the press which has not yet come out in this hearing?"

"I think you have a point, Senator," I said. "But I had no idea when I came here this morning that I would not be allowed to read my brief statement, uninterrupted, as I believe all of your friendly witnesses have been permitted to do. It is only fourteen pages long. I could have finished reading it in half an hour."

"What do you mean — 'friendly' witnesses?" Senator Breen spoke up. He was a West Coast real-estate operator who somehow, Rikind said, had got elected to the Senate.

"Well," I rejoined. "There are witnesses whom you treat with the utmost deference — several former Communists who have now turned informers, for example. And . . ."

"I would like to straighten you out, sir," Senator Breen cut in. "So far as I'm concerned there are no 'friendly' or 'unfriendly' witnesses here. Just witnesses, from whom we are trying to get the truth."

Senator Reynolds became aroused. "Do I understand this witness to cast aspersions on some of our previous witnesses by calling them 'informers'?"

"No, Senator," I said. "I was merely identifying certain persons whom you treat, it seems to me, with kid gloves."

"Strike it!" O'Brien shouted to the stenographer. "I will not have the impartiality of this committee impugned!"

Finally, after further wrangling, I was allowed to proceed.

"Gentlemen," I began, happy to get back to my text, "in view of the serious accusations made against me, I would like now to make, under the oath I have taken this morning, a solemn statement: I am not now, nor have I ever been, a Soviet agent or a member of the Communist party. I have never been connected in any way with a Communist organization. I have never believed in nor sympathized with nor advocated the principles and aims of Communism or of the Soviet Union or of its satellites. On the contrary, as a perusal of what I have broadcast and written for publication over the past quarter of a century makes crystal clear, I have constantly criticized and exposed the aims, strategy and tactics of Communism and of the Soviet Union. At the same time, in all I have broadcast and written — in the millions of words which cannot now be undone to, say, hoodwink a Congressional committee — I have proved my loyalty to this country and my devotion to its democratic ways and institutions.

"Yet, the chairman of this committee, who has been honored by his fellow citizens with election to the highest legislative body in the land, and two witnesses before this committee, have stated that I am, in fact, a Communist and a Soviet agent.

"Gentlemen, I say to you in all earnestness they have borne false witness. They have, to be frank, lied. . . ."

"That last sentence will be stricken," O'Brien interrupted, a slight sneer breaking out on his face.

"Do you realize the seriousness, suh," Reynolds broke in, "of what you have just said. That a member of the United States Senate has lied!"

"I do, sir! And I now repeat it. What Senator O'Brien has charged is a monstrous lie."

"Why should our distinguished chairman lie?" the cotton Senator demanded.

"I do not pretend to know the gentleman's motives," I answered. "Perhaps if there were time to be philosophical about it we could say that they are not unconnected with the spiritual and political climate of our times. But I would like to get on with my statement — it is not long."

"I might repeat," O'Brien declared, "that this committee has now become used to insults from the Communist brethren. You may proceed, Mr. Whitehead."

"I might say, sir," I interpolated, "that I have not come here to insult this august committee. It will be a dark day for American democracy when the truth, because it may be unpleasant to some, is mistaken for insult."

"Please go on with your reading," O'Brien instructed.

"I wish to make it clear" — I resumed reading — "that I am in general agreement with the objectives, if not the methods, of this committee."

"If I am not mistaken, the gentleman means to praise us," Senator Kleinschmidt broke in to say in his Mississippi Valley twang. The remark quite convulsed the solons.

"For your objectives, sir, but not for your methods," I replied, and again resumed my reading.

"Like all other Americans who care about the welfare of their country, I quite appreciate the fact that various investigating committees of the Congress have smoked out a few Communists who operated in the government before the war. That is all to the good, especially where there were cases of espionage. Of great value, too, was the light shed by some of the committees on the technique of Communist infiltration into various American organizations, including labor unions, though that technique was not exactly a secret.

"But against this good must be weighed great evil: the reign of terror in government and in such private areas of our national life as radio, the movies and education. Against the good must be weighed the witch-hunts, the character assassination, the reckless ruining of honorable reputations by hysterical, unsubstantiated charges, many of them hurled by former Communists.

"But worst of all, gentlemen, is the atmosphere of fear which you have created in this country. For the first time since the founding of the Republic, Americans, usually so courageous and outspoken, are afraid — afraid of their government, their Senators, afraid of a hundred self-appointed vigilante groups, afraid of their employers, of their neighbors even. They are afraid to speak out, to express their honest opinions . . ."

The Senator from the Far West, Breen, cut in: "Is there really any purpose, Mr. Chairman, in letting the witness continue with this nonsense?"

"That's what I was wondering myself, Senator," O'Brien said. There was a huddle of the Senators — a mumbling and a whispering. "How much more do you have there to read?" O'Brien asked.

"Very little, sir."

"If we cut you off, you'll go around bellowing you haven't had a fair hearing. On the other hand, Mr. Whitehead, as my colleagues have just reminded me, you are sorely trying the patience of the members of this committee. They are anxious, as am I, to get along with the job." He hesitated, and then broke into his half-smile, half-sneer. "Proceed, please."

"Gentlemen," I continued. "I agree with you that a democracy such as ours should have the sense to defend itself not only from without but from within. I believe we should be ruthless with any group who seeks to overthrow our form of government and substitute a dictatorship — either of the left or right. I happened to see — on the spot — German democracy overthrown some seventeen years ago because it didn't have the horse sense to stoutly defend itself against the Nazis. I hope we will not be so stupid.

"But do you think you can defend democracy with perfidy and defeat Communism with lies? Do you think you can preserve democracy by destroying its foundations: free speech and the freedom of Americans to honestly disagree with one another?

"Surely, the way to destroy those freedoms is to attach to them, as the chairman of this committee is doing, the penalty of abuse and vilification. For these American freedoms cannot long endure if decent, patriotic citizens of this country can disagree with Senator O'Brien or with this committee or with the ex-Communists only at the peril of being branded, as I have been branded, a Communist or a Soviet agent.

"That is why I venture to suggest, as a simple citizen who is deeply involved in this thing, who has been hurt by it, that after I am investigated, after all whom you now suspect have been investigated, that this Committee on Security and Americanism investigate its distinguished chairman. . . ."

I was so concentrated on what I was saying that the burst of applause came to me as a shock. O'Brien pounded his gavel.

"There will be no demonstration either for or against the witness!" he shouted.

"Mr. Chairman," the Senator from the cotton belt spoke up. "I must say, suh, that I greatly resent the impertinence of the witness."

"Senator," O'Brien smiled, "I am getting used to it by this time."

"The very suggestion, suh, that you be . . ."

"Senator —" O'Brien broke in, his smile as broad as his face now. "Though the witness's suggestion is rather unusual, I think I might say that I would not mind in the least being investigated if my colleagues in the Senate thought some good might come of it. Just so the Commies don't have a hand in it!"

"It would not be proper for me to suggest" — I continued reading — "and I am not suggesting, that in such an investigation the Senators look into the background of their colleague, including his income-tax troubles and indeed his income, how he got possession of highly secret government documents and how he used them, and all that. That is the Senate's business. I am merely suggesting, as a private citizen, that you try to ascertain whether the gentleman has lived up to his obligations and responsibilities as a member of the Senate by his irresponsible attacks on dozens of officials and private citizens and by the shameful falsehoods he has told about them. If he has lied, perhaps he should be deprived of his power to do further damage. If I have lied, you should — and I hope you will — send me to jail."

"Does the witness know that you can go to jail for contempt of the Senate?" Senator Breen asked.

"Yes, sir. Am I in contempt?"

"I was just asking you whether you knew the consequences," he retorted.

"Mr. Chairman —" the voice of Senator Reynolds rang out — "is the witness finished with his prepared statement?"

"Not quite," I answered.

"Good Lord, suh, I honestly do not believe the gentleman will ever finish. If we permit him to ramble on in this way we will forget what we wanted to question him about."

O'Brien beamed on the Senator from the South. "Senator, you are free to ask questions at any time."

"Mr. Witness," Reynolds said, screwing up his tired eyes and stroking his shaggy, walrus mustache, "you say you are not a Communist?"

"Correct."

"But sympathy with Communism is also a threat to our freedoms, is it not?"

"I believe I testified, sir, that I have no sympathy with Communism. Just the opposite."

"I see. Now, suh, membership in the Communist party is difficult to determine, is it not?"

"Is it? I suppose most members carry cards — or did."

"But do you not realize that many Communists — some of the biggest fry — never carried cards, never had cards, in fact?"

"I'm not very expert on that problem, Senator."

"You never carried a card, then?"

"Never had a card or was in any other way connected with the Communist party."

Next Senator Kleinschmidt took up the ball. He may have been an undertaker, as the papers said, but he certainly had picked up the lawyer's flair for questioning. Perhaps out in the prairies he had first studied law, perhaps even taken it up, and then realized there was more and quicker money in the burial business. At any rate, it was he who tried to lay the first trap. It may have been that the committee counsel put him up to it, for I noticed Kleinschmidt referred frequently to his notes.

"Mr. Whitehead, you said that you were not an expert on Communism. You do know something about it, do you not?"

"I try to keep myself informed, Senator," I said.

"Have you ever seen or read the *Communist Manifesto?*"

"By Marx and Engels?"

"Yes," he said, prompting me.

"Probably in college," I answered.

"So you were a young radical already in college?" Senator Reynolds exploded.

"No, sir. I believe it was required reading in some course I was taking."

"That is proof to me that the next job this committee should tackle is the colleges and universities. Hot beds of Communism, there's no doubt about it," Reynolds said, exhausting momentarily his ammunition.

Senator Kleinschmidt resumed. "Have you ever seen or read *State and Revolution*, by Lenin?"

"No."

"Have you ever seen or read *Left-Wing Communism: An Infantile Disorder*, by Lenin?"

"No."

"Have you heard of it?"

"No."

"How about *Problems of Leninism*, by Stalin?"

"I don't know that one either, Senator."

"Did you ever see or read *History of the Communist Party of the Soviet Union*, put out by the Central Committee of the Russian Communist party?"

"No."

"Ever hear of it?"

"Not that I recall."

"Did you ever see or read *Program of the Communist International and Its Constitution*, third American edition?"

"No."

"Any edition?"

"Neither the third, nor the second, nor the first."

"Did you ever see or read," Kleinschmidt persisted, *"The Revolutionary Movement in the Colonies and Semi-Colonies, a resolution of the Sixth World Congress of the Comintern?"*

"No. I'm afraid, Senator, my reading of Communist literature has not been very extensive."

"That's my very point," Kleinschmidt snapped. "How could you be first, for five years, a member of the American diplomatic service, and then a journalist and writer, and finally a broadcaster with a mass audience and not know something about Communism?"

"Senator, I don't think it is up to me to answer that question. I am what I am — and I do not apologize for it."

"Is it not surprising that one who had the public ear was so ignorant of Communism?"

"I don't think I'm ignorant of the subject. I'm just not a scholar, that's all."

I could sense the mortician trying to spring the trap in a most lawyerlike way.

"Given your admitted ignorance of Communism, Mr. Whitehead, is it not possible that some of your writings and broadcasts, perhaps some of your acts, were in line with the Communist line — and you didn't know it?"

"I know enough about Communism to have known it."

"How could you have known it if you were so ignorant as you claim?"

"Now, Senator, if I may say so, this is the kind of questioning that at times has made such a farce of this committee's proceedings. . . ."

"What does the witness mean?" Senator Reynolds put in.

"If I had answered that I had read all that Communist literature you would have hastily concluded that I was a Communist, or sympathetic with Communism. When I replied that I had not read it, you say this shows that in my ignorance I might have taken the Communist line, even though I didn't know it. Either way I lose."

"Does the witness contend that he hasn't ever read any writings of the Communists?" Senator Reynolds blurted out, impatiently.

"No, Senator Reynolds, I do not contend that. I remember reading, for example, Trotsky's *History of the Russian Revolution* — a fascinating book, by the way."

"Then you're a Trotskyite!" roared the Senator triumphantly.

"No. I'm not a Trotskyite, Senator. Unless reading his book automatically makes you one."

Rikind leaned over and whispered that I try to finish reading my statement. It was almost five o'clock. The time had passed quickly.

"Mr. Chairman," I addressed O'Brien, "may I — ?"

"Any more questions, gentlemen?" O'Brien chirped.

"I have a number of questions on points which the witness has covered so far," Senator Jones said quietly. "But I believe there is a vote in the Senate at five o'clock and I want to be there."

"Most of us want to be there," O'Brien agreed. I thought I saw a look of disappointment in his face. Perhaps he had been hoping for some telling point to be scored against me at the end so it would make the kind of headlines he wanted in the morning papers. I had already scored in the afternoon journals with my opening statement. Now my suggestion that O'Brien himself be investigated, and the uproar it provoked, would probably get the play in the morning editions. He would not forgive me for that.

"The committee stands adjourned until 10 o'clock tomorrow morning," he announced, and strode quickly out of the room.

I am more tired tonight than I care to admit. There is a certain strain in just keeping alert to the questions. However, after a good night's sleep . . .

NEW YORK, SEPTEMBER 29 (FRIDAY NIGHT)

TO COME up here this evening after the hearing in Washington recessed is like rocketing from one planet to another. Already that floodlit committee room, with O'Brien sitting unctuously in the middle of the long table and the Senators popping their sly questions to the purr of the cameras, seems like a scene from a bad dream. We returned so that we could be with the children over the week end.

I gather from Dick that his schoolmates see his father either as a villain or a hero — depending on what their parents are overheard to say. Maria was not much interested — she is too young — but Dick wanted a play-by-play account of all that had happened.

This Friday morning's session, which was recessed at noon until Monday, was taken up mostly with my efforts to finish my little statement and the Senators' determination that I should not finish it.

"I leave it to your imagination as to who won," I kidded Dick when I recounted the day to him.

I began this morning by suggesting to the committee that I be allowed to proceed with my statement to the end — I was nearing the finish, I explained — and then be free to answer any questions the members wished to ask. It seemed to me to be a reasonable enough proposal, but the Senators were outraged.

"Just a moment, suh!" Senator Reynolds shouted, stirring from his cotton-belt torpor. But O'Brien, who had a determined slant to his jaw all morning, took the play himself.

"Mr. Whitehead, you are not going to tell this committee how it is to proceed!" he said sternly.

"I was only trying to make a suggestion, Senator."

"Well, I suggest you let us run our business and you stick to yours. You are not, after all, a member of the committee."

"Fortunately!" Senator Reynolds mumbled, under the cover of his flying mustache.

I realize it doesn't do me any good to antagonize these curious gentlemen, but I cannot think of any way — short of surrendering — to avoid it. They are out to get me, regardless of what I say, and I am out to be not gotten.

I wondered what would happen next, since suggestions from my corner were ruled out of place. Senator Breen spoke up with a suggestion of his own, though I have no doubt O'Brien prompted it. Breen has the smooth manner and the skin-depth of the West Coast real-estate operator which, until lately, he has been. He can be rather ingratiating, even with me.

"Mr. Whitehead," he said, not unfriendlily. "We've all read your statement, which you handed to us yesterday. The whole country has seen it, or at least a generous extract of it, in the papers. Last night a good part of it was broadcast on the radio and you yourself were shown reading it on television."

"Shown reading a few paragraphs," I said.

"Well, let us say, it was certainly well publicized. Now at this point I would like to make what seems to me to be a reasonable suggestion. It would save us all a great deal of time if we could just put the rest of your statement in the record, dispense with further reading of it — and get on with the questioning."

"No one is more anxious to get to the questioning than I am, Senator Breen. But . . ."

I felt Rikind's hot breath on my cheek.

"Don't give in to him," he whispered.

O'Brien pounded with his gavel.

"Mr. Rikind, you are not to prompt the witness. I told you that yesterday at the very opening, I believe."

"I cannot even consult with my client?" Rikind sputtered, jumping up.

"I informed you yesterday of your rights, Mr. Rikind. You may consult with the witness when he asks you to. Not otherwise."

"Thank you, sir." Bill Rikind sat down, putting on one of his finest scowls.

"Senator Breen, I would like to accommodate you —" I spoke up in as conciliatory a tone as I could. "I am not asking to be heard to the end of this brief, prepared statement because I am in love with my own prose or my voice. But I do have a very good reason, I think, for wanting to finish this declaration. I have prepared it with some care. I have given it the best thought of which I am capable. It gives me an opportunity to answer the charges against me and at least some of the questions which are undoubtedly in your minds in my own words, in my own way, and as fully as I can. You don't have to be a lawyer — and I am not a lawyer, as are the chairman and some of the other members — to know that the coolest and most intelligent witness in proceedings of this kind may easily become confused under a barrage of questions posed unceasingly by some very distinguished minds. No doubt I shall become flustered before you are through with me. No doubt many of my answers will not seem to jibe exactly with others. That is the risk of appearing here. And having asked to appear here, I shall not dodge your questions, but shall attempt to answer them truthfully to the best of my ability. But in the beginning, sir, I should like to state orally for the record a few things that I think I have the right to give this committee."

"But every word of your statement will be placed in the record, just as you have written it, Mr. Whitehead," Breen persisted.

"In that case the witness would be deprived of enunciating every everlasting word of his manifesto over the air and over these newfangled — what-do-you-call-them — TV screens," Senator Reynolds broke in to say, chuckling at his own humor.

"Isn't that your real reason, suh?" Reynolds said, grinning at me with an air of triumphal discovery. "You want your picture on that screen, you want your voice to go rolling across the land into every kitchen and living room in the country — now, isn't that the real reason?"

I chuckled a bit myself.

"Speak up, suh. Answer the question, please," the old gentleman insisted.

"Senator Reynolds, it is not I who arranged for the broadcasting and the televising of these hearings. I believe that is the responsibility of your distinguished chairman."

"Any other questions?" O'Brien asked curtly. "If not, the witness may proceed."

"Gentlemen," I began, searching for my place. "I would next like to turn to the sworn statements of certain ex-Communists who have testified here in secret session before you. So far as I am aware, Senator O'Brien himself, has not yet presented to this committee any evidence for his grave accusations. . . ."

"I brought in several witnesses to back them up," O'Brien said.

"Two witnesses, was it not?"

"Well, two," O'Brien answered. "But they were just the first ones. As I have said before on many an occasion, we have just begun to scratch the surface."

"I will confine myself to just the two, who have so far testified here against me," I said.

"Whom are you speaking of?" Senator Kleinschmidt asked.

"I am coming to them, Senator. Since their charges are so serious — that I am a disloyal and traitorous citizen, no less — I shall ask the committee to allow me to state what I have here written about them with great care and after long reflection. . . ."

"He is trying to tell us how to proceed again," Senator Reynolds observed.

"And I am trying to preserve my patience, Senator," O'Brien said, forcing a smile into the television cameras.

"Mr. Chairman," Green, the committee counsel bobbed up to say. "May I remind you, sir, that the witness has not answered the question put to him by Senator Kleinschmidt?"

"Answer the question," O'Brien ordered.

"Senator, with all due respect to this committee, I should like to point out that I am about to answer the question — fully — in what I am about to read."

"Never mind the reading. Answer the question."

"Let me put it this way, Mr. Whitehead," Kleinschmidt said. "Are you referring to Miss Elsie McCabe and Mr. Frederick Newman?"

"Yes, sir, But can I read . . . ?"

"Mr. Chairman," Reynolds's voice rang out in the accent of Dixie. "Will you please, suh, remind the witness that he is here to answer questions and not to go on reading until hell freezes over? Personally, I have had enough of his reading. This is not a literary circle. This is not a gathering of eggheads!"

Reynolds's colleague from the South, the soft-spoken Jones, who had not said much, turned to him: "Pardon me, Senator, but I don't get the term."

"Eggheads! Damned intellectuals!" Reynolds roared. "Long-winded scribblers, like our distinguished witness. That's what I mean, suh."

When the laughter subsided I tried to go back to my reading.

[233]

"Just a minute," O'Brien halted me. "I believe Senator Klein-schmidt desires to question you further. Go ahead, Senator."

"Mr. Whitehead," the Midwest solon began. "Did you ever know Miss Elsie McCabe?"

"I did."

"Personally?"

"Yes."

"Did you know her well?"

"Yes."

"How well?"

I began to doubt whether the papers were right in saying this representative of the corn belt had been a mortician, by trade, before his election. He sounded more and more like a shrewd country lawyer to me — the kind who enlivened the county courthouses back in my own native Indiana when I was young.

"How well?" Kleinschmidt repeated.

"We were good friends — a long time ago."

"How long ago?"

"Well, a quarter of a century ago, Senator."

"Close friends?"

"Yes. Certainly."

"Romantically close?"

There was a titter in the room, which O'Brien suppressed with a stern glance though you could tell from his face that he was beginning to enjoy the line of questioning.

"I suppose you could say that."

"You were in fact engaged to marry her, were you not?"

"It is difficult to say, Senator, what my intentions were so long ago. We were never formally engaged, at any rate."

"Not formally engaged?" He paused, and I could feel him making ready to thrust in his stiletto.

"Not even formally engaged, and yet you lived with her — as man with wife, did you not?"

"No, sir."

I should have been more prepared for this than I was. The O'Brien committee was notorious for trying to smear the private life of "unfriendly" witnesses.

Bill Rikind sprang to his feet. "May I respectfully ask what this line of questioning conceivably has to do with the charges against the witness?"

"How many times do I have to tell you, sir, that witness's counsel has no right to pose a question to the committee," O'Brien said.

"Do I understand that this committee is now to investigate the purely private life of the witness?"

"You are to understand that you are to sit down and not intervene in these proceedings," O'Brien explained.

Rikind sat. He is getting used to it.

"Is it your testimony," Kleinschmidt resumed, "that you did not live with this woman?"

"That is my testimony, sir."

"Never lived with her?"

"Never. We had a few week ends together, no doubt, like couples sometimes do when they think they are in love."

"That is not the custom in my part of the country, at least," Kleinschmidt said, unctuously.

"Things must have changed out there, Senator, since my youthful days," I said.

"Perhaps it is you who have changed, Mr. Whitehead. Perhaps that's what Europe did to you — among other things. Is it not a fact that you were attracted to Communism over there?"

"No."

"But you were attracted to Communists, is that it?"

"I have been attracted to a fair number of human beings, Senator. But Communists usually repelled me because they had ceased being human beings."

"Did you not know," continued the little mortician — who by this time, I was convinced, must at the very least have doubled, back in the Midwest, as a trial lawyer — "that Miss McCabe was a Communist — I mean, at the time you were romantically attached to her?"

"I certainly did, Senator."

"So you knowingly associated with a Communist?"

[235]

"I associated, for a time, with Miss McCabe, knowing she was a Communist."

"Did you know she was a Soviet agent?"

"I suppose all Communists are that, to a certain extent, in that they try to advance the cause of the Soviet Union."

"Did you know," the Senator asked, "that Miss McCabe, at that time, was a member of an international Communist espionage apparatus?"

"No, I didn't. Did that come out in secret testimony here?" I asked, rather fascinated by this piece of information.

"The witness will please refrain from asking questions," O'Brien droned.

"Would the information surprise you, Mr. Whitehead — since you admit you knew the lady well?"

"Well, nothing really surprises me about Communists, Senator. But I admit this is an exception. It does surprise me, if it is true."

"Would it surprise you to know that Miss McCabe has linked you with her Communist espionage ring?"

"It would, sir."

"Why?"

"Because it's a lie. Lies about myself somehow surprise me."

"Are you testifying that you were not a member of Elsie McCabe's spy apparatus?"

"Yes, sir!"

"That you were not a member of any Communist spy ring?"

"I have already so testified, and I repeat it now."

O'Brien stepped in. "You testified you were not a Soviet agent. You didn't say anything about not being a Red spy."

"Well, it would be the same, wouldn't it, Senator?"

"Not necessarily."

"A Communist spy would be working for the Soviet Union, I presume, and therefore be a Soviet agent. At any rate, I was neither a spy nor an agent and I resent the very suggestion."

Senator Breen said he had a question. "You understand, Mr. Whitehead, that witnesses have testified here under oath that you were both?"

"If they did, they lied, Senator."

"But they would say you are lying. How are we to know who is lying?"

"If this committee would allow me to read a few more sentences of my statement, I go into that problem, Senator. That is precisely where this committee has done so much damage to innocent citizens, taking the word of former Communists for the Gospel truth." I turned to my manusciript.

"Lord! He wants to do some more reading, gentlemen," Senator Reynolds said, puffing through his untidy mustache.

"I for one," Senator Jones said, "would like to hear what the witness has to say on the subject. It is one of the most difficult problems we have. Here witnesses, former Communists who certainly ought to know something about a movement they spent many, many years in, come before this committee and say under solemn oath that, say, Mr. Whitehead was known to them to be a Communist and a Soviet agent. Mr. Whitehead says they are liars. Whom are we to believe? One or the other is lying and should be prosecuted by the Justice Department for perjury. I would like to get to the bottom of this. If the witness has prepared something on it, I would like to hear it — now."

"Thank you, Senator," I managed to say before O'Brien cut me off.

"Senator," he said glibly to Jones, "I would gladly accommodate you. But we have become so absorbed this morning in the witness's revelations concerning his connection with a former Communist and spy that none of us perhaps noticed how quickly time was passing. It is now a quarter past noon. As this is Friday, there will be no afternoon session. If it is not inconvenient to Mr. Whitehead, we shall invite him to return to the stand Monday morning."

"It is not inconvenient to me, sir. I must say, though, that I would welcome an afternoon session today. I rather hate to leave what you, sir, call my revelations concerning my connection with a former Communist and, as you claim, spy, up in the air. I had . . ."

"Suh, you will not spoil my week end," Senator Reynolds admonished me. "Not that I spend it in sport, or other pleasures. But it is necessary for me to return to the land of cotton and put my ear to the grass roots. That is the way democracy works in this country, Mr. Whitehead. You were away a long time, I believe, suh."

O'Brien adjourned the meeting. He looked more pleased with himself than he did at yesterday's adjournment. Was he thinking of the headlines this evening? If so, he could not have been disappointed. All the way up from Washington we bought the late-afternoon papers: the Washington papers, the Baltimore papers, the Philadelphia papers. The headlines were almost identical.

WHITEHEAD ADMITS KNOWING FORMER COMMUNIST AGENT

O'BRIEN COMMITTEE PRESSES SPY CHARGE AGAINST FORMER BROADCASTER

OCTOBER 2

PERHAPS it was because a good many week-end editorials had chided the O'Brien committee for not allowing me in three long hearings even to finish reading a half-hour voluntary statement — at any rate, after the usual preliminaries this morning, I was allowed to proceed.

"Gentlemen, at the last hearing on Friday we had come to the testimony of two former Communists, Miss Elsie McCabe and Mr. Frederick Newman, both of whom swore to you that I was a Communist and a Soviet agent. In executive, that is, in secret session, part of which — the damaging parts, so far as I am concerned — you have just made public, the following exchange took place between committee counsel and Miss Mc-Cabe:

COUNSEL: Miss McCabe, was Raymond Whitehead a Communist?
McCABE: Yes, sir.
Q.: Was Raymond Whitehead a Soviet agent?
A.: Yes, sir.

[238]

Q.: How do you know these two things?

A.: Well, I was close to him personally over many years.

Q.: And you personally knew him to be a Communist and an agent of the Soviet Union?

A.: Yes, sir.

Q.: Can you give the committee any other evidence?

A.: Well, he was known to my husband as a Communist and an agent.

Q.: Miss McCabe, will you tell the committee who your husband was?

A.: My husband was a Russian, a Bolshevik.

Q.: Where is he now?

A.: I do not know. He was taken away.

Q.: Dead, perhaps?

A.: Dead, or living a life worse than death. They took him away.

Q.: At any rate, he is out of the reach of this committee?

A.: Oh, certainly.

"Gentlemen," I continued, "it is surprising that the distinguished counsel for this committee and the distinguished members of this committee did not — and this is true also of Frederick Newman's testimony — think it worth while to put further questions to Miss McCabe as to the factual evidence, if any, of her very serious charges."

"Just a minute," O'Brien said. "This lady said she knew you. You have admitted the acquaintance. When such a person says she knew you to be a Communist and a Soviet agent, is it not evidence?"

"Why didn't you question her further — in detail, like you're questioning me?" I asked.

"He is trying again to tell the committee how to conduct its business," Reynolds broke in to remark.

"I was merely trying, Senator, to answer the chairman's question by one of my own."

"All right," Senator Jones said, intervening. I am almost coming to regard him as a friend in court. "What would you have asked, Mr. Whitehead, that committee counsel or members didn't ask?"

"In all justice, I think you might have asked the lady for more evidence. For instance, I was in Europe, living in Switzerland at the time I knew Miss McCabe. Which Communist party did she allege I belonged to? The Swiss? The American? The Russian? Did she ever see a party card on me? When did I allegedly become a member? When did I allegedly become an agent? Who allegedly recruited me? Where? For what? Can she name anyone except the mysterious Mr. Newman who claims to have known me as a Communist? Has she any letters to prove her charges? From me? From Moscow? From the comrades all over the world? Has she concrete evidence for one single act I committed as a Red agent or as a Communist? Can she show you one piece I wrote or broadcast that showed Communist bias? Sir, I could go on indefinitely. But the record shows you gentlemen did not go on at all. I wonder why."

"Does the gentleman impugn the motives of this committee in what he has just said?" Senator Reynolds wanted to know.

"I say it is curious, Senator, that once you get an ex-Communist witness to denounce someone as a Communist, you scarcely bother to go after the evidence. Whereas, with those of us who are not Communists, and never have been, you harass us with questions, many of them irrelevant, it seems to me, day after day."

"We do not harass anybody, Mr. Whitehead," O'Brien said curtly.

"Are you suggesting, Mr. Whitehead," Jones asked, "that we should not hear these ex-Communists as witnesses?"

"No, sir. In the first place, it is none of my business whom you hear. I would not contest your right to hear anyone you want. I would even agree that you can get valuable information about the Communist conspiracy — its technique of espionage, infiltration and so on — from these ex-Communists who once betrayed their country by spying on it for another.

"But since you asked me, Senator, I would like to make two observations on the subject."

"Go ahead," said Jones, though I did not gather from their faces that the other members were especially pleased with this line of talk.

[*240*]

"First, should one not be somewhat skeptical about the word of these former Communists? For years they conspired and lied for their cause. Now they have rejected that cause and taken up — I think that's how they would see it — a new one. I suspect their old habits of lying have not always deserted them. This is certainly true in the case of Miss McCabe and Mr. Newman.

"Second, Mr. Senator, what *does* pass my understanding is that you could do so much to make authentic American heroes out of admitted spies who admittedly betrayed their country. This, I believe, is a new phenomenon in American life; making heroes out of spies and, I might add, out of informers. . . ."

"You're against informers because they say you're a Communist, is that it?" old Senator Reynolds broke in to ask.

"No, Senator. I just am not very enthusiastic about informers in general. I must confess it hurt my sense of decency to see in the Soviet Union and in Nazi Germany informers being turned into heroes, being held up to the youth as worthy examples, which the young should try to emulate. I never thought that would happen here.

"If we had more time, and if you were interested, I could tell you from personal experience what the glorification of informers did to decent social life and indeed to family life in the totalitarian lands. It poisoned them; it destroyed them. A father became afraid to express his honest thoughts in his own house for fear that his son or daughter might betray him to the secret police. . . ."

"The witness is straying far afield, if I may say so, Mr. Chairman," Senator Reynolds protested.

"I know," O'Brien agreed. "The gentleman complains we will not let him finish his prepared statement, and then he tries our patience by disgressing all over the place."

"I was asked by Senator Jones for my observations on the subject, I believe," I said.

"Go on," Jones insisted.

"I believe it is pertinent to the charges against me to say one further word about the credibility of these ex-Communist witnesses. They are renegades. They have double-crossed the community by engaging in Communist activities, including admitted espionage, and now they are double-crossing their former comrades by informing on them and helping to punish them. I am not defending their former comrades. They should be exposed, and, if found guilty of violating the law, made to pay the penalty. What I am saying is that after the experiences which these former Communists have had, the telling of the truth does not come easily or naturally to them. In some cases they have to testify falsely — or think they do — in order to obtain immunity for their own crimes against the state. In that connection I would remind you that neither Miss McCabe, nor Mr. Newman, nor any of the other self-confessed ex-Communist spies who have testified before you have ever been prosecuted for espionage by the Justice Department.

"Later in these hearings, I may have, with your permission, something to say about the motives of Miss McCabe and possibly Mr. Newman for inventing the charge that I was a Soviet agent and a Communist, though I confess that there is a great deal in their behavior which completely baffles me. This much, I think, all of us here would agree to: the very work of a spy requires lying. He must deceive his associates: he must make them think he is one of them, though he isn't. In time, the boundary between truth and falsehood for a spy is bound to become blurred. I am not saying that when these ex-Communist spies come before you they are always lying. I am saying that they are not always telling the truth. And I respectfully suggest that this fact should be borne in mind."

Two or three spectators in the back of the room started to applaud. O'Brien quickly brought them to order.

Senator Jones spoke up. "Mr. Whitehead, is it your testimony then, that Miss Elsie McCabe is just a liar?"

"As regards me, completely."

"And you expect this committee to agree with you that you are right and she is wrong?"

"In this instance, yes."

"How are we to tell? You both have sworn to tell the truth." Jones seemed really puzzled.

[242]

"Well, that is for you to decide, Senator, after weighing the evidence and the reliability of witnesses. I have just made some observations about the reliability of ex-Communists. Undoubtedly you also have given the matter some thought. But since you ask me, there is another consideration."

"What is that?" Senator Jones asked.

"The accusations are not comparable. It is not a matter of my calling Miss McCabe a liar and of her calling me one. When I call her a liar, that doesn't hurt her very much. But when she calls me a Communist that hurts me a great deal — given the climate in America today."

"Just a minute, suh," Senator Reynolds intervened. I could see his beady eyes growing intense and his mouth watering beneath his coffee-stained mustache. "What bothers you is that Miss McCabe hurt you, is that it?"

"No, that she called me a Communist."

"And you don't like her calling you a Communist?"

"I don't like people telling lies about me, especially when they are as damaging as this one is."

"Miss McCabe might not like your calling her a liar — did that ever occur to you?"

"Then she shouldn't lie."

Senator Kleinschmidt spoke up and again showed his remarkable feeling for the law.

"Do I understand," he asked, "that you are accusing Miss Mc-Cabe of committing perjury before this committee?"

"I accused her of lying, Senator. I'm not sure I know the legal, technical difference between that and committing perjury, if there is a difference."

"Well, perjury is lying under oath."

"Then she's a perjurer."

"It's a little more than that, I believe," Senator Jones, whom I had vaguely heard of as being a legal light in the South, said.

"I stand corrected, Senator. I am not a lawyer," Kleinschmidt said.

"Perjury implies that a witness willfully and knowingly testifies falsely," Senator Jones explained.

"Then Miss McCabe is a perjurer," I said.

Kleinschmidt again took over the questioning. "All right, you accuse her of perjury. Now, you said a moment ago that what she said about you was much worse than what you said about her. You asked the committee to take that into consideration. I am sure it will. But let me ask you something. There is no law against being a Communist in this country. There is a law against perjury. Therefore what you said about Miss McCabe, about her being a perjurer, is much worse than what she said about you. You didn't think of it that way, did you?"

"No, I didn't, Senator. And I still don't. Calling a liar a liar is an old custom. It's a grave accusation among honest men. But it's a rather common one these days. It doesn't hurt a person much, or get him into much trouble. To call a man a Communist in 1950 does. In fact, it can ruin him. It can make him an outcast, deprive him of a job, of a living. In short, it can destroy him. That is the difference."

The people's representative from the West, Senator Breen, next raised a point.

"You know, do you not," he addressed me, "that Miss McCabe has been used several times by the Department of Justice in court cases dealing with Communists? Would not that suggest that the legal branch of the executive vouches for her veracity and for her credibility as a witness?"

Bill Rikind had prepared me for this question.

"I know that, Senator," I replied. "But is it not also a fact, sir, that the Justice Department in the prosecution of its cases often uses as witnesses for the state, gangsters, racketeers, narcotic peddlers, confessed murderers even and thugs?"

"It is not quite the same, is it?" the Senator from the West persisted.

"Well, there's a certain parallel, I think," I said. "Besides, Senator, we might note that the Justice Department has not used Miss McCabe to testify against me. In a court, she would be subject to cross-examination by my attorneys — a practice, I regret, which is not permissible before your committee."

"Are you suggesting, suh," Reynolds broke in, "that we allow your counsel to cross-examine our witnesses?"

"Yes, sir. Those who testify against me."

"It is against the rules of this committee, suh!"

I looked at my watch. It was a quarter to twelve noon. I still hadn't got to the end of my statement and I asked O'Brien, who had been singularly quiet all morning, if I could get along with it.

"If there are no more questions," he agreed.

I turned to my script, whose pages were beginning to deteriorate from being pawed at by sweaty, nervous fingers.

"Just a moment, please," Senator Kleinschmidt spoke up. "I would like to ask one further question before the witness proceeds."

"Go ahead, Senator," O'Brien said, almost urgingly.

"Aside from your relations with Miss McCabe — whatever they were . . ." Kleinschmidt began.

"I have tried to testify truthfully as to what they were," I said.

"All right. Would you deny ever having associations with other Communists?"

"I was just coming to that point in my statement, Senator. If you would allow me to proceed . . ."

"Answer the question, please," O'Brien ordered.

"Can I not read what I have noted down here on that?"

"He is dodging the question, Mr. Chairman!" Reynolds's Dixie voice rang out.

"I'm not dodging it at all, suh —" I replied heatedly, slipping in the "suh" quite unconsciously. There was a titter in the courtroom that made the cotton Senator furious.

"Mr. Chairman," he stormed, "I demand the room be cleared. I do believe, suh, that this unco-operative witness has filled this room with his camp followers and fellow travelers."

"I don't know a soul out there, I assure you, Senator," I said.

"Any further provocation, and I shall clear the room of spectators," O'Brien declared. He turned to me. "Mr. Whitehead, is it not possible for you just this once to answer a question forthrightly? You were asked whether you had ever associated with Communists — other than Miss McCabe. Now, please answer 'Yes' or 'No.' "

"Senator," I said. "With all due respect to this committee, I suggest there are some questions which cannot be adequately — or fairly — answered by 'Yes' or 'No.' In such instances I believe I have the right — if free speech means anything to this body — to answer in my own way. In this particular case I have given the question a good deal of thought and I would therefore like to answer it as fully as I can in the words I have written down here."

I knew perfectly well what O'Brien was up to at this rather crucial moment. The session would be adjourning in a moment. It was two minutes to noon. The committee would get me to admit that I *had* had some contact with Communists, but before I could explain the circumstances, that every diplomat and journalist worth his salt maintained such contacts for purposes of informing himself as to what was going on in the world, O'Brien would adjourn the hearing and my terrible confession, that I had had some association with Communists in the past, would make the headlines for the day. (O'Brien had announced in the beginning there would be no afternoon hearings today because of pressing Senate business.)

At this critical juncture, Senator Reynolds, bless his Southern soul, came to my aid quite unwittingly and himself ran out the clock.

He was fuming. "Suh, I do think that the witness might well be held in contempt of the Senate for refusing to answer the question, as you have directed. We can put up with the gentleman's evasions, with his unjustified impugning of the motives of this committee, which is only trying to do its duty and protect this great country of ours from the rodents who are trying to gnaw away its vitals. But, suh, I for one will not stand idly by and see a duly constituted committee of the United States Senate defied by a recalcitrant witness such as this!"

I saw O'Brien stealing a glance at his watch.

"I'm sorry, Senator," he said. "I couldn't agree with you more. And I suggest that when we have heard this witness out . . ."

"That will take us till doomsday, suh —" Reynolds interjected, provoking a ripple of laughter which further consumed time.

"Quiet, please." O'Brien rapped for order. "The Senator's point is well taken. As I was saying, at the end of this witness's testimony the committee may well wish to consider whether he has been in contempt of the Senate. But, gentlemen, it is now a couple of minutes past noon. There will be no hearings this afternoon because of Senate business. Meeting adjourned until tomorrow morning, usual time."

As O'Brien stalked out of the room, he glared at me. Perhaps he was thinking of the headlines he had come so near to provoking. I was thinking myself what they would have been like:

WHITEHEAD ADMITS
LINKS WITH REDS!

OCTOBER 3

YVONNE got into the act today — or, rather, was pulled in — much to her embarrassment and mine. It is plain that O'Brien and his colleagues, including the Senator from the land of cotton, are not going to behave toward my wife with any old-fashioned Southern chivalry.

When I am on the stand, Yvonne sits directly behind me. Whenever I am interrupted with cross-examination — I still haven't finished my prepared statement — she pores through her notes on the subject, if she can find them, and hands them to me.

Today, when I was being closely examined on my contacts with Communists, Senator Breen asked me if I had known any Reds in Geneva, when we made our home there. I couldn't think of any, but for the first time, I checked with Yvonne.

"Did we know any Commies in Geneva?" I whispered to her.

The committee's counsel, David Green, leaped to his feet, almost losing his horn-rimmed spectacles.

"I wish to call the attention of the committee," he snapped, "to the fact that the witness just then turned to consult his wife, who has no legal position before this body."

"That will not be permitted," O'Brien said sharply. "Mrs. Whitehead is here by courtesy of the committee, just like any other spectator. She must not interfere in these proceedings in any way. Is that clear?"

"I beg your pardon, sir, I was just . . ." Yvonne, quite abashed, started to say.

"I was not addressing you, madame. You have no right to speak here. I was addressing the witness. Do you understand what I said, Mr. Witness?"

"That I am not even to consult my wife?"

"That's right."

"It is she who has prepared a great deal of data in this case. I thought . . ."

"Mr. Chairman," interrupted Senator Jones, whose decency I am beginning to appreciate. "May I suggest that it is perfectly all right for Mr. Whitehead to consult his wife if he first asks your permission?"

"Very well," O'Brien conceded. "But you didn't ask my permission then, did you?"

"No, sir. I . . ."

"What did you whisper to her? What did you say?"

"Senator Breen asked me if I knew any Communists in Geneva, when we made our home there. Since my wife . . ."

"Your wife is a foreigner, is she not?" Reynolds cut in, stroking the flying wings of his mustache.

"An American citizen, sir."

"But foreign born, no?"

"Yes, like millions of other Americans, Senator — like all Americans originally, except the Indians."

"Mr. Chairman," Counsel Green spoke up, trying, I could see, to butter up O'Brien, his chief employer. "The witness has not answered your question."

[*248*]

"I asked you, sir," O'Brien said, with obvious relish, "to tell the committee what you whispered to your wife a moment ago. Just tell us what you said."

"Senator Breen," I began all over again, "asked me if I knew any Communists when we were living in Geneva. I couldn't remember any — I can't remember every last detail of my life. So I asked her."

"What did you say exactly?" O'Brien persisted.

"I said: 'Did we know any Commies in Geneva?'"

"What did she say?"

"She said she couldn't remember any."

"Well, you are not to do that again, Mr. Whitehead. If you have any questions to put to Mrs. Whitehead, you ask me first. Clear?" O'Brien was enjoying the game now.

"Clear," I said.

But Committee Counsel Green was not through with us.

"Mr. Whitehead," he began, "has Mrs. Whitehead been giving you advice and assistance thus far in these hearings?"

"A great deal, Mr. Green. She . . ."

"I mean here in this room during the proceedings."

"I believe a moment ago was the first time I directly asked her about something. But she passes me a note from time to time about something."

"She will please desist from doing that in the future," O'Brien admonished. "We want your answers to questions, not hers."

"Senator —" I tried to explain. "My wife did a great deal of work on this case, starting with when I was abroad and you made your outrageous charges . . ."

"Those last words will be stricken!" O'Brien said, addressing the stenographer.

"She has, for instance, gone over carefully an incredible number of articles and broadcasts to see where I stood on certain matters you are sure to question me on: what I thought of Communism, the Soviet Union, and so forth."

"Sir, if I may continue . . ." Counsel Green said. He turned to me. "Mr. Witness, to your knowledge, has Mrs. Whitehead ever had any contact with witnesses before this committee?"

"Why don't you ask her?" I said.

"I'm asking you. Has she?"

"Can't you just answer 'Yes' or 'No?'" O'Brien put it to me.

"No, I can't answer 'Yes' or 'No.'"

"Why not?"

"Simply because I don't know."

I was getting a little weary of the endless, irrelevant questioning, and for the moment I tended to forget what their purpose was: to wear me down and trap me. Bill Rikind, defying O'Brien, whispered to me: "Take it easy, Raymond. Don't let them ruffle you."

"Ask your wife then, if you don't know," O'Brien ordered.

I consulted Yvonne. "She says she did talk to one of the witnesses," I said, relaying the information.

"To whom?" Green said quickly.

"She says, Miss Elsie McCabe."

"What did she talk to her about?"

Again the silly consultation.

"She says, about her lies in the executive session."

This was news to me. Yvonne had not previously mentioned it.

"How did she know what went on here in executive session?" O'Brien demanded.

Yvonne, quite ruffled now, whispered to me.

"She learned it from our counsel, sir." Yvonne had mentioned it to me the day I returned, but I had forgotten.

"I shall look into that, Mr. Rikind," O'Brien said, with an ominous look in the direction of my eminent counsel. Bill did not bat an eye.

"I do believe, Mr. Chairman," Reynolds puffed, "the lady had been tampering with our witnesses."

"Did you put her up to seeing Miss McCabe?" O'Brien asked me sharply.

"No, I didn't. It must have happened while I was on the other side of the Atlantic, Senator. This is the first I knew of it."

And so the morning went, spent in endless, pointless wrangling, it seemed to me. But the pattern of O'Brien's tactics emerges rather clearly. It is to try to intimidate us, and to wear us down, to trap us. No session tomorrow. Senator O'Brien has to make a speech somewhere. Congress itself has just adjourned. But the O'Brien committee will continue to sit — at least until it is through with me.

NEW YORK, OCTOBER 4 (WEDNESDAY)

WE came back to see how Dick and Maria were faring, shifting for themselves. They seem to be doing all right. I was touched to learn that Barbara Fletcher had been coming in nearly every day to help. She is a very decent, generous person.

I went out to Lake Success to witness a historic action on the part of the U.N. By a vote of 47 to 5, with 7 absentions, the Political and Security Committee of the General Assembly gave tacit consent to General MacArthur to launch an all-out invasion of North Korea by U.N. forces. Actually South Korean troops are already fifty miles above the thirty-eighth parallel, but MacArthur has been holding back American and other foreign units until the U.N. decided whether North Korea should be disarmed by force and then unified.

I applaud the U.N.'s action today. If we don't go into North Korea, the Communists there can reassemble, form new armies with the help of Russia and Red China, and continue the war indefinitely.

WASHINGTON, OCTOBER 4 (LATER)

A GLOOMY trip in the train down for Yvonne and me. Fortunately Bill Rikind flew down, so that he was not with us to observe our discouragement.

Just before we left a special-delivery letter arrived from the landlord giving us six months' notice to vacate our apartment. He gave no reason, but we know perfectly well what it is. I have learned to accept the fact that "controversial" persons are no longer wanted on radio and TV, or in the press. But I was not quite prepared to be hounded out of my home.

[251]

SENATOR O'BRIEN postponed the hearings until this afternoon. At breakfast in the hotel this morning Yvonne told me of her talk with Barbara Fletcher yesterday. Barbara was deeply troubled. Bob Fletcher, she said, had been subpoenaed by O'Brien to testify at my hearing. Mark Robson had also been subpoenaed, she said. I wonder what they will say.

Conferred all morning with Bill Rikind about our strategy. He had some good ideas and seemed quite cheerful.

(LATER)— At the beginning of this afternoon's session I asked permission to make a brief statement. After a minimum of wrangling, O'Brien finally agreed to let me say a word of my own.

"Mr. Chairman," I said, "in the hearing before last, Senator Kleinschmidt asked if I had ever had any contacts with Communists. Questioning on that subject continued in the last hearing day before yesterday. Throughout both sessions I tried without success to read into the record a few words of my prepared statement which I thought pertinent to the subject. I now ask your permission to do that. If you agree, I, on my part, will be glad to abandon the reading of the closing part of my statement, provided that it is entered in the record. That will save us all time, and we can get on to whatever further questions you have.

"I might explain to the committee that the concluding paragraphs which I propose to skip, deal with a brief outline of my biography, which your counsel requested me to furnish you, and with a short summary of my thoughts on why I think this committee in general and Senator O'Brien in particular are doing grave injury to a number of patriotic citizens and great harm to the country. As to the biography, I will be glad to answer your questions relating to it. As to the final remarks, I trust you will allow me to come back to them at the conclusion of this hearing."

I sat back and awaited the committee's decision.

"I, for one," said Senator Breen, from the West Coast, "object to any bargaining with the witness."

"Senator Reynolds, have you any comment?" O'Brien asked the solon from the South.

"Yes, suh, I don't believe there is any end to the gentleman's statement. I think he intends to go on and on until the end of time."

"I could have read the whole thing, Senator," I repeated for the dozenth time, "in half an hour — had it not been for the interruptions."

"Well, I say, Mr. Chairman," Reynolds went on, "by all means, put the windy thing into the record and allow us, in the name of Heaven, to get on with the questions."

"Senator Jones?" O'Brien turned to the other Southern Senator, the representative of what must certainly be the "New South."

"Mr. Chairman, I would like to hear what he has written there," Jones said amiably.

"All right," O'Brien said grudgingly, "go ahead, Mr. Whitehead."

"Gentlemen," I started to read. "It is quite true that I have had some contact with Communists, but before you condemn me for that I would like to explain why. I fully realize that in the last four or five years — though it was not true before — 'guilt by association' has become accepted by many Americans as a valid theory, if the association happens to be with Bolsheviks. Probably most of us have always believed that you can judge a person by the company he keeps. But in the case of a journalist, like myself — and diplomats and teachers are in the same category — you have, I think, to make a distinction. You have to accord us not only freedom of thought and expression but what we might call 'freedom of contact.' An American journalist has to be free to meet and talk with all sorts of people, of every conceivable party and opinion, including Communists and fellow travelers, and even Russians. There happen to be in our unreasonable world quite a few Communists and Russians. In a good many places on our planet they exert considerable power.

In a good many others, they have great potential for influencing events and making trouble. That happens to be one of the facts of our time, whether Senator O'Brien and I like it or not. And the job of an American correspondent is to report the facts. To stear clear of Communists and Russians, to be afraid to associate with them in order to find out what they are up to — because Senator O'Brien will get you and destroy you if you do — is, for an American journalist, to betray his duty and the traditions of his profession. The result could also be catastrophic for America. For how are we to act wisely in our dealings with the rest of the world unless we have firsthand, factual information — however unpleasant — on which to base our actions?"

I looked up. O'Brien was pursing his lips. "I will not at this moment dignify the gentleman's remarks about me by the kind of reply he merits. But I will ask him a simple question. If, as you say, Mr. Whitehead, you have, as a newspaper fellow, the right to consort with Communists and Russians, do you not think we have the right to examine you on such dangerous contacts?"

"I don't dispute that for a moment, Senator," I said. "I would be happy to answer any questions on that, loaded as they might be. Incidentally, Senator, why do you distort my words by saying I 'consorted' with Communists and Russians?"

"I'll ask the questions, Mr. Whitehead, thank you," O'Brien said, smiling.

"Gentlemen —" I went on reading —"what I am trying to say is that contacts with people on the other side of the curtain are not only normal for Americans like myself — journalists, diplomats, scholars — but they are absolutely necessary if we are to do our jobs. The real question therefore is not whether I had such contacts — I tell you I did — but whether they contaminated me . . ."

"That's the whole point, suh. That's what we're trying to find out!" Senator Reynolds chimed in.

". . . and whether they led me into a single act of disloyalty to my country. The record, which I will submit, will prove that they did not."

"What record, suh?"

"Of everything I have written and broadcast."

"You are going to submit all that?" Reynolds asked, his walrus mustache fairly bristling.

"I have them here — for your perusal, sir," I said.

"Good Lord, Mr. Chairman," Reynolds said. "We will never finish with this witness if we have to wade through everything he has ever written and broadcast. He is long-winded enough, as it is."

"We will take the matter under advisement," O'Brien ruled. "Have you finished, Mr. Whitehead?"

"Yes. I assume the rest of my statement will be inserted in the record."

"That will be done."

There was no denying the sense of relief with which the committee members greeted my finish. Now they could get at me. I saw O'Brien glance at his watch. It was nearing five o'clock, the usual closing time. It would not do, of course, to adjourn now, however pleasant it might be for the Senators. O'Brien was knitting his brow. The headlines again, I wondered? The man was very shrewd in exploiting them. So far today, I had done almost all the talking. The headlines would reflect that.

"Very well," O'Brien said, clearing his throat. "There is not much time left today. But I would like to put a question or two. Will you please tell us, first, Mr. Whitehead, what Communists you associated with here in the United States?"

"Aside from Miss McCabe, I don't believe I ever knew any American Communists, Senator."

"Neither here nor abroad?"

"That's correct."

O'Brien's jaw dropped. He gave a sign, I thought, to the committee's counsel. Green bobbed up dutifully.

"You realize, Mr. Whitehead," he said, "that you are testifying here under oath?"

"Yes, sir."

"And that you have sworn to tell the whole truth?"

"Yes, sir."

"Would you not like to reflect a little on the chairman's question and perhaps try to refresh your memory? Now I ask you, sir, what other American Communists, here or abroad, did you know beside Miss McCabe?"

"None," I repeated.

"You are absolutely sure?"

"Absolutely."

"Is it your testimony that you never knew Frederick Newman?"

"Not as a Communist."

"But he was a Communist, was he not?"

"Not when I met him — a few months ago. He had repented long before."

"All right," O'Brien said, taking over the questioning. "What about your Communist friends abroad — the foreign Communists?"

"I had no Communist friends, with the exception perhaps of one or two Russians."

"Russians, you say? Who were they?"

"Diplomats. One was in the Soviet Embassy in Paris, the other in the Berlin Embassy."

"You frequented the Russian embassies abroad, is that it?"

"No. I didn't frequent them. Like most journalists — and diplomats — I went to them from time to time to see if I could find out what the Russians were up to."

"You had no other purpose?"

"None."

"And you made friends in the Bolshevik embassies?"

"I would say that I made perhaps two friends. It was rather a sad business, Senator, because both of the men I am thinking about were later liquidated in the Moscow purges."

Reynolds broke in: "You mean it saddens a person like you to see a Russian Communist liquidated?"

"Well, both of them happened to be rather decent human beings. And I say I was saddened not only because of that but because it often occurred to me that perhaps they were done in partly on account of having had contact with me. You may not know it, Senator, but in the Russian book I am down as a typical representative of the wicked, capitalistic, warmongering world."

"Well, all I say, suh, is that in *my* book, the only good Russian is a dead Russian."

"Come, Senator," I said, trying to chide him, "there are a lot of likable, decent Russians — among the people. The trouble is with their leaders."

"So you had friends in the Soviet embassies?" O'Brien took up the ball again. "What were their names?"

"The one in Paris had a German name: Hoffman. The one in Berlin was Bogomov. Both dead now."

"How do you know that?" O'Brien asked suspiciously.

"It was in the papers, for one thing . . ."

"Yes?"

"And, of course, word got back from Moscow to diplomatic circles in Berlin and Paris."

"You didn't hear from Russia directly?"

"No. I don't hear from Russia directly — if you are trying to imply anything."

"I asked you," O'Brien snapped.

"I answered you."

"All right, what about other foreign Communists you knew — beside Russians?"

"I might say, Senator, so as to keep this thing in perspective, that in the Thirties over there I also had contacts with quite a few Nazis and Fascists. It was all a part of my job."

"You're evading my question," O'Brien said, angrily. It was now five o'clock — adjournment time — and he was fighting for his headlines.

"Senator O'Brien, I am not evading your question. But I intend to answer in my own way. That is one right even you cannot deprive me of."

"Suh!" Reynolds broke in. "I must say that in all my long service in the United States Senate, I have never seen a witness as unco-operative as you."

"I'm sorry you think so, sir. I am not mindful of being unco-operative, as you say. But since I have to provide the answers here, they are going to be in my own words."

"Mr. Chairman," Senator Jones said, "I believe we have reached adjournment time. Unfortunately I have another appointment."

"Very well, Senator," O'Brien said. "But I did put a question to the witness and he evaded an answer. I think he should answer, and then we'll adjourn."

O'Brien glared at me. "Now, I asked you, Mr. Whitehead, whether you knew any other foreign Communists, besides Russians?"

"I knew a few in the sense that I had journalistic contacts with them," I replied.

"Who were they?"

"Well, I would have to think a little to name them all. They go back over a quarter of a century. There were some of the Tass correspondents at the old League of Nations in Geneva and in places like Paris, Rome, Berlin and London. I knew maybe a half dozen of them, just as I knew scores of other foreign correspondents from various countries."

"But they were Russians, weren't they?"

"Mostly."

"I'm asking for non-Russians, and I would be obliged if you would answer my question."

"In my work I occasionally interviewed French and German Communist leaders and there was once a British M.P., I recall, who was the lone Communist in the House of Commons. I took him out to dinner once in London and wrote a story about him. He was rather unique."

"So you admit you were in constant contact with a large number of Communists abroad. . . ."

"Now, wait a minute, Senator!" I started to protest.

O'Brien was grinning at me, like one who had really scored this time. He pounded his gavel. The session was over.

Bill Rikind was so furious he could hardly speak all this evening.

"I can't understand how the Senate lets the s.o.b. get by with it," he kept muttering.

He did not feel any better — nor did I — when the late evening papers came in. We stared at the headlines. An awful feeling of helplessness came over me.

WHITEHEAD ADMITS
KNOWING SEVERAL
COMMUNISTS ABROAD

Nothing in the headlines and very little in the stories about the circumstances. My long statement was dismissed with a short paragraph.

"Well, that's what we're up against." Rikind cursed. For the first time I felt a hint of his discouragement. Yvonne gave him an uneasy glance.

OCTOBER 6

TODAY being Friday, there was only one session, and it was short. It was long enough, though, to provide me with my first lesson from Senator O'Brien on what might be termed "guilt by omission," "guilt by paternity," and "guilt by matrimony."

Committee Counsel David Green, a heavy-set, sluggish man, who can be surprisingly nimble when O'Brien beckons, began by reporting that members of the staff had gone over some of my broadcasts and articles, copies of which I submitted yesterday.

"So far, Mr. Whitehead," said Green, peering at me through his dark-rimmed spectacles, "I must say we have been more impressed by what you did not say than by what you have said."

"Guilt by omission, you mean!" I spoke up. The idea came to me in a flash.

"Go on, Mr. Green," Senator O'Brien commanded.

"For instance, Mr. Whitehead," Green continued, "in what we have read so far you don't seem to have much to say about America — much good, anyway."

"Well, Mr. Green," I said, "I was not writing and broadcasting about America during the period you apparently have gone over. I was in Europe, reporting from there."

"When did you return to this country?" Senator Jones asked.

"A year ago last month," I said.

"And you broadcast then in this country?"

"Yes. In New York."

"Did you comment on the American scene?"

"Every Sunday evening, Senator."

"You're not broadcasting now, are you?" O'Brien cut in with a wide grin.

"No."

"Could you tell us why?"

"I certainly could. It's rather a long story, Senator."

"Good Lord, Mr. Chairman, there he goes again!" Senator Reynolds exploded. "As I told you, suh, before the committee reconvened, I have to catch a noon train for my homeland. I have a heavy schedule there over the week end. To tell you the truth, Mr. Chairman, I am in no mood this morning for another wordy marathon from this long-distance champion. May I respectfully suggest, suh, that at this point we pursue another line of questioning, and save the gentleman's long story for another time."

"Very well, Senator," O'Brien said amiably. Perhaps he thought he had disturbed me by the question. He looked pleased with himself.

"There are several other matters," O'Brien continued, "that have come to the attention of this committee about which we might question the witness at this point. Perhaps in regard to them he will be kind enough to keep his answers short."

"I must say, Mr. Chairman," Reynolds observed, "I do not see for the life of me why he cannot answer most of them 'Yes' or 'No.'"

"Nothing would please me more, Senator," I said. "But as I have said before I insist on my right to answer in my own way. I'm sorry if it takes your valuable time. It takes mine, too, of course."

"I was not addressing you, suh —" Reynolds cut me down. His colleague from the South next spoke up.

"Mr. Chairman," Jones said, "may I suggest that the committee staff go over, insofar as possible, a fair sample of Mr. Whitehead's articles and broadcasts, including what he has written and spoken here in this country over the past year, and then make a report. I do not think we have given our researchers enough time to do their job well."

O'Brien seemed glum at this suggestion, and Counsel Green glummer. However, O'Brien agreed. He next took up what turned out to be, for me, a novel line of questioning. It had to do with guilt by paternity.

"Mr. Whitehead, do you have a son?" he asked innocently. "I do."

"How old is he?"

"Going on sixteen."

"His name?"

"Richard."

"Mr. Whitehead, did your son ever attend a camp?"

"Yes."

"Where?"

"Up in Connecticut."

"When?"

"This past summer."

"What was the name of the camp?"

"I don't remember, Senator, if I ever knew."

"Who sponsored it?"

"I don't know who sponsored it."

"You mean to say you sent your boy to a camp without inquiring into its sponsorship?"

"Perhaps it was careless of me, Senator, but I had no grounds for suspecting the sponsorship."

"Why not?"

"Actually, the boy got a job as a counselor in this camp. He got it through a friend of mine, a man I trust."

"Who was he?"

"Christopher Chambers, the drama critic."

"He did not tell you who some of the sponsors were?"

"No. It's my understanding it was mostly Broadway theater people, who sent their youngsters to the camp."

"Did you not know that Broadway was full of Communists?"

"No, I didn't. And I don't."

"And that at least two or three of the sponsors were, in fact, what we might call Broadway Communists?"

"No. I didn't know it."

Senator Kleinschmidt, who had come in late, spoke up. "Would it have made any difference to you, Mr. Whitehead, if you had known?"

"It might have, Senator."

"You say 'might.' You are not sure?"

"It would depend."

"On what?"

"Well, whether these allegedly Communist sponsors took any part in the camp." I saw what the mortician was getting at, so I went on. "Senator, let me make myself clear. If there were any Communists there acting as counselors or instructors or leaders, it would have made a difference, naturally. I certainly would have spared my son from them."

"But you didn't even bother to find out."

"I had no reason to — from what I knew and from what Mr. Chambers, who got the boy the job, said."

O'Brien took over. "The fact remains, Mr. Whitehead, that you do not seem to have been worried over exposing your own son to the poison of Communist propaganda all summer at this camp."

"I don't worry, Senator, over what I don't know. There's enough to worry about in regard to what you do know. And I can assure you, sir, that I have seen no evidence that the boy was contaminated in the least."

"Your boy did not become a Communist, you think?" Reynolds asked, in all seriousness.

"No, sir. He remained a very normal American boy. At the moment he's daffy about the World Series. Nothing Communistic about that, I believe."

"Do the Russians play baseball?" old Reynolds asked.

"No, sir, not that I know of."

"I didn't think so," Reynolds puffed, as if this proved something fairly momentous to him.

A ripple of laughter ran over the room and helped to close the subject, at least for the time being. The concluding scene this morning also had its humor, I thought. For Senator O'Brien next switched to the field of guilt by matrimony.

"Mr. Whitehead, your wife is a foreigner, I believe you have testified?"

"No. She's an American."

"But naturalized, no?"

"Correct."

"What was her nationality before her naturalization?"

"French."

"Native-born French?"

"Yes."

"What did her father do?" O'Brien asked, suspiciously. Were we coming to guilt by paternity again? I wondered.

"He followed your profession," I said.

"My profession?" O'Brien snorted. "What do you mean?"

"Well, he was a politician. He was a Senator."

"What political party did he belong to in France?"

"I believe he was a member of the Radical-Socialist party. I would have to check with my wife to be absolutely sure."

"You may do so."

Yvonne nodded.

"Yes. Her father was a Radical Socialist," I said, relaying the confirmation.

O'Brien beamed. "He was not only a radical but a Socialist, eh? That is your wife's background, then. I assume you found it congenial."

"Very," I said.

"Mrs. Whitehead —" O'Brien turned to Yvonne. "Did you follow in your father's footsteps?"

Yvonne, her black eyes big with incomprehension at this turn of events, arose slowly. "I don't understand what you mean, Senator?"

"Were you a Socialist, too?" O'Brien asked her.

"But my father was not a Socialist — on the contrary —"

"I'm asking you, madame, if *you* were a Socialist — a Radical Socialist?"

"I'm not a Socialist, of course not. I did belong to my father's party — the Radical Socialists."

"Then you were a Radical Socialist. That's what I wanted to know."

Senator Jones spoke up. "I do believe, Mr. Chairman, that if you are to question the lady, you must swear her in first."

"We will do that later, Senator, when we call her to the stand," O'Brien answered. "I will not question the lady further at this time."

Bill Rikind was on his feet, bristling. "Sir, would it not be highly improper to insert in the record what Mrs. Whitehead has just said, inasmuch as she has not yet been sworn?"

"You have no right to put questions here. How many times do I have to tell you that, Mr. Rikind?" O'Brien bawled.

"The record will show, Senator," Rikind insisted on saying, "that on a previous occasion you ruled that Mrs. Whitehead had no right to speak here. That was when she wanted to say something. Now, to suit your pleasure, you overrule your own ruling. I object, sir, to your making the rules — and breaking them — as you go along. And I object to your questioning the witness's wife without first swearing her in."

"You have no right to make objections here. Please sit down, Mr. Rikind," O'Brien ordered.

Once more my troubled counsel sat.

"Mr. Chairman," I sang out. "May I relieve your ignorance?"

"You too have no right to ask questions here, especially insulting questions," O'Brien retorted.

"In the interest of elementary information, not to speak of justice, I believe I have a duty to at least inform the committee that the so-called French 'Radical-Socialists' are not Radical Socialists, but just the opposite — conservatives. If you do not realize that, you are going to get way off the track."

"You mean to tell us, suh," Reynolds snorted, "that 'Radical Socialists' are not Radical Socialists? Do words, my good man, have no meaning for you?"

"Yes. But in this case, Senator Reynolds, I fear the meaning — quite naturally — is confusing you. This is a case where words do not mean what they seem."

"Well, go ahead and explain it then," Reynolds said. "But in the name of heaven, in a few words, please. I have a train to catch. Can you explain it in a sentence or two?"

"Yes, I can, sir," I said. "I can show you how absurd Mr. O'Brien's attempts to link me through my wife through her father to Socialism are."

"Never mind Mr. O'Brien for the moment. I want you, suh, if you can, to tell me why a 'Radical Socialist' is not a Radical Socialist."

"Well, in France, Senator, the so-called Radical-Socialist party, which pretty well dominated French governments and indeed the French parliament between the wars, was neither radical nor Socialist. It was conservative."

"Conservative!" Reynolds puffed. "You mean the French called a conservative party Radical and Socialist?"

"It's an old Western European custom, Senator," I tried to explain. "Many of the conservative parties used the name, probably to attract the votes of the masses. Even the extreme, right-wing parties used it. Take the German Nazis, for example. They called themselves National Socialists. The name didn't mean a thing. In fact, it was misleading."

At this point the old man from the South had to depart to catch his train and O'Brien adjourned the hearing until next week. He did not look so pleased as he left the committee room. As we departed, I saw him talking earnestly to a couple of reporters from the Clark press. On the whole, I felt that though the morning was a great waste of time, being rather typical of how these investigations wander all over the lot in order to try to trip you up, that we had come off rather well.

But not with the Clark press, at least. All the way up to New York from Washington this evening we bought the papers. The Clark rags had an identical headline.

WHITHEAD'S WIFE AND SON
LINKED WITH RED GROUPS

It begins to dawn on me that in the yellow press, at least, with its immense circulation, and therefore in the minds of a big chunk of the public, O'Brien is building up his case.

NEW YORK, OCTOBER 7 (SATURDAY)

CHRIS CHAMBERS snared three tickets to what turned out to be the final game of the World Series here today. He and Dick and I spent a fine afternoon out in Yankee Stadium. The game lacked the excitement we had looked forward to, the Yanks winning easily 5 to 2, and sweeping the series with four straight wins. But young Dick was excited by the very spectacle, and that was enough for me.

NEW YORK, OCTOBER 8 (SUNDAY)

STEVE BURNETT'S boat docked last night. We were on hand to greet him and the three girls at the pier, an experience that gave young Maria her share of the week end's excitement. Steve a little dazed. He cannot quite get accustomed to coming back to his native land in disgrace, though I argued that it was Washington which had disgraced itself in his case, not he. By a little doubling up, we are putting him and the children up until they find an apartment.

The presence of five rambunctious youngsters — four of them females — in the house, enlivened the Sabbath day.

OCTOBER 9 (MONDAY)

WHEN Bill Rikind joined us for breakfast this morning, he had a worried look. He had spent the week end in Washington, he said, sleuthing around. And he wanted to talk very seriously with me.

"Raymond, it is obvious that O'Brien has nothing on you," he said.

"Then why the worried look, Bill?" I asked.

"Raymond, I think he's going to try to frame you!"

"How can he do that, Bill?"

"By more perjured testimony by Elsie McCabe and that slippery liar, Newman and others. Possibly by forged or phony documents. The man will stop at nothing."

"Well, how do we expose a frame-up?" I asked.

Rikind didn't know.

However, nothing much came up in the two sessions today and I am inclined to think that Bill Rikind is beginning to see spooks under his bed at night. O'Brien opened the morning hearing with a question I was not looking for.

"Incidentally, Mr. Whitehead, do you keep a diary?"

"As a matter of fact, I do, Senator," I admitted.

"Does it cover these hearings?"

"Yes, sir, it does."

"I want you to turn it over to the committee, if you please."

I refused. There was a long wrangle. I was again threatened with contempt. I maintained my refusal. There are some rights I will not give up until they are taken away by force.

"Am I a citizen of Soviet Russia or of the United States?" I exclaimed angrily at one point.

"Just a minute, suh," Reynolds, who looked worn out from his week end in Dixie, bellowed. "There is absolutely no justification for such an outburst. It is an insult to the members of this committee."

"I consider the chairman's request an insult to freedom in America," I rejoined. "If I want to keep a diary, it is my own damned business, Senator."

"You think it may be incriminating — is that why you refuse to show it to us?" he asked.

"No. I refuse because I value my personal freedom under the Constitution, Senator."

Next Senator O'Brien wanted to know what newspapers I read.

"Are you a subscriber to the *Daily Worker?*" he asked.

"I take it, along with the *Times, Herald Tribune* and . . ."

"You read the *Daily Worker* every day?"

"No, I said I subscribed to it."

"To be sure what the party line is?"

"Not in the sense you mean it, Mr. O'Brien."

"What do you mean?" Senator Jones asked.

"I mean, Senator, that every journalist in this country commenting on the daily news finds it interesting from time to time to see what the party line is. So he reads the *Daily Worker* to find out. For instance, I found it interesting at the time the Korean War started, to see the paper wait and see what the line from Moscow would be."

"You weren't commenting on the daily news then, were you?" O'Brien cut in.

"Not on the radio, no."

"For any other medium?"

"No, I was unemployed at the time, Senator."

"Still, you read the *Daily Worker* just the same?"

"Well, I try to keep informed — in case I am re-employed again."

"You think you will be?"

"That may depend on how this hearing comes out, Senator." I smiled. "I hope to get a job."

Committee Counsel Green took up the general subject.

"You say you were a subscriber to the *Daily Worker*. Were you also a contributor?"

"No, sir."

"Are you sure?"

"Positively."

"You don't want to reflect on that answer a moment?" Green persisted. I wondered what kind of a trap he thought he was preparing.

"No. I never contributed to Communist publications, Mr. Green."

Then he sprang it.

"Mr. Chairman, at this point I would like to introduce into

the record an article by the witness which appeared under his byline in June, 1943, in the *Daily Worker*. It is in praise of the Red Army for its stand at Stalingrad."

"May I see it?" I asked. Green handed it to me with a contemptuous gesture.

"Mr. Chairman," I said quickly, after glancing at the photostatic copy, "that is a piece I wrote for the magazine *U.S.A.* It was obviously lifted by the *Daily Worker*. We can easily check it."

"The important thing," O'Brien announced, "is that whether lifted or not, the newspaper of the Communist party in America obviously liked your point of view enough to print it. The *Daily Worker* doesn't print anything against the party line, does it?"

"No, but most American papers in 1943 had some praise for the Red Army at Stalingrad. *U.S.A.* didn't publish what I wrote because it was the party line."

"Do you mean to say, suh," Reynolds spoke up, "that you praised the army of Communistic Russia?"

"Well, in 1943, Senator, the Russian Army was killing Nazi Germans. It was our ally, I believe."

"Mr. Whitehead, may I ask you this?" O'Brien took up the questioning. "Have you ever written a book attacking Russia?"

"I haven't written a book about Russia."

"Why not?"

"Well, for one thing, I don't know much about it."

"You've written a couple of books about other countries, haven't you?"

"Yes. I thought I knew something about them."

"You were in Russia, were you not?"

"Yes. But not for long."

"And you never felt moved to write a book about it?"

"Guilt by omission again," I said, forcing a smile. "Senator, aren't you trying to cast suspicion on me for what I haven't done?"

"I'm trying to ask you some questions," O'Brien retorted, "and you're trying not to answer them."

"Well, I can't answer for what I haven't done."

[*269*]

He then took up my books, which had attracted little attention in America, though they had sold fairly well in England and, in translation, on the continent — a suspicious point in itself, it seemed to O'Brien.

O'Brien, who was beginning to take over now, asked most of the questions.

"Were your books, Mr. Whitehead, ever sold in Communist bookstores?"

"I haven't the slightest idea, Mr. O'Brien."

"Would it surprise you," O'Brien went on, his mouth creased in a slight smile, "if you were told that Communist bookstores promoted your books?"

"It would, certainly."

"Along with other left-wing books?"

"I object to the last part of that question," I spoke up.

"The witness has no right to object to questions here," O'Brien said quickly. His colleagues nodded approval.

"I want to tell you why I object . . ."

"Since you have no right to object, you have no right to tell us why you object."

"I think, sir," I said, "the record would be more balanced . . ."

"Never mind about the balance of it," O'Brien cut me off. "That is the concern of the committee."

I was determined to get in my word. "Senator O'Brien, you asked a question and I want to answer it."

"Please."

"The question was whether I was surprised that the Communists should promote a book of mine. I said I certainly was surprised. This is the first time I heard it. But I might add, in elaboration of my answer, that if the Communists, for example, promoted my book about the failure of the Western European democracies to stop Hitler while there still was time, this was merely because they happened, for the moment, to be vitally interested in that failure. Later, when they joined Hitler, they had a different point of view, and no doubt pushed my books off their shelves."

"Just a minute," Senator Reynolds bawled. "Can you prove that the Reds ever removed your book from their shelves?"

"No. I was just speculating, sir."

"Well, suh, please stick to the facts here and leave the speculation to your books."

"All I am trying to say, gentlemen," I persisted, "is that sometimes the Communists happen to favor what we are for — they were, for instance, for defeating Hitler — at least after June 21, 1941. So were many of us before that date and afterward. That does not necessarily stain us with the Bolshevik brush."

"Do you say" — O'Brien pounced on me — "that we were for defeating Hitler after June 21, 1941, or even before? We weren't in any war then."

"Well, say we were in the same boat with the Russians after December 11, 1941," I answered.

"Mr. Whitehead," Senator Kleinschmidt, who like a good many others from the Middle West, I remembered, had been lukewarm about the war against Germany, spoke up, "did you urge us to get into the war with the Russians?"

"No. But I certainly urged us to get into the war against Hitler."

"In other words, on the Russian side?"

"Not when I began my urging, Senator. Your implication is false. In the beginning, remember, Russia was on Hitler's side. They both attacked Poland and divided it up. The side I was on — since you ask — comprised the British, the French, the Poles, the Danes, the Dutch, the Norwegians and some other decent folk. I was for them, and I defy even Senator O'Brien to say that made me a Red."

At the mention of his name, O'Brien glanced ostentatiously at the ceiling. There was a slight pause in the questioning, so I popped one myself in an effort to dispose of O'Brien's bookstore trickery.

"Incidentally, Mr. Chairman, apropos of your questions about my books in the Communist bookstores, how many such stores were there — or are there — in America?"

"That is a question, I'm afraid, Mr. Whitehead, and you are not here to ask questions, remember?"

"The reason I asked, Mr. O'Brien, is that I remembered reading some testimony before this committee which put the number at 5. There are, I believe, some 2500 legitimate bookshops in the country, all of which, I presume, handled my book. I think the ratio is significant, so far as this particular little smear is concerned."

"Strike that last about 'smear,' " O'Brien ordered.

And so the morning went. I fought against weariness and against losing my patience, forcing myself to remember that one of O'Brien's objectives is to wear me down. At one point, though, Bill Rikind's patience became exhausted. He jumped to his feet toward the close to protest that the questions had no pertinence to O'Brien's charges.

"The committee, sir," O'Brien told him, "is the sole judge of pertinency here."

The afternoon session was even more inane, I thought. I was asked about some things which did not concern the committee — and should never concern the American government: my thoughts. Here again the Senatorial questions were unbelievably trivial; some were so silly that I found it difficult to dignify them with answers. But I was in no position to withdraw from the incredible nonsense. Under the law, I had to sit there and I had to keep answering.

"Mr. Whitehead," O'Brien asked, shortly after the session got under way, "do you believe in the American way of life?"

"Very much."

"Is it superior to the Communistic way, in your opinion?"

"Definitely. Positively."

"Do you claim you have always said so in your writings and broadcasts?"

"They speak for themselves, Senator. You have them there."

"Answer the question, please."

"I answered it."

"You have nothing more to say on that subject?"

"Well, I could talk about it for hours, Senator, if you . . ."

"In the name of Heaven, no!" Senator Reynolds implored, stretching his great arms toward the heavens.

"You lived some time in Western Europe, did you not?" O'Brien resumed.

"Nearly all my adult life."

"Would you consider the way of life there superior to our own?"

"Well, it has its points."

"Kindly answer the question."

"I think the way we do things is pretty good, on the whole."

"You don't wholly approve, is that it?" Reynolds snorted.

"Not of everything, Senator. Not of O'Brienism, for instance."

"Then, suh, why don't you go back to Europe — and stay there?"

"Because I prefer to live at home."

Committee Counsel Green cocked his legalistic eye.

"Mr. Whitehead," he said, "is it your testimony then that in what you have written and broadcast you have generally supported the American way of life?"

"Well, most of what I have written and broadcast, Mr. Green, concerned reports from abroad."

"Then you were not concerned with the American way of life?"

"I was concerned with such things as democracy and freedom. They're a part of the American way, I believe."

Counsel Green was evidently preparing the way for something, but I could not guess what.

O'Brien now took over. "Mr. Whitehead, do you believe in free enterprise?"

"Decidedly."

"You've never opposed it in your writings and broadcasts?"

"I have never opposed it. I've certainly criticized it. Who hasn't?"

"Is it not a fact that in many of your articles and broadcasts, you were unfriendly to business?"

"Not unfriendly, Senator; critical sometimes."

"The Communists are critical of business, are they not?"

"I am critical of business, *ergo*, I am a Communist. Senator, how childish can you get?"

"I must ask you, Mr. Whitehead, to dispense with your insults," O'Brien snarled.

At that moment he sprang some surprise witnesses. Into the committee room traipsed three familiar faces: Sidney Goodrich, little Archy Oaks and columnist Bert Woodruff — as curious a trio as I have ever seen. Goodrich was sworn first. The change in the demeanor of the committee members — Jones excepted — was a sight to see. Their hostility vanished. They were all smiles. They were courteous, solicitous.

"Mr. Goodrich," O'Brien began. "You are the author of a forthcoming book, are you not?"

"Yes, sir," Goodrich said.

I turned to study him for a moment. It was obvious that life as an editor of *World Review* under Verne Gibson was less rugged than on the Public Power Committee.

"What is the title of your book, Mr. Goodrich?" O'Brien asked in his most soothing tone.

Goodrich stole a glance at me, started to smile — a bit sheepishly, I thought — and then wiped the smile away.

"We're going to give it the title *World Review* has used for the articles, which are the basis for the book."

"And what is that, Mr. Goodrich?" O'Brien prompted him.

Again Goodrich's eyes met mine.

"The general title, Mr. Chairman," he answered, "for the pieces now running in *World Review* is 'I Believe in Big Business.'"

"Well, I'm happy to hear that somebody does," old Reynolds chimed in.

"And the subtitle," Goodrich added, "is 'It's the American Way.'"

"So I think we can conclude, Mr. Goodrich," O'Brien continued, "that you are considered something of an authority today on business and the American way."

"I believe my articles have attracted some attention," Goodrich said.

"Now, Mr. Goodrich," O'Brien went on, "could you tell us whether you ever followed the articles and broadcasts of Mr. Whitehead?"

"I think I can say that I have — like many others."

"Would you say that they were unduly critical of the way we do things in America?"

"They were often critical, I believe. Of course, in a free country like ours, he was free to say what he pleased."

O'Brien pouted and hastened to get the witness back on the track.

"The Communists have been very critical of American business, have they not?" O'Brien asked.

"They certainly have been."

"And of what we call our American way of life?"

"Yes, certainly."

"That being so," O'Brien smiled, "what conclusions would you draw, Mr. Goodrich, about the general line Mr. Whitehead has taken in his broadcasts and articles and books?"

"Senator, it is not for me to draw any conclusions," Goodrich said. "That is your job, I believe."

O'Brien's face fell. "Did you yourself ever consider Mr. Whitehead to be a Communist?"

"No, sir."

"You didn't know he wasn't one, did you?" O'Brien said, growing a little peppery.

"No. It just never occurred to me."

"You couldn't prove he wasn't?"

"No."

"But, in your opinion, he was against business and the American way?"

"I would say he was sometimes critical."

"Very well. Thank you very much, Mr. Goodrich." And with that Goodrich was dismissed.

Bert Woodruff, gruff and glowering, was next, and he was more positive. The widely syndicated Clark columnist has long seen the world in absolute whites and blacks, and his grudges make him see most of it as black. He delighted O'Brien, whose

[275]

mouthpiece he often is in his column. But he was a little too much for Senator Jones.

"You say Mr. Whitehead is a Communist?" Jones started to say.

"Yes, sir," Woodruff barked.

"How do you know that?"

Woodruff was exasperated by the question. "How do I know it, Senator? Why from his writings, for one thing. From his broadcasts, for another."

"You mean he took the party line?"

"Yes, sir. He never deviated from it by a hairsbreadth."

"How do you know?" Jones persisted.

"How do I know, Senator? I listened to the man. I read his stuff. Every word Communistic!"

"I mean, how did you know it was the party line? How did you know what the party line was?" Jones asked, a twinkle in his eye.

"Listen here, Senator," Woodruff exploded. "You're not calling me a Red, are you?"

"No. I'm asking you how you knew the party line so expertly?"

I felt almost a sense of relief to see someone like Woodruff getting the treatment I had received.

"Well, all I can say, Senator," Woodruff muttered, "is that I make it my business to know it and I can tell you that Whitehead followed it. Does that satisfy you?"

"We do the questioning here, Mr. Woodruff," Jones said quietly.

"Do you consider the present administration Communist?" Jones asked.

"I certainly do," Woodruff shot back, "from the President on down."

"That's all I have to ask, Mr. Chairman," Jones said smilingly. He had pretty well debunked the redoubtable columnist, but O'Brien, who got in the last word, tried to re-establish his friend. He questioned him meticulously about the various rewards and prizes he had received for his Americanism, his patriotism, his anti-Communism.

Archy Oakes, despite the new assurance he carries as a vice-president of his ad agency, was as scared as a rabbit on the stand. However, with O'Brien's help, he managed to get over the idea that, in his opinion, I took the "Communistic" line in my broadcasts.

"And you heard them all, didn't you?" O'Brien prompted him.

"I was at his side every Sunday evening, yes, sir," Archy explained.

I couldn't bring myself to feel any resentment toward him. Archy was one of the ciphers of society. Through no fault of his own, he must have brought a lot of trouble on himself in his own agency and in the little gutless world of ulcered advertising men along Madison Avenue for having been so closely connected with me so long. I certainly didn't hold it against him when he tried to make up for his obvious guilt by association with me. I even found my sympathy going out to him when Senator Jones popped a question or two that greatly embarrassed him.

"You say Mr. Whitehead took a Communistic line in the broadcasts you heard?" Jones said, repeating the technique he had used on Woodruff.

"So it seemed to me, sir," Archy answered.

"All right. How did you know what the Communistic line was?"

Archy stared glassily at the Senator. The silence was almost pitiful.

"Please tell us how you knew," Jones said, patiently.

"Well . . . uh . . . It was like someone said here earlier . . . uh . . ."

"Don't tell us what someone else said. What do *you* say?" It sounded strange to my ears to hear the tables reversed.

"Well . . . uh . . . from what I knew, sir, it did sound kind of Communistic."

"You didn't know much about Communism, did you?"

"No, sir."

Jones had one more question.

"Mr. Oakes, did you ever mention to Mr. Whitehead that his broadcasts sounded kind of Communistic to your ears?"

[277]

"Uh . . . no, sir."

"Why not?"

"Uh . . . sir . . ."

The bell saved my former colleague of the air. It was five o'clock. Senator O'Brien grabbed for the gavel and pounded it for adjournment.

So ended one of the most tiresome days of my life. Where are the charges against me? Where is this hearing leading to? Am I to be here all winter? I put the questions to the unhappy Rikind tonight.

"Don't ask me, Raymond," he replied gruffly. "How can I tell where this lunacy is leading? To the bughouse, probably. For all of us."

He started to sing, as if he were mad.

OCTOBER 10
O'BRIEN made his great pitch today. Fraudulent though it was, it may have wrecked me.

The session started dully enough. At first I thought it would be a repetition of yesterday's tedious ordeal. At O'Brien's order, the committee's counsel led me through a long series of questions about my life history. I had already filed a biographical sketch, but this did not satisfy the suspicious chairman. He had to have repeated to him where I was born, raised, educated, why and when I went abroad, what I did there, and so on, ad infinitum.

Later the questioning took this turn:

"Mr. Whitehead," O'Brien asked solemnly, "did you stick up for your country when you were abroad?"

"Through thick and thin, Senator. Even when I thought it was in the wrong."

"You think your country was in the wrong, do you?" old Senator Reynolds, coming to life, blubbered.

"Occasionally, I suppose. But abroad you usually defend it anyway. Out of national pride. I don't mean to say I went around flaunting Old Glory, but I did . . ."

[278]

Reynolds's nostrils quivered. "You were ashamed of the Stars and Stripes — is that it?"

"No, that isn't it, Senator."

Next came questions concerning my five years in the diplomatic service when I first went abroad.

"Did you have much contact with Russians when you were in the service?" O'Brien wanted to know.

"Just the normal diplomatic ones, Senator."

"Did the Russians ever approach you?"

"Approach me? How do you mean?"

"To try and pump you."

"Every diplomat does that, Mr. O'Brien."

"I am asking you if the Russians did?"

"They did."

"And do you testify that you withstood the temptation?"

"Well, there was no temptation in the first place. If your implication is that I gave away diplomatic secrets to the Russians, the answer of course, is that I did not."

O'Brien pursed his lips and gazed at the ceiling.

"Why did you leave the diplomatic service, Mr. Whitehead?" he said, breaking the silence. I was glad of the opportunity to answer that one.

"Senator, if I had known how the foreign service officers of my generation would be hounded out of their jobs and disgraced for life by your machinations — after, in many cases, a lifetime of honorable, selfless, courageous service to their country — I never would have gone into it in the first place."

"I didn't ask you why you went into it, but why you left it?" O'Brien shot back.

"I'm coming to that. The reasons that led me to leave it are not very interesting, I'm afraid."

"I ask you to state them."

"As I recall, I came to the conclusion that I was not cut out to be a diplomat. For one thing I hadn't gone to the right college."

"What were the right colleges?" Senator Kleinschmidt, sniffing a clue that was always pleasing to us Midwesterners, spoke up.

"Harvard. Yale. Princeton."

"You mean if you hadn't been to one of them, you . . ."

"You didn't get very far, that's right, Senator —" I helped him out. I wondered what college he had attended to fit him for the undertaker's life.

"What other reasons, please?" O'Brien asked.

"Well, little things mostly, Senator. The formal social life bored me. The red tape, and so on. And I had a hankering for writing, for journalism. That was one of the chief reasons, I think."

"How many Communists were there in the State Department in your time?" O'Brien suddenly shouted.

"None — that I knew of."

"In the foreign service?"

"Same answer."

"You didn't resign from the diplomatic service because you wanted to be free to work for Communism, did you?"

"I had no such desire, Senator — then, or since."

"But you admit that by the time you resigned, you had met a lot of Russians, hadn't you?"

"A few. But they had not infected me."

And now Senator O'Brien closed in on me.

"Mr. Whitehead," he began, "have you ever wangled any special diplomatic assignments from the State Department since your resignation back in — when was it?"

"In 1929, Senator."

"Have you?"

"I never tried to wangle any, Mr. O'Brien."

"Do you say you never carried out any such assignments?"

"No. I don't say that, Senator. I carried out three or four, in fact."

"Were they secret assignments?"

"They were confidential."

"Did you carry one out recently — within the last couple of years?"

"I did."

"When?"

"A year ago last summer, I think it was."

[280]

"Where?"

"Kabul."

Senator Reynolds, who had been catching a nap, awoke.

"Now that's a new one on me, suh. What did you say the name of the place was?"

"Kabul, sir. Capital of Afghanistan."

I could feel O'Brien itching to bear down. He resented the intervention of the Southern relic, if not his ignorance.

"Is it not a fact, Mr. Whitehead, that you went to Kabul to contact a certain Radislav?" O'Brien asked, his eyes squinting slyly.

"I wanted to see that gentleman, among others, yes," I said.

"Did you see him?"

"Oh, yes."

"Will you tell the committee who he was?"

O'Brien sat back triumphantly, his mouth curling into a smile. It was clear to me now what he was up to. This is what he had been leading toward for nearly a fortnight. Admittedly he had me in a position where my hands might be tied.

"I would be glad to, Senator," I replied. "But first it would be necessary, in all fairness to this committee, not to mention fairness to me, to explain the nature of the assignment given me by the Secretary of State. Unfortunately it was — and I presume, still is — confidential."

I had been asked by the Secretary of State to go to Kabul to see what the Russians were up to in Central Asia. But I could not tell the committee that. Not without the permission of the secretary certainly. It would be embarrassing for him to give it. And even more embarrassing, obviously, to Senator O'Brien. At the moment, I realized, he had me in a corner and both my hands were tied behind my back, so to speak.

"You're afraid to answer my question, is that it?" O'Brien beamed.

"Not at all, Senator. As I was trying to explain . . ."

"The fact is," O'Brien interrupted me, "that this Radislav is a Russian, isn't he?"

"That's right."

"A Soviet agent."

"Agent and diplomat," I conceded.

"And you constantly visited him in the Soviet Embassy in Kabul?"

"I saw a good deal of Radislav, certainly. But we can't shed much light on it, Senator — other than the false light of suspicion you are now trying to throw on it — until, or unless, I can explain to this committee and to the millions who may be watching and listening over TV and radio why I was sent to Kabul in the first place."

At this juncture, Senator Jones tried to come to my aid.

"You do not feel free to divulge the nature of your mission to Afghanistan?"

"No, sir. Not unless the State Department permits it."

"If the permission is forthcoming, you will tell us?"

"Gladly."

"Mr. Chairman," Jones turned to O'Brien, "may I suggest that we adjourn until this afternoon and that in the meantime you, or one of the other committee members whom you care to designate, consult with the Secretary of State?"

But O'Brien was not to be put off his track. "Senator Jones," he said, "I think one of us could contact the secretary during the luncheon recess. In the meantime, in the interest of bringing this witness's testimony to a close before the end of this week — the gentleman has now been on the stand for nearly a fortnight, and I realize the strain on him . . ."

"On all of us, suh!" Reynolds piped up.

". . . I propose that we go ahead with the questioning. I myself, if that is agreeable to the other members, will endeavor to see the secretary over the noon hour."

They all murmured their approval. I was reminded of what Bill Rikind remarked once of the U. S. Senate. It was a rather cozy club, he said. Despite the party quarrels and the personal antagonisms, the members tended to be very accommodating to one another. Even to the likes of O'Brien. I studied him for a moment. He was almost spitting on his hands in anticipation of what he thought was about to take place.

"Mr. Whitehead," he began gingerly, "you had known this Radislav for some years, had you not — before you saw him again in Kabul?"

"I had known him slightly," I said.

"Where was that?"

"In Paris once, when he was in the Soviet Embassy there. And in Geneva, when on two occasions, I believe, he was a member of the Russian delegation to the League."

"You were close friends?"

"Not at all."

"Friends?"

"Well, I don't want to get into semantics here, Senator. Let's say he was the kind of a contact American newspapermen like to have. An acquaintance, if you like."

"But you knew this Communistic agent over a number of years — you concede that?"

"I say I knew him, yes. But, Mr. Chairman, before you go any further —"

"Are you going to give me some more advice as to how to conduct this committee's business?" O'Brien tried to cut me short.

"No. But I want you to know that from now on I answer all questions about this mission to Kabul under protest."

"Whitehead," O'Brien said, "you can invoke the Fifth Amendment if you feel that truthful answers to questions here might incriminate you."

"I know I can, Senator. But I am not going to. Too many witnesses before this committee, in my opinion, have invoked the Fifth Amendment and the implication has been accepted in this country that they were guilty, that they were Communists or worse."

"What could be worse than a Communist, suh?" Reynolds bellowed.

"A traitor. A spy, Senator."

I turned again to O'Brien. "I am not afraid, sir, that my truthful answers will incriminate me before the law. But until I can explain what I was sent to Kabul to do, I quite realize that your questions and my truthful answers can be very misleading, that they can arouse suspicion and cast doubt. That is why I shall answer from now on under protest. I want the record to show it."

"The record will show it," O'Brien said.

"Mr. Chairman!" Senator Jones's voice rang out. "It is now five minutes before noon. I think this is a good place to adjourn."

O'Brien looked at his watch in amazement, as if he were being cheated by the clock. "I did not realize it was so late," he muttered. "The committee stands adjourned until two P.M."

"Just a minute, Mr. Chairman," Jones said. "Am I correct in assuming that you will endeavor to get in touch with the Secretary of State during the lunch recess? In view of the point we have now reached in the questioning, I think it is important that this witness be permitted to tell us what he was doing in this Asian capital, in the first place. I think you should press the secretary for that permission."

"I shall so do, Senator," O'Brien said grudgingly.

At the beginning of the afternoon session O'Brien announced, not without an air of triumph, I thought, that he had been unable to "contact" the Secretary of State.

"The gentleman appears to be out of town," he said, beaming, "and out of reach."

"Out of reach?" Senator Jones asked.

"Out of mine, at least, Senator." O'Brien grinned.

"In that case, Mr. Chairman," Jones said, "may I suggest that Mr. Whitehead step aside for the moment so that we can hear that other witness?"

"What witness, sir?" O'Brien asked curtly.

I wondered myself who it could possibly be.

"That young lady over there," Jones said, pointing his finger at a woman in the first row of spectators. I had not noticed her before, but the face struck me at once as vaguely familiar. I had seen it somewhere, though it was not a countenance you would recall easily, being rather plain except for the outsize aquiline nose and the somewhat bulging eyes, which were too close together.

"I believe, sir," Jones went on, "you had the young lady flown back from Afghanistan last week to testify here."

I remembered now. She was a stenographer in our embassy at Kabul who had been lent me for a day or two to take some dictation of routine letters. For some reason I had not quite trusted her to take down my highly confidential memoranda of what I was learning there. I had asked our chargé to give me another one, a young man who seemed less suspicious and more discreet. This had not pleased Miss Jenkins — that, I now recalled, was her name. She was thirty or so, and a bit on the spinsterish side. Nothing much in Kabul pleased Miss Jenkins. A wild, lonely, primitive, tribal capital was not an ideal spot for her. Shortly before I left she had asked me to put in a word for her with the Department. She would like to be transferred to New Delhi. She was interested in Hindu philosophy, she said. The Mohammedanism of the Afghans, she added, repulsed her. I had promised to do what I could and then had completely forgotten it — and her.

There followed a wrangle among the Senators whether to hear Miss Jenkins or continue with me. Senator Jones was rather insistent on Miss Jenkins. O'Brien, of course, was itching to finish me off. Strangely enough, he gave in. Perhaps it was largely because he is trying to keep Jones in line. O'Brien wants a unanimous report on me. The somewhat liberal Senator from the South gives more and more evidence of asserting his independence and, what is more important to me, his fairness. I was certainly grateful to him for his timely intervention.

There now followed a scene so ludicrous it could only have taken place in an O'Brien committee. Still, it relieved the tension. For at first, O'Brien by his questions, and Miss Jenkins by her answers, had managed to build up quite a bit of it.

"Are you acquainted with Mr. Raymond Whitehead?" O'Brien asked, after Miss Jenkins had been sworn in and had identified herself.

"I saw him on numerous occasions in Kabul," she answered in a flat, nasal voice.

"Did he spend much time at our embassy?"

"Some. But . . ." she hesitated.

"But what?" O'Brien prompted her.

"I got the impression he spent more time at another embassy."

"Which embassy was that?"

"The Russian Embassy —" Miss Jenkins obliged.

At this moment I began to feel a little helpless. Bill Rikind, Yvonne and I were now seated amidst the spectators and had no more right than those around us to intervene. I could feel Bill getting hotter and hotter under the collar.

"Have you any idea, Miss Jenkins," O'Brien said, in his most friendly manner, "whom Mr. Whitehead might have been seeing at the Russian Embassy there in Kabul?"

"Yes, sir. It was the talk of the town. . . ."

"Well, who was it?"

"Mr. Radislav."

"Could you tell us a little about him?"

"Well, he was the counselor of the Soviet Embassy."

"He was more than that, wasn't he?"

"Well, sir, I am only a stenographer. I don't know much about these things.

"Wasn't this man Radislav," O'Brien hastened to say, "a notorious Russian agent? Did you ever hear that said about him?"

"Yes, I did, sir."

"And you say that Mr. Whitehead, while he was in Kabul, saw a great deal of this notorious Russian agent?"

"I said that was the talk around Kabul, yes, sir."

"And around our embassy?"

"Yes."

Rikind sprang up, purple-faced. "Mr. Chairman, I object to this line of questioning until at least we have heard from the Secretary of State as to whether my client . . ."

"Mr. Rikind, you certainly know you have no right to object, or even to open your mouth at this particular moment, when your client is not even on the stand." O'Brien cut him off, genially enough. "You are just a spectator now. Please sit down."

"Sir," Rikind cried, "in the name of elementary American justice I insist on being heard! Mr. Whitehead does not deny seeing this man Radislav. He . . ."

"I would not like to be forced to ask you to leave this committee room, Mr. Rikind," O'Brien said, still suavely.

Bill sat down.

"There is no doubt whatsoever, then, Miss Jenkins," O'Brien resumed, "that Mr. Whitehead spent a great deal of his time in Kabul with this notorious Russian agent and spy, Radislav?"

"I would say it was common knowledge, sir — in Kabul," Miss Jenkins replied.

"Did he try to keep it secret?" Jones cut in to ask.

"I never heard him mention it," Miss Jenkins said.

"Would he necessarily have spoken of it to you? What is your job, exactly, in the embassy there?" Jones persisted.

"Stenographer, sir."

"Isn't it just possible, Miss Jenkins," Jones went on, "that someone carrying out a confidential diplomatic mission for the Secretary of State might not think of sharing his confidence with any embassy stenographer?"

"I had ears, Senator," Miss Jenkins said slyly. But the slyness quickly dissolved with the next question.

"Isn't it a fact, Miss Jenkins, that you are more than a stenographer in the Kabul embassy?" Jones asked. It was his turn to be a little sly. "Isn't it a fact, Miss Jenkins, that you are a so-called security officer there?"

O'Brien quickly intervened. "Senator Jones, I don't believe we should ask the witness to answer that question. It takes us into diplomatic secrets which, in the case of Mr. Whitehead this morning, you were so anxious not to tamper with."

"Very well, Mr. Chairman," Jones said. But he had made it clear to me, at least, who had reported on me from Kabul.

The Senator from the South was not quite finished, however. One further question of his touched off the incredible antics that convulsed the audience and made this hearing look, for a moment, even more of a farce than it probably is. It certainly brought out a quirk of Miss Jenkins's personality that no one, at least here in the committee room, had previously been aware of.

"One more question, if I may, Miss Jenkins," Senator Jones began. "Wouldn't it be quite natural and customary for an American diplomat to call at the Soviet Embassy? How do you know that the nature of his mission to Afghanistan — and we do not know yet exactly what it was — did not make it necessary for him to see this mysterious Mr. Radislav?"

Miss Jenkins's eyes started to pop. The Senator had touched some curious string deep within her that aroused her to a pitch that I am sure surprised even O'Brien, not to mention the rest of us in the vast room. In fact, Miss Jenkins seemed to go into a trance.

"Senator," she said, staring at him, her eyes nearly bulging out of their sockets. "There is something in life known to the ancient Hindu philosophers as vibrations. . . ."

"What's that?" Senator Jones asked.

"Vibrations, sir! Every living soul vibrates. They send out waves."

"Waves?" Senator Jones exclaimed.

"Vibratory waves, sir," Miss Jenkins said, staring at him as if she were trying to hypnotize him. "A few of us are born to understand them, to catch their meaning."

"Does Mr. Whitehead vibrate?" Senator Jones asked. He kept a straight face, but there was a titter in the room. Miss Jenkins, I saw, had become pale and terribly intense, her eyes glassy.

"Yes, sir," she said, "he does. The waves he sends out to me are unusually strong. On two occasions in Kabul, while he was giving me dictation, his vibrations nearly drove me to distraction."

So that was why it had been so difficult, somehow, to dictate to her a few routine letters. My vibrations. I had not been aware of them. She had not mentioned them.

This time Chairman O'Brien had to gently pound his gavel to halt the giggling.

"Did they convey any meaning to you — I mean, his vibrations?" O'Brien asked.

[288]

"Very decidedly, sir," Miss Jenkins said, fixing her gaze now on the chairman. "Their meaning was clear. In fact, overwhelming! They warned me this man was not to be trusted: that he was disloyal, subversive, a traitor!"

The warm room exploded with laughter, and it took a time for O'Brien to restore order. Miss Jenkins, it was obvious, was too deep in her trance to even hear the outburst. She sat in the witness chair, staring glassy-eyed at the Senators.

"Did you make a report of your impressions to the State Department, Miss Jenkins?" Jones asked.

"Yes, sir. I certainly did."

"One last question, Miss Jenkins, if I may," Jones said, and you could feel the spectators leaning forward with anticipation. Jones, who has a sense of timing as good as O'Brien's, hesitated for just a second or two. "Is Mr. Whitehead," he asked, his face dead pan, "vibrating now?"

Her answer was lost in the roar of laughter, but I could see her nodding her head.

"Any further questions?" O'Brien snapped, as soon as the room had quieted down. The query brought snickers from here and there, but he paid no attention to them. There were no further questions in the minds of the Senators.

"Very well," O'Brien said. "Mr. Whitehead, will you kindly return to the witness chair?"

He would get at me yet, I saw, in the half hour that remained before the evening recess. He had no intention, I realized, of letting Miss Jenkins's preposterous testimony capture the headlines tomorrow morning. He had a half hour in which to grab them for himself.

Senator Jones spoke up. Perhaps he would rescue me.

"Mr. Chairman," he said. "It is only half an hour before our customary recess time. I move that we adjourn now."

But this time he was overruled. All the other Senators supported the chairman in his desire, as O'Brien said, to enable the witness to finish his testimony as soon as possible. O'Brien, clearly, was not going to let me escape from his trap this time.

"In all fairness to the witness," Jones argued, "I think we

should wait at least until tomorrow. By that time we should have the decision of the secretary. Until or unless we do, there is no point, it seems to me, in going into his activities in Afghanistan."

To cut short the argument, O'Brien called for a vote. Senators Breen, Kleinschmidt and Reynolds, who had been silent all day, sustained him. Followed by Rikind and Yvonne, I traipsed back to my familiar seat, feeling that I was about to be thrown to the lions.

"Mr. Whitehead," O'Brien began calmly, in a voice so low I had to strain at first to catch his words. "We had got to the point this morning, I believe, of your close relationship with a notorious Soviet Communistic agent by the name of Radislav."

"Close relationship, Senator?"

"Well, you said you had known him for several years, didn't you?"

"I said I kept up a contact with him, just as I did, in the course of my work, with other Communists, and with Fascists and Nazis. And may I remind you again, Mr. Chairman, that until I am permitted by the Secretary of State to reveal the nature of my mission to Afghanistan, I am answering all these questions under protest."

"It has been so entered in the records, sir," O'Brien droned.

"And I might add, Senator, that I think in questioning me now along this particular line, you are demonstrating the truth of one of the accusations that has been hurled at this committee."

"Which accusation, suh? There have been so many," old Reynolds asked.

"Of its unfairness, sir," I said.

"Well, I declare!" Reynolds puffed. "We have you in a hot spot. We have you admitting a close relationship with a notorious agent of world Communism. So you say we're unfair to question you further," Reynolds jabbered.

"Now let's go back a bit, Mr. Witness," O'Brien resumed, warming to his task. "Your 'contact,' as you put it, with this Soviet agent goes back many years, does it not?"

"Yes."

"How many years?"

"Well, as I said this morning, Senator, I first met the gentleman . . ."

"So you call a Soviet spy a 'gentleman'?" Reynolds burst out.

". . . in Paris . . ."

"Answer my question, please, suh?" Reynolds shouted.

"It was a manner of speaking, Senator," I said, trying to keep my temper.

"In my vocabulary, Mr. Whitehead —" the old windbag got in the last word — "a Communistic spy is not a 'gentleman.' "

"So you first met this Radislav in Paris? When was that?"

"In the late Twenties, that would be."

"And then you said this morning you saw him again in Geneva with some Soviet delegation?"

"That would be in the early Thirties."

"And over those years you became friends?"

"Acquaintances would probably be more accurate, though I don't want to split any hairs, Senator."

"Is it your contention, Mr. Whitehead, that you got valuable information from the gentleman?"

" 'Gentleman' you say?" I exclaimed, turning to Senator Reynolds.

"I apologize. It was a slip of the tongue," O'Brien said, actually breaking into a smile.

"I do not feel at liberty to answer that question, Senator," I said.

"You rather liked the fellow, didn't you?"

"Well, he was a rather charming old ruffian. We even had one thing in common."

"You had something in common with a Russian agent?" Reynolds puffed.

"Yes, sir. Chess. We played it fairly often when I was in Kabul last summer. Usually he trimmed me."

"Where did you play it?" O'Brien asked.

"At the Russian Embassy."

Senator Breen, the West Coast realtor, pricked his large ears up.

"Do you not realize, Mr. Whitehead, that it sounds suspicious that you should want to spend any time at all in the Soviet Embassy?"

"I realize that, Senator — as long as I am not free to give you a full explanation."

"So in Kabul," O'Brien resumed, "you admit you played chess with this Soviet spy."

"Well, every diplomat is a sort of a spy, isn't he? I hope ours are, anyway. And I presume all Soviet diplomats are."

"Sometimes," O'Brien rejoined, "I wonder who ours are spying for. For us, or for the Russians. That, if I may say so, is what we're trying to find out about you."

"I resent the implication, Senator."

At this point I volunteered a word that I might well have kept to myself, seeing what company I'm in.

"I might say," I said, "that what I am revealing here about old Radislav may well cost him his neck."

"You seem very solicitous, Mr. Whitehead, of Russian necks —" Senator Kleinschmidt, who had been silent all day, broke in to say.

"Well, I hesitate to contribute to a man's untimely death, even a Russian's," I said.

"That is understandable in a man of your sympathies," O'Brien said.

"Mr. Whitehead," Reynolds's stentorian Southern voice rang out. "You may have heard me say this before, but it bears repeating. I say that the only good Russian is a dead Russian!"

A titter ran through the audience that was encouraging.

"Now, let us get straight where we are," O'Brien said, glancing at his watch. There was not much time left. "You have freely testified that you were a good friend of one of the most noted Soviet spies of our time, that he was a man you personally liked, that you often sought him out, that you played chess with him, and . . ."

"Senator," I broke in, "your technique fascinates me. What

you are trying to do, for the headlines anyway, is to link me with what you call a noted Soviet spy. And by this to prove that I myself was, as you have formally charged in the Senate, a Soviet agent. I say it's a fraud. A lie."

"I think the witness is beginning to squirm," Reynolds volunteered.

"Mr. Whitehead," O'Brien replied, "facts are facts. Did you, or did you not, testify to every word I have just pronounced?"

"I testified, Senator, that I knew a Russian diplomat by the name of Radislav and I have told you the circumstances — in so far as I am free to today — of that professional contact."

"Are you denying that he was a Russian agent?"

"Obviously all Russian diplomats are Russian agents."

"And that he was a Soviet spy?"

"Again, we assume all Soviet diplomats indulge in espionage."

"And do you now deny your own words that you went out to this faraway country, Afghanistan, to see this Russian agent and spy? That was your testimony."

"It was my testimony that in carrying out a government assignment I found it valuable to see Mr. Radislav when I got to Kabul."

"Is it not a fact, Mr. Whitehead," O'Brien continued, "that this fellow Radislav was known to you as one of Russia's great authorities on Asia?"

"On Central Asia, certainly."

"This so-called confidential mission of yours could have been a cover, couldn't it?" O'Brien said, raising his voice dramatically.

"A cover?"

"Yes. To enable you to see Radislav, pass along your information to him and get your new instructions."

"Come, Senator," I laughed. "You're letting your imagination run away with you."

"Do you deny that you worked with Radislav as an agent?"

"If it is necessary to deny the preposterous, I deny it."

"Tell me," O'Brien said, trying a new tack. "Do you happen to know if one of Radislav's friends was a former American diplomat by the name of Stephen Burnett?"

"I believe they knew each other, Senator, in Asia."

"Is Burnett a friend of yours?"

"Yes, sir! I so testified before this very committee."

"He was recently kicked out of the diplomatic service for being disloyal to his country, was he not?"

"He was suspended, I believe, on the ground that there were doubts about his loyalty. He has appealed this cowardly decision."

"You think it's cowardly to get rid of a diplomat who is disloyal to his native land?" the old cotton Senator sat up to ask.

"I think it was worse than that, Senator, to make such a charge against a patriot who had served his country well."

"He is defending a traitor!" Reynolds bellowed.

"Burnett was not a traitor, sir!"

"He was a friend of yours and a friend of Radislav," O'Brien cried. "In fact, you three — an admitted Russian spy, an American diplomat who had to be discharged for disloyalty and you, Mr. Whitehead — you three certainly had a very close — and I must say — interesting relationship. You were good friends. It is a fact which this committee will be forced to take into consideration."

It was five o'clock, but O'Brien was not quite through.

"Before we adjourn, gentlemen, I believe the committee's counsel has something he desires to read into the record at this point."

"Yes, sir." David Green, who had been conspicuous by his silence today, sprang up, bursting to get a word in even if it were not his own. "Mr. Chairman, this is a memo from Security Agent X-143 concerning the witness's activities in Kabul in the summer of 1949. It is marked 'Exhibit Number 186.' I quote:

During the four weeks Mr. Whitehead was in Kabul, he spent a total of fifty-one hours in the Soviet Embassy. It has been established that he spent most of this time with Alexis Radislav, counselor of the Embassy of the U.S.S.R., and known to the American Embassy to be one of Russia's foremost experts on Central Asia and a Soviet agent, notorious for stirring up strife in this unsettled part of the world. Mr. Whitehead also saw at the Soviet Embassy the ambassador, the first secretary, the second secretary, the military attaché and Mr. Kotchov, who is generally believed to be the ranking representative here of the Russian secret police. It has been ascertained that Mr. Whitehead played a great deal of chess with Mr. Radislav and that on several evenings a great deal of drinking, chiefly of vodka, went on, in which Mr. Whitehead fully participated. As is well known to American security officers, this is a common method employed by the Russians to get American officials to talk while their guard, so to speak, is down. Mr. Whitehead appears to have been an easy victim. On at least eight occasions when Mr. Whitehead returned to his hotel after midnight from the Embassy of the U.S.S.R. it was established by embassy security officers, that his breath smelled of alcohol, probably vodka.

It was Mr. Whitehead's habit, on returning from the Soviet Embassy, or from any place else, to make random notes of his day's talks. Later some of these were used as the basis for memoranda, dictated to one of the embassy stenographers. The original notes were torn up by Mr. Whitehead and deposited in the wastebasket in the embassy office which he occupied while in Kabul. It has been possible for security officers to piece many of these notes together, and they are attached to this report. . . ."

The chunky committee counsel paused for breath. "Mr. Chairman, may I respectfully suggest that these notes — forming special exhibit SE-1 — which I shall not now read, be kept confidential — at least for the time being. I can tell the committee that it contains material that appears to leave no doubt that Mr. Radislav and Mr. Whitehead were working together in a common Communistic conspiracy. . . ."

"Just a minute, Mr. Chairman!" Rikind jumped to his feet. "What kind of a star-chamber procedure is this? I demand that the counsel's last remark be stricken from the record."

"You have no rights here to object, Mr. Rikind, as I believe I have told you a hundred times," O'Brien said, quite good-naturedly. He had scored heavily and was feeling in a happy mood. At this juncture he could even afford to appear reasonable and accommodating.

"We will take the matter under advisement," he ruled. "Also, if there is no objection from other members, I propose that the rest of this particular memo be inserted into the record without further reading. It is now past five o'clock. The witness has had a long — and trying — day. Unless there is objection, the committee stands adjourned."

(LATER)— Midnight — Rikind and I have tried desperately all evening to reach the Secretary of State. We finally traced him to the Virgin Islands, where he is on a brief holiday. We have urgent long-distance calls in to him there, but so far without result.

Yvonne just came in with the morning papers. The headlines are the worst we've had:

WHITEHEAD ADMITS
LINK TO NOTORIOUS
SOVIET AGENT, SPY!

HEARINGS OF FORMER BROADCASTER
REACH CLIMAX IN TENSE COMMITTEE SCENE

OCTOBER 11

SENATOR JONES opened the hearings this morning with a dramatic statement.

"Mr. Chairman," he asked, "have you been able to get in touch with the Secretary of State?"

"No, sir," O'Brien said. "I regret I haven't. I tried to last night, but the gentleman is still out of town."

"Mr. Chairman," Jones continued somewhat gravely, and now O'Brien gave him an uneasy glance. "I would like to report to the committee that last evening I succeeded in reaching the secretary by telephone in the Virgin Islands, where he is on a brief vacation. He authorized me to give the committee the following statement —"

"Couldn't we just insert it in the record, Senator Jones?" O'Brien interrupted. "We have a couple of important witnesses here this morning whom we ought to hear."

"I'm sorry, Mr. Chairman," Jones persisted, "but I should prefer to read it. For it is something, I am sure, we will all want to consider — in the light of yesterday's hearing."

"Very well, Senator," O'Brien said, scarcely concealing his annoyance.

"The statement is as follows —" Jones said, taking up an old envelope on which he had scribbled the words.

> The Secretary of State is glad to confirm that a year ago last summer he asked Mr. Raymond Whitehead to undertake a confidential mission to Kabul, the exact nature of which must necessarily remain secret. The secretary wishes to emphasize, however, that whatever contacts Mr. Whitehead made in the Afghan capital were necessary in the carrying out of his assignment. It would be a matter of deep regret to the secretary and an unthinkable injustice to Mr. Whitehead were the committee to attach any suspicion whatsoever to Mr. Whitehead's action or conduct on this particular mission.

I sat back, tingling with a feeling of relief. The secretary's courage had saved me.

"Mr. Chairman," Jones said quietly but earnestly, "you will note that the secretary does not feel able to reveal the exact nature of Mr. Whitehead's mission. It will therefore serve no purpose to question the witness further about it. But the secretary's statement, I submit, does put yesterday's testimony in a new light."

"That is a matter of judgment, Senator," O'Brien replied tartly.

A murmur ran through the audience which he quickly squelched with his customary hypocritical observation. "There will be no demonstration for or against the witness," he growled. But he must have felt that he had been thrown on the defensive again, for he went on:

"I say it is a matter of judgment, Senator, because there are some of us on this committee — a majority, I dare say — who are not unmindful of the secretary's demonstrated softness toward Communists, if not his affinity for them — has he not filled the Department of State with Communistic Moscow-lovers?

"As for me, Senator Jones, I am content to let the record show that the witness claims — and the Secretary of State backs him up — that he hobnobbed with one of the most famous of living Russian spies in the so-called interests of his country. If that is the way to serve the true interest of this great nation, then I say: God help America!"

"And I say Amen to that, suh!" the voice of the Old South rang out. "And I must say," Reynolds went on, stroking the handle bars of his flying mustache, "to my distinguished colleague from the South, that it passeth my understanding how he or any other member of this committee, loyal as we all are to our country, its flag, its constitution, its institutions, could help but be suspicious of this witness's patriotism and loyalty — indeed of his Americanism — in view of all we have heard about him, of his activities, of his 'contacts,' as he calls them, with all his Red friends, including Bolshevistic spies. I say this man has consorted with the enemy! I don't give a damn, suh, what the Secretary of State says!"

I had not been vindicated, then, after all. Had I been naïve in thinking that I ever had a chance to be — before such inquisitors? A weariness began to come over me. Of what use to bare the truth of your unimportant life, hour after hour, day after day, to such prejudiced primitives? It got you nowhere. It merely exhausted you. It was no defense. How could you defend yourself against such men? Had any man ever been able to defend himself — successfully — against the Spanish Inquisition?

"The next witness will be . . ." O'Brien's voice droned out, fetching me from my rumination. "In fact, if it is all right with committee members, I should like at this point to call two witnesses to the stand."

I glanced over toward the spectators' seats. Elsie and Newman were rising — confident and smiling. I had not noticed them.

"Miss Elsie McCabe and Mr. Frederick Newman, will you kindly take the stand," O'Brien said affably, and it must have seemed to many, even to my well-wishers, that the walls were beginning to tumble down upon me. As if in a nightmare, I could feel them trembling, myself.

I got up from the witness chair.

"Just a moment, Mr. Whitehead, please," O'Brien said, raising his voice. "If it is all right with other members, I would like you to remain on the stand. I want the three of you on the stand together. Miss McCabe and Mr. Newman will first be sworn." He swore them to tell the truth, and nothing but the truth.

"Mr. Chairman!" Bill Rikind called out. "I believe it is highly irregular to have more than one witness on the stand at a time."

"We make the rules here, Mr. Rikind," O'Brien smiled.

Elsie and her friend took seats immediately to my right. She was smartly attired in a trim dark-blue suit and her hair was freshly done. She made a rather attractive figure, I had to admit, for one her age. She must have knocked off fifty or sixty pounds in the last year. I gazed at her, trying to catch her eye. Perhaps it would give some hint of why she had come here to bear false witness again. But she avoided my gaze. I could not even get a clue. She turned to whisper to Newman. He was of a slighter build than I had remembered from my one glimpse of him at Elsie's. But when he turned to her to whisper back I caught the burning fanaticism in his eyes. His intense look was the kind that in the past, and now in the present, seemed impatient to hurry the heretic off to the stake.

I glanced back for a second at Yvonne. She was staring at the two witnesses, as if she were both fascinated and repelled.

A low buzzing of voices had spread over the room as Elsie and Newman came forward to the stand. O'Brien rapped for order.

"Miss McCabe and Mr. Newman," he began, "have already testified at length in executive session. It is not my intention to ask them to repeat themselves today. The relevant parts of their testimony have already been made public."

"Can we cross-examine them on it?" Rikind asked, popping up.

"No, you may not. There is no cross-examination in a Senate committee except, in a sense, by members."

Rikind, muttering under his breath what may have been foul oaths, sat down.

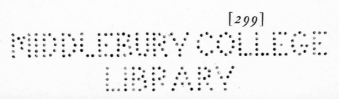

"In view of the categorical charges made by Miss McCabe and Mr. Newman, I do think, in fairness to Mr. Whitehead, there should be a confrontation," O'Brien said in a kindly voice that he must have thought masked his hypocrisy. "Perhaps," he said, and now his voice grew unctuous, "there has been a case of mistaken identity. Miss McCabe and Mr. Newman, former top Communists themselves, have sworn that they knew Mr. Whitehead as a Communist and as an agent for Communistic Russia. Mr. Whitehead has sworn that he was neither.

"Were there perchance," O'Brien went on, his lips curling in a smile, "two Whiteheads, or even more? It is not an uncommon name. I say: let them confront each other here — and we shall see."

"Splendid idea, suh!" Reynolds blubbered, his mouth watering in anticipation of an obscene scene.

It was the purest nonsense, the most utter hypocrisy, the meanest kind of shabby trick — and I sat up in my seat to say so.

"Senator, this is ludicrous," I said. "Whom do you think you are fooling?"

"Strike that!" O'Brien admonished his clerk.

"I have told you, gentlemen, that Miss McCabe and I were once very close friends, and that I met Mr. Newman once — in fact, it was at Miss McCabe's home. Why this farce of a confrontation, then? How dishonest can you get?"

"We will conduct the hearing, if you don't mind, Mr. Whitehead," O'Brien said. He was obviously determined to go ahead with this ridiculous scene.

"Miss McCabe," he continued, "I will ask you to look at the gentleman on your left and tell us whether this is the Mr. Whitehead you have sworn to be, from your own knowledge, a Communist and a Soviet agent?"

Elsie turned slowly around and for the first time our eyes met. But there was not much in them that I could make out, except a gleam of triumph. But for what purpose, I wondered? Was there a vindictiveness in them too? Perhaps, but I could not be sure.

"This is the Mr. Whitehead I knew," she said slowly, but in a firm voice.

"As a Communist?"

"Yes."

"And as a Soviet agent — like yourself?"

"He was one of us. Yes, sir."

"There is no doubt at all in your mind, now that you confront the gentleman face to face?"

"No, sir." She spoke the words with emphasis.

"And there is nothing you would like to retract from your previous testimony in regard to him?"

"Nothing," she said flatly.

She smiled at me, and then turned away, but I did not get the meaning, if any.

Senator O'Brien next led Frederick Newman through the same rigamarole. He swore too — this man whom I had never laid eyes on, nor even heard of, until the other day — that he had known me as a Communist.

"Any questions?" O'Brien asked.

"I have some, sir," I said.

"You are here to answer questions, not to ask them, Mr. Whitehead," O'Brien said, breaking into a grin, ". . . as I believe I have had occasion to point out to you before."

"Do you mean to tell me, Senator . . ." I started to say. This was a crucial moment, I quite realized. I would have to fight back hard.

"I mean to tell you," O'Brien cut me off, "for the hundredth time that your questions are out of order here."

"This is outrageous, sir!"

There was some — not much — applause from the audience. O'Brien quickly squelched it.

"I have a question or two —" Senator Jones spoke up. The very sound of his soft, Southern voice cheered me up. But how probing could he afford to be at this point? I wondered. He had shown courage these last days. But he came from a conservative state in the South. He would be up for re-election, I remembered, in 1952. It would not help him if it were remembered then that he had been unduly hard on two of the new heroes in America, two ex-Communists who in a burst of patriotism were putting a finger on their former comrades. Senator O'Brien would go into Carolina and remind Jones's constituents of that. Was he not this very month barging into three or four states where liberal Senators were up for re-election and branding them as pro-Communists? There were limits, I saw, to how far Senator Jones, at this point, could go.

He turned first to me, "Mr. Whitehead, do you now deny what these two witnesses have just sworn?"

"I do, sir. I say they have lied."

"One or the other of you is lying — there's no doubt about that."

"Suh, while I have no doubt myself as to who is telling the truth here and who isn't —" Jones's Southern colleague intervened — "I have a proposal that may clear up the matter."

"What is that, Senator?"

"Suh, I propose we submit all three of the witnesses to the lie detector! That's as good a way as any to ferret out the culprit."

"With all due respect to you, sir," Jones said, "I myself do not believe in them."

"They are used in my state, suh, with good effect, I believe. How about it, Mr. Chairman?" Reynolds bellowed.

"We will take it under advisement, Senator," O'Brien answered. "Any other questions?" he asked.

"I am not yet through, Mr. Chairman," Jones said. "Now, Mr. Whitehead, you stand by your sworn testimony that you are not and never were a Communist?"

"Yes, sir. I most certainly do."

"And that you were not an agent of the Soviet government?"

"I have so sworn, and I stand by it."

"Then it is your word against theirs?"

"Well, Senator," I said, snatching at the opening, "I would think that since they are making such serious charges you might expect them to give more than their word — some evidence, I mean."

O'Brien was about to admonish me, but Senator Jones cut him off.

"I was just coming to that point," he said quickly, turning to Elsie and her fellow witness. I could feel Bill Rikind's ears pricking up.

"Mr. Newman," Jones said, "you have testified that Mr. Whitehead was a Communist. How did you know?"

"From official reports, sir."

"What official reports?"

Newman seemed astounded that he should be questioned in more detail. I could understand his astonishment. Rikind and I had checked his testimony on a score of occasions before this and other committees. Not once, after charging that a man was a Communist, had he been asked by any Congressman to go beyond explaining that he knew this "through official reports" or "through official communications."

"Why, official reports that passed between our top officials," he answered.

"Do you have any of these reports you could show this committee?"

"Of course not, Senator," he said, exasperated.

"We must take your word for them?"

"If you like. All the other committees have."

"This committee, Mr. Newman, makes its own way," Jones said spiritedly. "You realize, don't you — or do you? — that when you say you knew 'through official reports' that Mr. Whitehead was a Communist, it is not evidence?"

"Just a minute, Senator Jones, if I may intervene," O'Brien said. "I think we must all keep in mind that Mr. Newman was himself a top member of the American Communist party for many years. He knew all the important people in it. Therefore when he says he knew someone — Mr. Whitehead, for example — as a fellow Communist, then I say *that* is evidence — very important evidence, it seems to me."

Unruffled, Jones continued. "Is it your testimony, Mr. Newman, that during the years you were a top Communist, you knew Mr. Whitehead?"

[303]

"I knew him as a party member."

"Did you know him personally?"

Newman hesitated. "Not personally, no."

"Isn't it a fact, as he has testified, that you never even saw him, face to face, until recently — that is, long after you had turned anti-Communist?"

"That is correct, Senator."

"He told the truth about that, did he?"

Again O'Brien intervened. "Is it not true, Mr. Newman, that even those of you who were in the Politburo didn't — and couldn't — know every last agent who was working for you and Moscow?"

"How could we?" Newman said, obviously grateful for the chairman's intervention. "There were hundreds of them. We couldn't know each one personally. But we could — and did — know about them."

"The thing that bothers me, Mr. Newman," Jones said, "and I say this most sincerely because I appreciate what you and other former Communists have done to expose the Communist threat, is that you and Miss McCabe and other reformed party members are now in a position to denounce anyone as a Communist. We must take your word. You offer no proof."

"We offer the truth, sir!" Newman fairly shouted.

"I appreciate that," Jones smiled. "But tell me this, Mr. Newman. In your Communist days, did you ever tell a lie?"

"Of course I did, Senator!" the little man exclaimed. "I don't think you understand the nature of Communism, sir, judging by your question. All Communists have to lie. How else can you carry on a conspiracy against America?"

"And when you leave the party," Jones said quietly, "you cease lying? You begin to tell the truth?"

"Yes, sir. You do. Because you're a free man again. A man with a conscience."

"Thank you. That is all."

To my disappointment, if not my astonishment, Jones was through. I was grateful that he had exposed Newman as a liar. But could he not have delved into the motives of this man?

They were far from clear to me. Some of course were fairly obvious. Frederick Newman, after a life of relative poverty, was now making big money from his nationally syndicated column on the Communist danger. He was much in demand as a paid lecturer and as a paid performer on radio and TV. He basked in the limelight. He had become an important public figure, a "celebrity." If it were necessary to lie, to throw a few innocents to the lions, in order to retain that position, was it not a small cost to a man with his shady past? And was it not becoming increasingly necessary to lie, to put the finger on the "liberals" and denounce them as Communists? Was there not a time — and had it not now come? — when his real ammunition began to run out, when his firsthand information about Communists and conspirators became exhausted and it was necessary to turn to those who were not Communists but who were suspect in America because of their liberal, independent, nonconformist minds?

But these were questions which the O'Brien committee did not care to go into. The answers might have spoiled the game.

Once, in executive session, I remembered from my reading of the testimony, Senator Jones had actually got on the track of such questioning. He had asked Newman:

"Could you tell us whether the *Daily Worker* or any other Communist publication ever identified Raymond Whitehead as a party member?"

"I would have to check on that, sir," Newman had replied. "It would take a lot of time, reading back through the years. I'm sure that you would find that the *Daily Worker* and *New Masses* often praised him for his broadcasts and his articles."

"He has admitted," Jones said, "that on some occasions they did. But he has specified them. They praised him for being against Franco. And against Hitler."

"Precisely, Senator. He was taking the party line."

"Then I took it myself," Jones laughed. "A lot of us, Mr. Newman, opposed Franco and Hitler. And we were not Communists."

"I appreciate that, Senator. But Whitehead was."

"How do you explain then," Jones persisted, "that White-head, in his broadcasts, opposed Hitler at the time of the Nazi-Soviet pact? He wasn't following the Moscow line then, was he?"

"Admittedly, Senator," Newman said. "But you must understand that occasionally we allowed our secret members to oppose us so that they could continue to get by with the public as non-Communists."

"In other words, no matter what evidence Whitehead furnishes us of his anti-Communist broadcasts and articles, you still maintain he was a Communist?"

"I do, sir."

"One more question, Mr. Newman. Mr. Whitehead has given us various clippings from the *Daily Worker* showing that they referred to him as a 'liberal' or a 'progressive,' but never as a Communist. How do you explain that?"

"Easily, Senator. The use of such terms as 'liberal' or 'progressive' in the *Daily Worker* is a sign to the comrades that the person so described is a Communist, or at least pro-Communist. It is a reminder that the person so described can be trusted as taking the party line."

It was plain to me, on reading this, that Newman was preparing the ground for henceforth including "liberals" and "progressives" in his long list of "Communists." Obviously he was running out of Communists.

But Jones did not pursue the matter further. And no other Senator pursued it at all.

Neither did any of them, not even Jones, attempt today to delve into the motives of Elsie McCabe. Even had they tried, perhaps, they would not have gotten very far. I, who knew her so well, could not penetrate very far into the mystery of why she had so brazenly lied about me. The personal reasons — and I was thankful to be spared having them aired in public — her spite over my marriage, over my refusal to follow her into the party long ago, over my relations with her since I came home — undoubtedly were factors which had induced her to do what she had done. But they could not have been the only ones.

Elsie, of course, like Newman, had stumbled into a lucrative career as a professional ex-Communist. Like him, she had become a nationally known public figure, basking in the limelight.

But there must have been other reasons and it baffled me that I could not, for the life of me, make them out.

I glanced at my watch. It was already past noon. I wondered why O'Brien had not adjourned the hearing — not that I cared one way or the other. He must have noticed my gesture for now he said:

"Gentlemen, we are running over today because there will be no afternoon session. Several members, I am informed, have pressing out-of-town engagements this evening. Your chairman has one himself — a pro-American meeting in Pittsburgh. Before we adjourn I want to ask Mr. Whitehead, in fairness to him, if he has anything to say."

Surprised at this generosity I perked up. "I have plenty to say, sir. But it would take me more time than I fear we have, seeing the hour. There are a number of questions I would like to put to these two witnesses . . ."

"You did not understand me correctly, Mr. Whitehead," O'Brien said, with a smile that was almost kindly. "I did not ask you to question the two witnesses. That would be completely out of order. I merely meant: have you any general observation to make about their testimony?"

"I have, Senator. But it would take some time to express it."

"Mr. Chairman, the man is insufferable. I object to him taking any more of our time today —" Reynolds blustered.

I saw that I ought to snatch at just a moment of time to say two things which otherwise I might not get a chance to say.

"Could you sum up, perhaps, Mr. Whitehead, what is on your mind — say in a minute or two?" O'Brien asked. "Otherwise I shall have to adjourn the hearing."

"Very well, Senator. I will say that the two witnesses have brazenly lied. And I will point out to the committee, if I may, that neither of them have offered one iota of evidence . . . *evidence*, I repeat — that I ever was a Communist or a so-called Soviet agent. I simply refuse to believe, gentlemen, that you can let witnesses get by with damning me as a Communist —

with all that means today in America — without their offering the slightest bit of evidence other than their unsupported word."

"They supported each other's testimony, didn't they?" O'Brien asked.

"Not with any evidence, sir."

Old Reynolds, pulling at his mustache, cleared his voice. "How about you, young man, giving us some evidence that you are *not* a Communist?"

It was a question that was bound to pop up sooner or later, and Senator Reynolds, I mused to myself, was bound to ask it.

"Senator, how do you prove you are not something somebody says — falsely — you are? How do you prove you are not a Communist when you are not one?"

"That is my question, suh. Answer it, if you can."

"You are asking me to prove my innocence."

"I am asking you to give us some scrap of evidence which proves you are not a Communist."

"I thought it was the American tradition — not to mention the law — to assume my innocence unless or until there was some evidence to prove my guilt."

"Suh, do you not realize," Reynolds said, bellowing at me, his voice deep and resonant and quivering, "— do you not realize, for your own good, that the evidence here against you has been . . . uh . . . well nigh overwhelming?"

I had not realized it, of course. It seemed incredible that even such an old windbag as this Southern relic could have thought so. But his words stung me into another realization: If Reynolds was impressed by the "evidence," then the ex-undertaker, Kleinschmidt, and the former West Coast realtor, Breen, undoubtedly were too. (O'Brien didn't want or need any evidence to pillory me.) Inane though it would be in the presence of more normal Americans, it was necessary, I saw, to say something at this moment in defense of my innocence.

Bill Rikind reacted similarly, for he turned and whispered: "Answer the old bastard. Say something for the record. Remember, you're on the air, on TV."

I had forgotten the cameras and the mikes, I had forgotten momentarily — what O'Brien never lost sight of for a moment — that I was also being tried before a nation-wide audience gazing at their television screens or listening in on their radios.

"Senator Reynolds," I said, trying to throw off my weariness, "I am not sure I know of any way to prove you are not a Communist. But since you ask me to try, I will say this: One can only bare the record of his life, as I have done here, and invite you to find one shred of Communism in it. Fortunately, what I have believed happens to be a public record, contained in a thousand or so broadcasts, scores of articles and some books. You have these: you can judge.

"If I were not sure you would think it a waste of your time, I could bring in a score of citizens, from the Secretary of State on down, to testify that they knew me, not as a Communist, but as an anti-Communist, and as a loyal, patriotic American. Perhaps that would be the kind of 'evidence' you are seeking and which would 'prove' that I am not a Bolshevik nor an agent of Moscow."

"It would not be evidence to me, Mr. Whitehead," O'Brien chuckled. "At least, not if it came from the Secretary of State. From him, it would be evidence to the contrary. No man, as I have said before, has done more to promote Communism and Communists in this country."

With that parting quip he moved to adjourn the hearing. He had saved one little surprise for the end.

"Gentlemen," he said, amiably, "I believe we can finish with this witness at the next hearing."

"The Lord be praised!" Reynolds sang out.

"I suggest," O'Brien continued, "that we convene tomorrow at two P.M. That will give members time to return to Washington and get a little rest beforehand. There will be, so far as I know, only one witness."

"May we have his name?" Senator Jones asked.

"Yes, sir. Mr. Robert A. Fletcher, vice-president and general manager of the Federal Broadcasting Company."

"What is his connection with the witness, may I ask?"

[309]

"It was F.B.C., Senator Jones, for which Mr. Whitehead made those thousand broadcasts he mentioned a moment ago. Mr. Fletcher was Mr. Whitehead's boss and, I am told, his friend — going back many years. So perhaps," O'Brien grinned, "we may kill many birds with one stone. The hearing stands adjourned."

So Bob is to be the last witness. For me, or against?

OCTOBER *12*

BOB strode briskly to the witness stand. I had not seen him since that day last June when he had called me in to fire me, except for a chance encounter a month or so later in Radio City when, pausing for a hurried moment on the avenue, he had been most affable. Despite the briskness of his manner, as he took his seat and listened to O'Brien intone the oath, answering with a crisp "I do," his face looked drawn and tired. This was a busy season at F.B.C., with the big fall shows for the million-dollar sponsors being launched or resumed on radio and TV, and Bob, no doubt, was up to his ears in work and worry. Mark Robson, I had heard, was so engrossed in his approaching marriage to Dora Faye, the ballerina, that he had left Bob Fletcher to struggle by himself with the daily headaches of running a vast radio and television network. It was a killing job and the pace obviously was telling on Bob, as it was bound to on any man in such a position.

There were dark blotches under his intense black eyes and his forehead seemed more deeply furrowed than before and his cheeks more hollow. For the first time I noticed that his well-groomed dark hair was graying above the ears, and thinning around the temples. The air of weariness, however, somehow enhanced his appearance of distinction. He must have made an engaging figure on TV as indeed he did in this committee room under the strong lights, which threw his handsome features into sharp relief.

Barbara Fletcher sat three or four seats away from us in the first row of spectators. She looked as attractively wholesome as ever, though there was a strain in her face that I had not seen before. Perhaps Bob's appearance here was more of an ordeal for her than for him. She nodded a greeting to us, but it was an effort, I felt, for her to smile.

"Mr. Chairman," Bob spoke up at once in his well-modulated, deep voice. "May I say just a word at this point?"

"Certainly, Mr. Fletcher," O'Brien replied obligingly.

"Do you have a statement to make?" Senator Jones asked.

"No, Senator. I would like to say merely a word or two by way of explanation, if I may."

"Go ahead, please," O'Brien said affably.

"I would like to make it clear," Bob began, "that I am not here either to attack or defend Mr. Whitehead. I am here solely to explain the role of F.B.C., for which, next to Mr. Mark Robson, I have, as general manager, the responsibility . . ."

I had forgotten that Bob could be stuffy — it became him so little.

"We understand F.B.C. has figured in these hearings — because of Mr. Whitehead's connection with the network. If I can be of any help to the committee — or to him — in shedding light on this matter, I am ready now to do so."

"That is precisely why we have called you here to testify today, Mr. Fletcher," O'Brien said, beaming.

"Are you here voluntarily or under subpoena?" Senator Jones asked rather brusquely.

"I was subpoenaed, sir," Bob replied.

"Wasn't the president of the company, Mr. Robson, also subpoenaed?" Jones asked.

"I believe he was, Senator," Bob said, smiling ingratiatingly. "But, as you can understand, he is a very busy man and we agreed that I could well speak for the both of us — and for F.B.C."

"Well, we're all busy men these days, Mr. Fletcher."

O'Brien seemed a little taken back at his colleague getting off first with the questioning. "Do you want Mr. Robson subpoenaed too, Senator?" he asked Jones rather sharply.

"I understand he was subpoenaed, Mr. Chairman," Jones said.

"That's right. But I'm asking you if you want him brought here?"

"No, sir," Jones answered. "I am sure Mr. Fletcher will suffice. I merely wanted to point out to the witness — and for the record — that no man in America is too big or too busy to answer a Senate subpoena."

Bob seemed a little flustered, as did O'Brien and the other members of the committee. Jones had certainly acted a little strangely the last few days, they must have thought. Apparently this was a "friendly" witness. And "friendly" witnesses heretofore had always been treated with kid gloves. What had got into Senator Jones? his colleagues must have wondered. I wondered myself. He had been growing in stature these past few days, it seemed to me.

He was not yet finished with his preliminary questioning.

"Did I understand you to say, Mr. Fletcher," he resumed, "that you were here to testify solely in regard to F.B.C.'s experience with Mr. Whitehead?"

"That's correct, sir," Bob said, clipping his words.

"You understand, don't you," Jones went on, "that once you're on the stand, you must attempt to answer whatever questions any member deems relevant to this hearing — not necessarily merely those which concern your company?"

"I would prefer, sir," Bob said, but not quite so confidently as a moment before, "to confine myself to company relations with Mr. Whitehead. As I said . . ."

"I am not sure that I, at least, can accommodate you —" Jones cut in. "But we shall see."

O'Brien intervened. "I am sure, Senator Jones, that Mr. Fletcher will be more than glad to answer any questions that members may care to put to him."

"That is correct, sir," Bob said quickly, relieved at O'Brien's assist.

But Jones was still not quite through.

"Mr. Fletcher," he said, "someone — I think it was the chairman — told us yesterday that you were an old friend of Mr. Whitehead."

"That is correct, sir."

"More than a business friend — I mean, were you a close personal friend?"

Bob hesitated and glanced at Barbara. She had been leaning forward, hanging on his words, and now she seemed to eye him searchingly.

"That is correct, sir," he said, and now he turned to me, forcing a smile. I, of course, could say nothing. At this point, I was a mere spectator, seated in the audience.

"Then that fact, sir," Jones said, "both broadens the nature of your testimony and limits its objectivity, does it not?"

Bob looked flustered. "I hope, sir," he said, "that I can be objective."

I was puzzled. It would have been easy for Bob merely to state the truth: that we were no longer friends.

"Are you through, Senator?" O'Brien leaned over the table to ask Jones.

"For the moment, sir, yes."

O'Brien sat back, relieved. He pursed his thin lips. He smiled at Bob. He cleared his throat.

"Mr. Fletcher," he began, "is it true that Mr. Raymond Whitehead is no longer with F.B.C.?"

"That is correct, sir."

Bob was still very taut, but perhaps, I thought, O'Brien's kindly questions would now help to relax him. I can't say that at this moment I was very relaxed myself. Deep down there was the uneasy feeling which had kept me awake most of last night that, for reasons still beyond my grasp, this man I once loved and admired was out to destroy me — or at least to assist in my final destruction. All through the sleepless night in the hotel room, I kept trying to put the thought aside. It could not be true. There was no logic in it. There was no motive for him to try to do so. I was no longer even an embarrassment to his loyalty and devotion to F.B.C. and to Robson. I was no longer a thorn — if I had ever been — in his climb to success and position and power. And he did not need, at the pinnacle he had reached, to bolster his position in business or society by pandering to the witch-hunters or helping O'Brien smear and destroy one more innocent citizen. Neither he nor Robson nor, God knows, F.B.C. were suspect, nor had anything in their past, as had Elsie McCabe and the other ex-Communists, to live down and make up for.

O'Brien's oily voice aroused me from my thoughts.

"I wonder, Mr. Fletcher, if you would tell the committee why Mr. Whitehead is no longer with F.B.C.?"

"Well, it's a long story, Senator," Bob replied, a weary smile breaking on his handsome face.

This remark brought Senator Reynolds to life. "We've become hardened to long stories, suh, after two weeks of listening to the endless elucidations of Mr. Whitehead. Perhaps you could tell me, suh, why you folks on radio tend to be so infernally verbose?"

"Well, we have to fill a lot of air, Senator," Bob smiled.

"And that makes you just naturally long-winded," the old gentleman from the cotton country retorted, chuckling at his little joke.

"Perhaps" — O'Brien spoke up, obviously impatient to get along with the business he had in mind — "we can keep the story to its bare essentials if we ask you a few questions."

"I would much prefer it that way, Mr. Chairman," Bob said.

Had they worked out, beforehand, a pattern for the questioning? I wondered. As repulsive as you would have thought O'Brien must be to a man like Bob Fletcher, had they not been on pretty good terms for years? I remembered now that at all of Bob's big parties which I had attended, in the country or in town, Senator O'Brien had invariably been among the guests. I could not believe that Bob had anything but contempt for the man. Perhaps it was just that, like most everyone else in America, he found it prudent to stay in the good graces of the slippery little Washington witch-hunter.

"Mr. Fletcher," O'Brien said. "Is it true that about six months ago F.B.C., in common with a good many other American business enterprises, asked its employees to sign a loyalty oath?"

"Yes sir."

[314]

"You simply asked your personnel to state, under oath, that they were not and never had been Communists?"

"Yes, sir — and further that they had never been a member of any organization advocating the overthrow of our government by force."

"That would be the Communists, would it not?"

"It would."

"Did Raymond Whitehead sign the loyalty oath?" O'Brien snapped.

"No, sir."

"He did not?" Senator Breen asked sharply.

"He did not," Bob answered curtly.

"He refused to sign?" Senator Kleinschmidt asked. Neither the representative from the Far West nor the one from the Midwest had been in a questioning mood during the last few days. But now, with the final witness, they strove to get into the act.

"That's right. He refused to sign," Bob replied.

"In other words," O'Brien declared triumphantly, "Mr. Whitehead did not dare to take an oath that he was not a Communist, or had never been one, or that he did not, or had not, belonged to a conspiratorial organization advocating the overthrow of our constitutional government by force."

"I said he did not sign the oath," Bob said.

"It is clear he did not dare to," O'Brien added.

Jones spoke up. "Did Mr. Whitehead offer any explanation for his refusal to sign?"

"Yes, sir, he did."

"What was his justification?"

"As I recall," Bob replied, "he said it was against his principles."

"That's what they all say," O'Brien chirped.

"Didn't he invoke the Fifth Amendment?" Senator Reynolds put in, raising a chuckle in the audience.

"How many at F.B.C. refused to sign the loyalty oath?" O'Brien asked.

"Mr. Whitehead, and some half a dozen other employees," Bob said.

"Out of how many employees?"

"Out of nearly 2500, sir."

The audience was now following the questions and answers with rapt attention. Obviously the tide was running against me. I thought of the millions who probably were listening or viewing the broadcast. To them my guilt must have seemed to be growing very plain. No one sensed this more clearly, I suppose, than O'Brien. I could feel him trying to close in. And I was helpless to intervene. While Bob was on the stand I was a mere spectator.

"Mr. Fletcher," O'Brien began, switching skillfully to a new, but connected, line of interrogation, "our research staff has gone over copies of hundreds of Mr. Whitehead's broadcasts for F.B.C. It has been impressed, for one thing, by the fact that he rarely had anything good to say about America. We have questioned him about that and he has given us the plausible explanation that most of these broadcasts were made from Europe and that he naturally was confined to comments on these foreign, European countries." O'Brien paused.

"What about his broadcasts when he came home — about a year ago, wasn't it?"

"That's right," Bob said.

"He began broadcasting from New York every Sunday evening, I believe."

"Correct."

"Is it not a fact, Mr. Fletcher, that these broadcasts from New York were very critical of America?"

"They were often critical, Senator. But that was his right."

"And the Communists, of course, were critical of America, weren't they?"

"They certainly were, Senator. But I am not saying there was any connection."

"You are not. But I am. I say an objective study of his radio scripts proves that in criticizing America as he did, he took the Communist party line. We have had expert testimony along that line from Miss Elsie McCabe and other former Communists, who certainly should know. I merely wanted your corroboration that his broadcasts, after he got home to his native land, were full of disapproval and disparagement of the American way of life."

Bob might have said something at this point, I thought, but he did not. After all, he probably thought, no question had been put to him.

"Next I would like to ask you, Mr. Fletcher," O'Brien resumed, "about Mr. Whitehead's attack on well-known and proven anti-Communists. I shall pass over his contemptible assaults on me for having tried to rid this government, and this country, of Commies. But let's take some others who became targets for his venom. Isn't it true, Mr. Fletcher, that Mr. Whitehead in his broadcasts — and I'm speaking of the ones he made after he got home, and should have known better — isn't it true that he attacked Franco and Chiang Kai-shek?"

"I believe he did, yes," Bob said.

"Nearly every Sunday?"

"Well, quite often, say."

"And isn't it true that both Franco and Chiang have been two of the leading fighters against Communism in our day?"

"They have certainly fought Communism, Senator."

"Then what it boils down to, does it not, is that Mr. Whitehead attacked two valiant warriors against Communism over your F.B.C. network?"

"As I said, Senator, he certainly opposed both of those gentlemen."

"Now, let's take another case," O'Brien said. He was really warmed up. "Are you acquainted with the case of a certain Stephen Burnett, now under suspension by the State Department for disloyalty to his country?"

"I am," Bob said. I saw him glance quickly at Barbara. I had not noticed her for some time. Her chin was buried in the palm of one hand. She had a dejected look. This time she did not smile back at Bob.

"Is it true that Mr. Whitehead, in his Sunday broadcasts, staunchly defended this disloyal diplomat, this Mr. Burnett?"

"As I recall, he did, sir."

Who at F.B.C., I wondered, had given Senator O'Brien such leads? I could not believe that it was Bob.

"What did the management at F.B.C. do about *that?*" O'Brien thundered.

"We told him to lay off defending Mr. Burnett."

"And did he lay off?"

"He did. He had to."

"You didn't try to prevent him from testifying before this committee *for* Burnett, did you?"

"As a matter of fact, Senator, we did," Bob said.

"He refused to heed you?"

"Yes."

"Well," O'Brien said with a smirk. "His testimony didn't amount to much. But that isn't the point. The point is he insisted on coming before this committee to defend Burnett, as he had done on the air — a man whom this committee was forced to find, after listening to all the evidence, guilty, of being a participant in a Communist conspiracy to turn China over to Red Russia!"

O'Brien's voice was rising in a mighty crescendo, and now he turned his face toward the whirring television cameras, which no doubt (the thought passed swiftly over my mind) had him in close-up and shouted:

"I say that birds of a feather flock together! I say that Raymond Whitehead, in defending Stephen Burnett, as he did on the air and before this committee, was defending a fellow Communist! I say the evidence before us proves beyond fear of contradiction that both of these men participated in the Communist conspiracy, that they were, in truth, agents of the Soviet Union, that they were more than disloyal to their country, that they were traitors!"

So I was getting O'Brien's verdict in advance, even before my hearing was over, delivered with a purple face that was close to convulsions. Finally he stopped and mopped his brow.

"Suh" — Reynolds turned to O'Brien — "I couldn't agree with you more."

The spokesman of the ol' South was rendering his verdict too.

There were a few more scattered questions to Bob, and then he was dismissed with a word of praise from the chairman for his "co-operation."

It had to be admitted that Bob's other answers all afternoon, so far as they went, were pretty factual. It was only that by keeping them short he omitted to say a great deal that might have put a different light on various matters. He might have added, for instance, during the questioning on the loyalty oath at F.B.C. that Robson himself had accepted my word that I was not a Communist and had therefore not cashiered me for not signing. Bob might have answered squarely the question Senator Jones put to him at the end.

"Mr. Fletcher, the charges here are that Mr. Whitehead was a Communist and a Soviet agent. Having known him over many years and having worked with him closely, would you say that either accusation — or both of them — were true?"

"Senator, I am not here to pass judgment. That, sir, if I may say so, is your task," Bob replied.

NEW YORK, OCTOBER 13
            IT FINALLY came to an end in Washington, D.C. on this Friday, the thirteenth, and Yvonne and I lost no time in getting back here to the children. Steve Burnett, with plenty of time on his hands, has been looking after them and his own. Tonight we had a big reunion. Steve got up a dinner of Chinese specialties. After the youngsters had gone to bed, he and Yvonne and I celebrated with a bottle of champagne. Not that we had much to celebrate, except the pleasure of being together again and, in my case, the feeling of being out from under a staggering load.

Actually Bill Rikind is bubbling with optimism. At lunch today in the Mayflower in Washington after the last session of the hearing he exclaimed: "Raymond, I'm telling you. You're cleared — once and for all!"

We shall see. I myself wouldn't give much more than a nickel

[319]

for my chances. If I am cleared, I shall be pleasantly surprised.

Still, we did not do so badly today, I think. I got in a final word despite Chairman O'Brien's ruling that I could not make a concluding statement. Lawyer Rikind, in briefing me for this last hearing, had emphasized that an opportunity would probably come to get in a parting shot.

It came about the middle of the morning when after committee counsel and Rikind had argued endlessly about admitting into evidence certain exhibits and depositions, O'Brien cleared his voice, leaned over the table, and eying me almost kindly, said:

"Before we come to the end of this hearing, there is one question which I would like to put to the witness." His voice was positively dulcet. "Mr. Whitehead, do you feel you have had a fair hearing?"

"No, I don't, Mr. Chairman."

"What was that?" O'Brien asked quickly, as if he had not quite heard correctly.

"Senator O'Brien, I know it has been the custom of most of your witnesses, no matter how outrageously they have been pilloried here, to answer that question in the affirmative. Perhaps they were weary and answered as they did because they wanted to have an end to the torture.

"Sir, I admit to being near exhaustion. I am thankful the hearing is nearly over. But since you have asked me whether I have had a fair hearing I must, in all truth, say 'No.' And I would beg your indulgence for a moment while I tell you why."

"Mr. Chairman," Reynolds's voice rang out, "I protest! The man is off again!"

"I, too, Mr. Chairman," Senator Breen cut in, "could easily dispense with any further dissertations from the gentleman." Senator Kleinschmidt nodded his approval.

"Senator Jones?" O'Brien asked.

"Well, Mr. Chairman," Jones replied, "since a question of some importance to all of us was put to the witness, I believe he should be allowed to explain his answer — briefly, of course."

"I shall be brief, Senator," I said, grateful once more for his understanding.

"Just a minute, Mr. Witness —" O'Brien cut me down. "That doesn't mean you can go ahead."

There was a hurried consultation among the members. Finally O'Brien, not trying to hide his exasperation, emerged from the huddle to say: "All right. It is the consensus of the committee, Mr. Whitehead, that you should be given five minutes to elaborate on your answer. After that the chair may have something to say. Proceed, please, subject to any questions members may wish to ask as you go along."

"Gentlemen," I said, "I do not question for one moment the ancient right of investigation by the Congress and its committees. I do protest against the abuse of that right by Senator O'Brien."

"Mr. Whitehead," Senator Jones interrupted. "Do you think there are any Communists in this country?"

"Obviously, Senator. But I think we're lucky to have so few — compared, say, to democracies like France and Italy."

"Do you think that this committee of the Senate should concern itself with exposing these Communists?"

"Yes, sir, I do. And as I have said here before, I think that some of the committees of the Congress, including this one, have done a service in exposing the infiltration of Communists into some of our organizations and even, in a few cases — and these were mostly before or during the war — into the government. But, sir, Senator O'Brien has been running out of Communists. Recently he has begun to smear as a Communist anyone who disagrees with him. He has managed to institute a reign of terror in our foreign service, in the State Department, in other departments, in our schools and universities, in the films and radio."

"I will answer the gentleman in due course —" O'Brien broke in. "But may I remind you, sir, that you have been given time to explain why you think your hearing has not been fair, not to abuse the committee chairman."

"Very well. It was Senator Jones's question which got me off the track — though perhaps not as far off as you think.

[321]

"Gentlemen, to begin with, do you not find it singular that the man who publicly made such grave charges against me should preside over my hearing? Is it fair that he should be both prosecutor and judge?"

"This is not a court, as I reminded you in the beginning," O'Brien snapped.

"I know it. But it renders a verdict. It finds its victims guilty. It sentences them, in effect, to destruction. No legal court could do more."

"We pass no sentences, suh. We inflict no punishment," Senator Reynolds cried out. "That, suh, is beyond our competence. It lies outside our jurisdiction."

"You punish by publicity, Senator. When you stigmatize a man as 'disloyal,' as a 'Communist,' as a 'Soviet agent,' and publicize it throughout the nation, you destroy him. His name. His reputation. His standing in the community. His ability to earn his living.

"A fair hearing, you ask? How can there be a fair hearing without the right of cross-examination, without the right of one's counsel to intervene, without some slight concession to rules of evidence? I presume I am to be found guilty of Senator O'Brien's ridiculous accusations on the word of a couple of former Communists. On the 'word,' I say. For they have not provided — nor has Senator O'Brien or anyone else — one shred of evidence. Had my counsel been allowed to cross-examine them, as he would have been in any ordinary court, he would have had little difficulty, I imagine, in exposing them for the liars they are.

"The unfairness of these proceedings — I am trying to stick to the one question posed me by the chairman — goes back a long way. Even before Senator O'Brien made his speech in the Senate last August castigating me as a 'Soviet agent' — a charge he has not dared repeat outside the Senate and this committee room, where he would risk a libel suit — even before last August the Senator leaked a number of completely false stories about me to his favorite columnists in the Clark press.

"Where did they come from? From the files of this committee. One of your own staff members has boasted in a magazine article

[322]

that your committee has more than a million names, complete with dossiers, 'pertaining to subversion,' in its files. From examples already made public we know that many persons named therein are prominent citizens of the highest probity and patriotism. Also, we know that your data is unverified and unevaluated, consisting mostly of idle gossip and rumors, often supplied by demented crackpots, of clippings from the yellow press or the Communist press — both irresponsible — of names found on letterheads of alleged subversive organizations. And Senator O'Brien 'leaks' the contents of these files or uses them as the basis of charges hurled in the Senate to smear men in advance of their appearing before this committee.

"Fairness, you ask? Would it not be mere elemental justice, not to mention decency, for this committee to have the courage to verify the material in its one million dossiers and evaluate it before turning it over to irresponsible zealots to use as a sinister tool to besmear innocent reputations?

"Or better still, Senators, would it not be fairer just to make a bonfire of your million files? Why should a man's standing in a splendid democracy depend upon secret files, consisting of the most incredible rubbish? We are not a police state."

"How else," O'Brien intervened, "can we determine a man's thoughts — remembering that a man's thoughts determine his actions."

"You have no business in a democracy, Senator, trying to determine a man's thoughts!"

O'Brien looked exasperatedly at his watch. I hurried on.

"I realize, gentlemen, that in assessing the fairness of this hearing we must take into account today's climate in America. I know it is popular, but is it just, is it even common sense, to hold, as some members here have held, that there is such a thing as guilt by association, by nonassociation, by silence, by omission, by paternity, by matrimony even? The finger of guilt has been pointed at me in all of these ways.

"I will pass over the obvious bias of the committee as shown in the kid-glove manner it treats certain ex-Communists who come here to bear false witness in contrast to the hammer-and-tongs treatment it gives witnesses such as myself. I will pass over comment on the kind of questions you have badgered me with for a fortnight: leading questions, tricky questions, trivial questions, silly questions, irrelevant questions, even what I think were dishonest questions such as the ones inquiring into whether I had ever read a long list of Communist works. I was damned as an ignoramus because I hadn't read them, but had I admitted to reading them, you would have taken that as proof of my Communism.

"One final point, gentlemen, if I may. No judge ever expresses an opinion about a case being tried in his court. Yet yesterday, even before you had a chance to go over the record of this hearing and consider it on its merits, the chairman and one other Senator rendered their verdicts. Fair? I put it to you.

"So much for my answer to your question, Mr. Chairman."

"Are you through?" O'Brien asked sarcastically.

"Can I have one minute more to make one last observation?"

There was a murmur from Reynolds.

"Go ahead," O'Brien said, with feigned weariness. "If I said 'No,' you would claim we were abridging your right of free speech. Go ahead."

"Thank you. I would like to suggest that one reason for O'Brienism in this country today, for the atmosphere of suspicion and intolerance, for the reckless assassination of innocent men's characters and reputations before this and similar committees, for the hysterical hunt for 'disloyal' men in government and out of it, is that since the end of the war things have not gone in the world exactly as we Americans had hoped. We have failed to achieve a decent peace. Indeed we have been drawn into a war in Korea — a faraway place for American sons to die in. Large parts of the world — some of the most ancient and civilized lands — have passed into hostile hands, have been taken over, that is, by the Communists. These things quite naturally disturb us. So the O'Briens, taking advantage of our uneasiness, attempt to find scapegoats here at home for all that has gone sour in the world. And this leads us to a great illusion, shared in part by all of us: that whatever has gone wrong in the world, whatever annoys or distresses or frightens us, must be blamed on Americans — that is, on disloyal, subversive, traitorous Americans. The truth is that we have not had things exactly as we like since the war because, strong though we were, we were still not powerful enough to shape all events to our desires. Blame history for that, but not a handful of Americans, who may often have been wrong in what they did or failed to do, but who were not disloyal therefore, or subversive or 'Communistic.'

"Thank you, gentlemen, for hearing me through."

I sat back so utterly exhausted that I scarcely heard what Bill Rikind told me afterward was a severe castigation from Senator O'Brien for my "outrageous, contemptuous and contumacious" conduct before the committee. Soon came the welcome pound of his gavel. The hearing was over.

OCTOBER 16

STEVE has found an apartment — out on Riverside Drive near Columbia. He signs the lease day after tomorrow.

We have enjoyed having him and the three girls here, even though we were away in Washington most of the time. Irita and Marcia, his two youngest (eight and eleven), have gotten along splendidly with Maria. Marguerite, the eldest, is the same age as Dick, fifteen, but they have not hit it off too well.

OCTOBER 17

A DELIGHTFUL surprise! Wendell Lewis Philpots cables from Paris that he and Wanda are sailing on the *Queen Mary* tomorrow and will be here this week end. He says he has been offered a job at the United Nations Secretariat here. How wonderful! At last he can come home — decently. We cabled our delight.

OCTOBER 18

FOR the first time since he returned, Steve, a proud man in any predicament, had a beaten look when he came in this afternoon. He said nothing until after the children had gone to bed and he and Yvonne and I were sitting up having a nightcap.

"I guess you'll have to bear with the Burnett brood a while longer," he said lugubriously.

"We would love it, my dear," Yvonne said, with a warm smile. "But didn't you sign the lease for the new apartment today?"

"No, I didn't."

Neither Yvonne nor I said anything.

"I was turned down," Steve said after a while.

"How do you get turned down on an apartment lease — I mean, if you are white, preferably Gentile, and put up the dough?" I asked.

"It is very simple, Raymond. The landlord simply refused to sign. I was a little taken aback, I must say. I mean, I wasn't expecting it. I . . ."

"What in the hell happened, Steve?" I broke in.

"He was a pudgy, puffing, rather self-righteous little man, the owner," Steve answered. "He said he wasn't signing. I asked why. 'Because,' said he, 'I don't want no disloyal American in my building.' "

OCTOBER 19

WE TOLD Steve last night to forget about apartment hunting, that he and the youngsters could hole up with us for the winter. We're a bit crowded, but we're happy together.

I forgot, though, until this minute — I don't think we ever told Steve — that we ourselves got notice the other day to vacate these premises in six months.

OCTOBER 20

BILL RIKIND phoned today to say that the O'Brien committee would make public its findings in my case on November 2. He thinks we ought to be in Washington on that date to make a public statement — whichever way the verdict goes.

"Personally, Raymond," said he, "I have no doubts."

WE ALL piled down to the dock this afternoon to greet Wendell and Wanda Philpots. It was a joy to see them. Wendell seemed much more sprightly than in Paris last summer, a handsome, distinguished-looking figure with his white hair, lean, sensitive face and lively eyes sparkling with good humor. Wanda too looked better, I thought. She has not tried to regain her once trim figure, but she has retained that Slav vitality common in many Polish women even at fifty. To me, she is still a beauty, with her large, dark, luminous eyes and her high cheekbones and amply generous mouth. They seemed excited to be here.

We had a fine reunion at dinner here and then far into this Saturday evening over drinks. Whatever Wendell may feel deep inside, whatever uneasiness at finally coming home at sixty-six to a land he left at thirty and which, for the last sixteen bewildering years, rejected him, he was outwardly exuberant, bubbling with wit and charm, full of good talk about the latest goings-on in Europe, keen to learn what was happening here, enthusiastic about his job at the U.N.; so that as the evening wore on, he recalled to me the urbane, cultivated, graceful figure I had first got to know in Paris in the Twenties when he was the dean of the American correspondents there and the friend and confidant of European statesmen, intellectuals, artists and writers.

"In Paris last summer, Raymond," he chided me, "I joked with you about coming home to die."

"Of course you were joking, Wendell." I remembered how sadly he had smiled.

"The truth is I've come home to *live* — a few more years anyway. And I'm looking forward to them. It's my country, as well as yours, Raymond, or yours, Steve — or Mr. Rockefeller's or — what's his name? — Senator O'Brien's."

"We're going to be very happy here. I can feel it," Wanda added. She had sold her millinery shop, she said. They were rich — she laughed — in French francs.

"And my salary at the U.N., I'm told, is tax free. We shall

indeed be rich, Wanda." Wendell smiled, looking at her admiringly.

He had got the job, he said, through French friends in the Paris Foreign Office and with the blessings of the American Ambassador.

"But first," he said, "I'm going to take Wanda up to the little town in Connecticut where I grew up. If it is at all like I remember it, especially now with the maples turning and the smell of autumn in the air, I think she will like it." He turned to her and smiled again. "We will buy a car, Wanda — with your money from the hat shop. We'll galavant about New England. You will see what a beautiful country this is."

OCTOBER 22 (SUNDAY)

YVONNE, Steve and I drove up to Chris Chambers's place in West Cornwall. The maples along the Housatonic River were ablaze with color. Chris told us of a 200-acre farm nearby that is up for sale, cheap. We all drove over to see it in the late afternoon. It is a bit run down; some of the fields look a little worn out; the stately old frame house needs painting, as do the barns. Still, it may be something for us, Steve and I agreed. You could probably live off it, if you worked hard. At least you wouldn't starve. And there would be spare time for writing the books.

At noon, just before we reached Chris's, we caught Sunday Brunch With Betty and Bob on the car radio. The frenetic couple were all steamed up about a social item we had all missed. They said Mark Robson and Dora Faye would be married next week. They said café society in New York was agog about the wedding. Bob Fletcher would be best man. They kept calling Dora Faye "Lady Kingsbury."

OCTOBER 23

THE inimitable Senator O'Brien is now turning his attention to our scientists. In a speech in the Senate today he claimed five hundred of them were openly associated with

Communist-front groups. He smeared seven of them by name, most of them distinguished physicists who helped make the atom bomb and one of them a Nobel Prize winner.

OCTOBER 24

TODAY was United Nations Day, the fifth anniversary of the U.N. charter coming into force, and Steve and I went out to Flushing to hear President Truman address the Assembly. The air at the U.N. was thick with eloquent words. But the U.N. itself just manages to stumble along.

The only sour note of the day was sounded by Senator O'Brien. In a statement issued at Washington he said that United Nations Day was a good occasion for all loyal and patriotic Americans to wake up to the fact that the U.N. was "corrupting America," that it had become a "hot bed of Communists," and that "it was dominated by atheistic Russia." He invited it to remove its "sinister premises" from our "hallowed shores."

I guess if O'Brien didn't exist, I'd miss him.

OCTOBER 25

WE HAD a drink with Wendell out at Flushing yesterday. It warmed my heart to see him in such fine fettle. This is the kind of world he loves and in which he is so effective: the world of politics and diplomacy. All the big shots from the foreign delegations seemed to know him. He said his new job was to be special assistant for European affairs to the secretary general and that he had been asked to start work immediately — today, in fact. He complained that would rob him and Wanda of their New England vacation, but I could see how happy he was to have a regular job again, and one that was not an affront to his talents.

OCTOBER 27

WENDELL and Wanda came over for dinner tonight and we had much good talk. They are looking for an apartment nearby, as Wendell will be working in the new secretariat building just down the river, the first fifteen stories of which are already in use.

He said there was considerable worry at the U.N. today over reports that Red China was pouring troops across the Yalu River frontier into North Korea.

OCTOBER 29 (SUNDAY)

STEVE BURNETT and I took another look at that farm today. It has possibilities.

On the way back from the country we decided to go down to Washington together Tuesday evening. Steve thinks it is time he saw the secretary again and, if possible, the President about his appeal. The findings of the O'Brien committee in my case are due on Thursday. I promised Bill Rikind to be on hand.

Both of us depressed at the news from Korea tonight. We sat up until midnight listening to the radio. Apparently the war is not over, as we had believed. Red China has intervened!

OCTOBER 30

IT HAS happened to Wendell Philpots!

Even before he arrived this evening, very troubled, I had heard the news on the radio. Senator O'Brien announced this afternoon that he had asked the State Department to hold up clearing Wendell Philpots for his U.N. post until the Senate Committee on Security and Americanism has looked into the matter.

"It would be interesting to learn," O'Brien was quoted as saying, "why Mr. Philpots, like Raymond Whitehead, stayed away from his native America most of his life. Besides, they're friends!"

Wendell was in a sorry state. "What do I do?" he said, his fine, sensitive face twitching.

"Fight back," I said.

"How do you fight such guttersnipes?"

"That's what Steve and I are still trying to find out. You just have to keep at them."

"I'll go back to Paris before I'll let O'Brien haul me up before his god-damn committee," Wendell said. He was really hurt.

"No, you won't!" I chided him. "In the first place, O'Brien will subpoena you. In the second place, he will get the State Department to hold up your passport. So, you've got to stay and fight, Wendell. If enough of us do, we may win yet!"

WASHINGTON, NOVEMBER 1

THE capital agog. This afternoon two Puerto Ricans attempted to assassinate the President! One was shot down and badly wounded on the steps of Blair House, where the President happened to be taking a nap. The other was killed leaping a hedge near the house. One guard is dead, two wounded.

NOVEMBER 2

WITH all the excitement in Washington, it was difficult last night for Rikind and me to do much thinking about how to handle our statement concerning the O'Brien findings. We needn't have bothered. O'Brien postponed the announcement until tomorrow. He's not fool enough to try to compete for headlines with an attempted assassination of a President of the United States. Actually Rikind and I sat up late at the Press Club listening to the correspondents discuss the shooting.

Give the prize for comment on it to the leading French Communist daily, *L'Humanité*. It blandly tells its Paris readers today that the attempt to murder the President was staged as an election publicity stunt!

Rikind still persists in telling me that in all probability I shall be "cleared" tomorrow. It's a good sign, he says, that the committee, according to his grapevine, is having difficulty on agreeing. He hears that Senator Jones is leading the fight against

O'Brien, and that Breen and Kleinschmidt — those colorless solons! — are on the fence.

NOVEMBER 3

A FURTHER delay of the verdict on me. But Senator O'Brien promises it definitely for tomorrow.

I feel rather depressed this evening. Steve tried to cheer me up, but I could sense that he felt pretty low himself — not only on my account but because of his own frustrations. The secretary has told him that nothing can be done until after next week's elections. But I think Steve feels that even then nothing will be done. In the meantime, he goes about branded as a "disloyal" citizen. Can't even get a roof of his own to put over his head.

NOVEMBER 4 (SATURDAY)

UNLIKE a proceeding in a court, there was no session today of the Senate Committee on Security and Americanism to render its verdict. At four P.M. Senator O'Brien simply made available to the press the text of the committee report. There were actually two reports, a majority and a minority finding.

The first, signed by all but Senator Jones, sinks me, I guess. But I should be grateful to Jones. He strove valiantly to save me. As Rikind says, his minority report is classic in its Jeffersonian eloquence.

But O'Brien has the votes — 4 to 1. And the majority finds me guilty as charged: that I am a Communist and a Soviet agent! Moreover, it holds that I lied when I denied I was neither the one nor the other and recommends to the Department of Justice that it submit to a grand jury the question of whether I did not commit perjury before the committee.

My troubles, therefore, are far from over. In fact, you might say, they are just beginning. In the meantime, what do I do? How earn a living, for instance? The hell with trying to defend your good name. I have to start thinking about mere physical survival.

YVONNE, looking fresh and lovely, was standing on the platform at Penn Station when the overnight train got in at seven this morning. She drove us through the empty streets in the rain to the house where she had, with Marguerite Burnett's help, an enormous breakfast ready. For the first time since yesterday noon I was able to eat.

The morning papers are full of O'Brien and me. I spent most of this Sabbath Day poring through them and pondering the verdict. Its reasoning is unbelievable. But there it stands before me, the incredible words written down indelibly in black on white.

. . . Raymond Whitehead was proven to have had a long and intimate association with Communism and Communists. Two former American Communists have sworn on oath that he was a member of the party. One of them, Miss Elsie McCabe, his life-long friend, has testified that he, in fact, joined her in the Communist conspiracy. . . .

Much was made by Whitehead of the fact that no evidence was offered that he ever had a membership card. But Mr. Frederick Newman and Miss McCabe have testified, from their long experience as top Communists, that many leading comrades were never issued cards. . . . Raymond Whitehead, on several occasions during the hearing, demanded that specific evidence, other than the word of Mr. Newman and Miss McCabe, be produced to show that he was a Communist. The committee, Senator Jones dissenting, finds that the corroborative evidence was overwhelming.

For instance, it has been proven that the bulk of Whitehead's magazine articles and broadcasts constantly reflected the Communist party line as laid down by Moscow. Bert Woodruff, the well-known columnist and authority on Communism in America, Archibald Oakes, who supervised Whitehead's Sunday broadcasts in New York for the sponsor, and Robert A. Fletcher, vice-president and general-manager of F.B.C., have all testified that Whitehead took the party line in what he wrote and broadcast.

But this is self-evident to any fair-minded, patriotic American who reads, as committee members did, an ample sampling of what Whitehead said and wrote. There are, for instance, a dozen articles, hundreds of broadcasts and whole chapters in his books in which he savagely attacks such renowned anti-Communist leaders as Franco and Chiang Kai-shek. This was the pure party line as laid down by the Kremlin . . . In answer to a specific question by Senator Reynolds, Raymond Whitehead admitted that he had praised the Red army of Communistic Russia during the war. . . .

Mr. Whitehead admitted that he subscribed to, and was a regular reader of the *Daily Worker*, the leading Communist daily newspaper in the United States. His purpose was obvious: to learn daily what the Communist party line on any given issue was, so that he could reflect it in his Sunday broadcasts. In this connection, Mr. Newman has explained to the committee that such was the principal objective of the *Daily Worker*: to keep the comrades up to date on the twistings and the turnings of the Moscow party line. Though he had no specific written evidence on the point, Mr. Newman told us that Whitehead, as a member of the Communist party and therefore under its rigid discipline, was obligated to take that line in whatever he broadcast or wrote. We have seen that he did.

Even Raymond Whitehead's family life was Communistic, as the evidence presented to us made clear. He admitted, for instance, that he sent his innocent son to a Communist summer camp as recently as last year. The hearings brought out that Mr. Whitehead's wife was the daughter of a well-known French Socialist. She herself admitted to being a member of her father's political party in France, the Radical-Socialist party. As is well known, Socialism is the next step to Communism. In fact, as expert witnesses pointed out, they are often inseparable. And it need hardly be pointed out that creeping Socialism is a direct threat to the American way of life. . . .

The committee heard evidence that Raymond Whitehead refused to sign the loyalty oath at F.B.C. Indeed, Whitehead, under questioning, admitted that he refused to sign. Why? He was asked merely to swear that he was not, and never had been, a Communist. The majority could not help but come to the conclusion that Whitehead's refusal to sign the loyalty oath at F.B.C. was strong evidence that he was a Communist. If he were not, why didn't he sign? . . .

In the light of this mountain of evidence, the committee, Senator Jones dissenting, concludes that Raymond Whitehead was in fact a member of the Communist party and that he served it loyally and effectively in the best interests of Soviet Russia and against the best interests of the United States of America, of which he is a native-born citizen.

Was Raymond Whitehead also a Soviet agent?

The committee believes that all American Communists are *ipso facto* Soviet agents in that, as pointed out above, they serve the interests of the Soviet Union. But the evidence before us has convinced the majority of members, Senator Jones dissenting, that Whitehead was more than an agent by that definition; that he was, in fact, a conscious, deliberate, active and effective instrument of the World Communist Conspiracy.

His close contact with Russian Communists, indeed with Russian spies and agents disguised as diplomats, goes back a long way. He admitted to the committee that during the long years he chose to live outside the United States and reside abroad, he had a number of close friends in Soviet Russian embassies, especially in Paris and Berlin.

But it is in his intimate relations with one, Alexis Radislav, that his guilt becomes manifest. Radislav, according to the evidence presented to us — and not denied by Whitehead — is perhaps the most notorious Russian Communistic spy living today. Radislav's special field is Asia, where he is credited with having stirred up much of the trouble that has affected that unhappy part of the world and which has led so much of it to go Communistic and hence become hostile to the United States of America and its democratic allies.

It was established beyond doubt in these hearings that Radislav and Whitehead have, for years, been in cahoots. Only one conclusion can be drawn from this sinister relationship and the majority of members have drawn it.

Mr. Whitehead and Comrade Radislav became close friends many years ago. They saw a good deal of each other at Paris, Geneva and other places. A year ago last summer Raymond Whitehead made a mysterious journey to that almost inaccessible city of Central Asia, Kabul, the capital of Afghanistan. His chief purpose, according to the evidence presented to us and indeed according to Whitehead's own admission, was to get in touch with this notorious Soviet agent and spy, Radislav.

Mr. Whitehead has tried to explain and the Secretary of State has sought to confirm that Whitehead was sent to Kabul by the secretary on a so-called confidential mission. We have asked in vain for the secretary to explain the nature of that mission. He has refused. Mr. Whitehead has refused.

The majority, having weighed all the evidence, is of the opinion that whatever the nature of Whitehead's 'mission,' he used it as a cover to contact Russia's most famous spy. It is interesting to note that he chose what is undoubtedly the most out-of-the-way capital in the world for this meeting. It was the safest place imaginable to get in touch with the enemy.

However, as the evidence before us revealed, it was not completely safe. Whitehead's sinister contact with Radislav could not be kept secret. We had a full report on it, from one of the trusted American stenographers in our embassy there, a young woman for whose patriotism we herewith wish to express our appreciation. We had another report from Security Agent X-143 in Kabul. And finally Whitehead himself, on being confronted with this startling evidence, admitted to his compromising contacts with the Russian spy.

It is true that Raymond Whitehead offered an explanation of why he met almost daily with this notorious Kremlin agent, always — be it noted — within the confines of the Soviet Embassy where his plottings, he thought, were safe from scrutiny by American security officers. He conceded to us, on questioning, that he played chess nearly every day with Radislav, and that on numerous occasions he sat up all night with him drinking. His excuse was that this was necessary to accomplish the 'mission' which the Secretary of State had entrusted him to carry out. But the majority of this committee cannot believe that it was necessary for any loyal American citizen, no matter what his assignment, to have such close contact with so sinister a Russian under such suspicious circumstances.

Miss Jenkins, the embassy stenographer mentioned above, to whom Whitehead dictated some of his correspondence, has testified that she instinctively felt Whitehead to be a disloyal, subversive, traitorous American.

But the compelling evidence comes from U. S. Security agent X-143, who reported fully on Whitehead's activities in Kabul and whose vivid account has been admitted into the evidence before us. It is a damning document — for Raymond Whitehead! A total of fifty-one hours spent at the Soviet Embassy in the four weeks he was in Kabul! Most of those fifty-one hours spent plotting with Russia's most notorious spy! But meetings also in the Red Embassy with the Russian Ambassador, the first secretary, the second secretary, the military attaché — and revealing! — with a certain Kotchov, identified as a Russian secret-police higher-up! Evening after evening of heavy drinking, which as the security officer points out, is a common method employed by the Russians to get American officials to talk and to make them pliable to Russian design! The spectacle of a supposedly American official, as Whitehead ostensibly was — even though temporarily — returning on at least eight occasions from the Soviet Embassy to his hotel, so the security agent reports, with his breath reeking with alcohol — undoubtedly vodka!

And finally — and here Whitehead's guilt becomes clear as day — the security officer piecing together the original notes which Whitehead had jotted down on returning from his nocturnal plotting at the Soviet Embassy and which he thought he had safely disposed of by tearing them up and throwing them into a wastebasket. They are contained in the special exhibit, SE-1, attached to this report. In the opinion of the majority, they leave no doubt whatsoever of the

Red conspiracy in which Raymond Whitehead was participating with Radislav at the Soviet Embassy in Kabul. They reveal what the barbaric Russians were up to in Central Asia, moves against the United States and our Allies. They reveal that the Russians took Whitehead into their confidence as regards their most secret and sinister plottings. It is clear beyond a shadow of a doubt that they would not have done so had Raymond Whitehead not been in on the plots himself as an agent of Soviet Russia. . . .

In the light of all the evidence, which in this case seems to the majority to be overwhelming, we conclude that Raymond Whitehead was in fact a conscious, deliberate, active and effective instrument of the World Communist Conspiracy, a Soviet agent who betrayed his own country on behalf of the Soviet Union and World Communism!

I admit to reeling dizzily when I read this for the first time in Washington yesterday. It has the same effect on rereading today. Who can blame an innocent citizen, devouring these heady words in this morning's Sunday newspaper, for concluding that I am guilty as hell? Old Mephistopheles O'Brien has done his dirtiest with consummate skill.

Or will Senator Jones, perhaps, in his eloquent minority report, redress the balance in the mind of a decent citizen? He not only finds the charges against me unproved; he dares to do what few Senators, public officials, newspapers and radio commentators dare today: lash out at O'Brien for his irresponsibility, his lies and his malice.

But he is one lone Senator against four others. Will the average reader not conclude, as do we all so often, that the majority is right? Or will some, at least, heed his words?

Never before in my long exprience in the Senate have I seen such a concoction of half-truths and untruths, of idle gossip and hearsay, of ungrounded suspicion, of unproven accusations, as were presented to this committee for its serious consideration. . . . For the first time in our history, so far as I am aware, we have seen a democratic institution borrow from the Communist totalitarians the contemptible technique of exploiting the "big lie," "guilt by association, by paternity, by matrimony" and so on. . . .

And what has been the principal result of this hearing? Aside from the tragic and, in my opinion, wholly unjustified destruction of the good name and reputation of one American citizen, the result has been, when you add this case to others like it before this and other committees of the Congress, to further divide and confuse the American people, to sow suspicion among them, to undermine their confidence in each other and in their government — and all this at a time when they should be unified and confident in the face of the Communist attempt to foment dissension amongst us. . . .

As for the specific charges made against Raymond Whitehead by the chairman of the committee, and now sustained by him and three other members, that Mr. Whitehead was a member of the Communist party and a Communist agent, I find them not proven. . . .

As to both accusations, and especially the first, we are asked to take the word of two former American Communists, Miss Elsie McCabe and Mr. Frederick Newman. They offered not one scrap of evidence to support their charges. They asked us to take their word, though when I questioned them they admitted that as Communists they had often lied. I myself am not convinced that a Communist automatically overcomes his predilection for lying as soon as he leaves the party. . . .

It has been pointed out during the hearings that Whitehead proved he was a Communist by taking the party line in his writings and broadcasts. But he did not take the party line when he denounced the infamous Nazi-Soviet pact of 1939 or when he opposed Hitler at the moment Stalin was embracing him. He did not take the party line when he made his bitter broadcasts at Russia's aggression against Finland in the first year of the war. One could cite dozens of other examples. But it is held against him that he attacked Franco and Chiang Kai-shek. We are told that to oppose these two gentlemen was to follow the party line. What nonsense! Like many others I myself have publicly spoken out against these two enemies of democracy. I defy anyone to prove that I am therefore a Communist. . . .

During these hearings we have been offered the sorry spectacle — and I hope for the last time in America — of attempting to prove a man's guilt by association, by paternity, by matrimony. It was brought out, for example, that the father of Whitehead's wife was a well-known French "Socialist" and that she herself, following in her father's footsteps, was a "Socialist." Even if she were, even if she were a Communist, that would not be proof that her husband was. We have not yet reached a point in America, I hope, where we establish "guilt by matrimony." But here, it seems to me, honorable members were doubly guilty of failing to search out the truth. For even the accusation that Mrs. Whitehead, and her father, were "Socialists" is manifestly absurd. The so-called "Radical-Socialist" party which Mrs. Whitehead's father represented in the French Senate and of which she herself was a member was not "Socialist" at all, but a middle-of-the-road, bourgeois party leaning to the conservative side and supporting, as do conservative groups in general, the *status quo.* . . .

I find therefore that on the basis of the evidence submitted to us there is no reason to believe that Raymond Whitehead was a member of the Communist party or a believer in, or supporter of, Communism. . . .

The even more serious charge that Whitehead was a Soviet agent rested largely on his relations with one Alexis Radislav, the counselor of the Soviet Embassy in Kabul, and admittedly a notorious and skillful agent of Russian imperialism in Asia. But why did Whitehead make contact with Radislav in Kabul, as he freely admits he did? This is the nub of the whole sinister indictment. Majority members say Whitehead made the contact in order to carry out his duties as a Soviet Communist agent. But this is demonstrably false if we consider what Whitehead's mission was in Afghanistan. The majority complains that neither Whitehead nor the Secretary of State would tell. I hold they were justified in not telling, though the failure to do so, as Whitehead said, obviously hurt his case by casting unfair suspicion on him. For how can we conduct diplomacy in a goldfish bowl? How can we ascertain what the Russians are up to if we publicize our attempts to find out?

But the purpose of Whitehead's mission came out at the very end of the hearing when the special exhibit known as SE-1 was admitted in evidence. This pasting together by an overanxious and gullible security officer of Whitehead's notes, which he had torn up and thrown into a wastepaper basket after dictating memos on them to an American Embassy stenographer, revealed that he had been able to find out from Radislav and perhaps from other officials of the Russian Embassy in Kabul, what the Soviets were up to in Asia, what their moves against us and our Allies would be. Obviously this was most useful and vital information for our government.

But the majority have willfully and falsely misinterpreted these notes. They contend that Whitehead never could have obtained such highly secret information about Russian intentions unless he was in on the plots themselves, as a trusted Soviet agent.

I say that this is a vicious and unwarranted assumption. I say it is obvious to any fair-minded person that exactly the opposite assumption is true, namely, that Whitehead was sent out to Kabul by the Secretary of State to find out what the Russians were up to in Asia, that he did find out, and that he reported his findings to the American government. Instead of condemning him in a manner to ruin him for life this Senate committee should praise him and honor him for serving his country skillfully and well in a difficult and perhaps dangerous diplomatic assignment. . . .

I therefore conclude that the charge that Raymond Whitehead was a Soviet agent was not only not proven but shown to be utterly false, and I deeply regret that a man who has shown himself to be a loyal and patriotic American should receive from the majority members this unforgivable blot upon his name. I am sure that when our tempers have cooled, when the foul suspicion that permeates the American air today has subsided, that this committee, or some other of the Senate, will make good the wrong it has done.

This leads me to make an observation or two at the end.

Like almost all Americans, I believe that Communism and the new imperialism of Soviet Russia constitute a very real threat to our country and our democratic way of life. But in coping with it I do not intend to sit idly by, in silence, while those who shout loudest about curbing Communists and Russia, rapidly undermine the very freedoms which are our chief strength against the enemy.

We have lately seen in this country the ugly spectacle of private citizens, as well as government employees, being destroyed by public condemnation whose only basis is rumor, hearsay, gossip and deliberately false accusations. This has been accomplished, sometimes in such hearings as this, by the crass disregard for the most elementary rules of evidence and fair play. The mere hurling of a charge of disloyalty or Communism, however irresponsible its perpetrator, has been accepted by too many Americans as the same thing as establishing guilt. We have seen come true the line of Shelley that "the breath of accusation kills an innocent name."

Such a situation is no doubt normal in a totalitarian land. In my humble opinion, it has no place in America. . . .

We might well ponder a warning I read recently in May's Constitutional History of England:

> Next in importance to personal freedom is immunity from suspicions and jealous observation. Men may be without restraints upon their liberty . . . but if their steps are tracked by spies and informers, their words noted down for crimination, their associates watched as conspirators, who shall say that they are free?

We might further ponder the vision of one of our greatest living judges* in remarking the other day on the same subject:

* Judge Learned Hand — R.W.

I believe that the community is already in the process of a dissolution where each man begins to eye his neighbor as a possible enemy, where noncomformity with the accepted creed, political as well as religious, is a mark of disaffection, where denunciation, without specification or backing, takes the place of evidence, Risk for risk, for myself I had rather take my chance that some traitor will escape detection than spread abroad a spirit of general suspicion and distrust, which accepts rumor and gossip in place of undismayed and unintimidated inquiry.

Senator Jones saved one little surprise for the end.

"I recommend," said he, "that the Department of Justice submit to a grand jury the question of whether perjury has been committed before this committee by Miss Elsie McCabe and Mr. Frederick Newman."

NOVEMBER 6

Steve and I, with nothing else to do, spent most of the day at the U.N. out at Lake Success. We ran into Wendell Philpots, who was a picture of gloom — not only because of the Korean news but because of Senator O'Brien. The esteemed solon is threatening further "revelations" in his case. What they could possibly be Wendell hasn't the slightest idea. In the meantime the secretary general has been embarrassed because the State Department has not yet "cleared" Philpots for employment at the U.N. Its stalling is obviously a sop to O'Brien, as if you could appease him!

We brought Wendell home to dinner to cheer him up, phoning Wanda to join us. To get his mind off O'Brien, we chewed the fat over tomorrow's mid-term elections.

The more responsible commentators agreed tonight that this has been, as one of them put it, one of the "dirtiest" election campaigns of this twentieth century. So many smears, they said — and vilification and unproved charges. Wendell, who has had a lot of experience with unsavory elections in France, said he was shocked by what the newspapers reported — and they probably overlooked a good deal.

[*341*]

"To read the papers and hear the candidates on the air," Wendell said, frowning, "you would think that this election was between a huge Communist party, such as we have in France, and the non-Communists. In one state after another, from Maryland to California, they've managed, by means beyond my simple comprehension, to make Communism the big issue. Yet there are no Communist candidates in those states. Will someone please explain to me how Communism arises, then, as an issue?"

Neither Steve nor I, I'm afraid, were of much help.

NOVEMBER 10

I REALLY got down to work on the book today, laboring at it all morning and all afternoon. To my surprise I found that my notes — aside from those in this journal — are so voluminous that if I work at it every day — and what else is there to do? — I should be able to finish the book by the end of the year.

NOVEMBER 11

ARMISTICE DAY, but somehow it does not stir me as it used to. The second war was too big and too recent.

Colette Robson came to dinner last night. I have never seen her looking lovelier. She did not so much as mention Mark. She has taken a small apartment in the East Sixties and is looking for a place in the country. I told her I hoped she would now return to the theater. There is such a dearth on Broadway of great actresses.

"Write me a play, Raymond," she said, "and perhaps I shall."

This morning she drove off with Steve and the four girls — Steve's three and our Maria — for a week end at Chris Chambers's. They made a merry carful. Dick is out on Long Island. He is beginning to organize his own week ends. It is a good sign, I think, of his growing up. I hope — the ugly little thought just occurred to me — that he is not restless to get away from me because of my disgrace. I must have a frank talk with him next week. Maria, I think, is too young to realize what has happened.

If her schoolmates ever mention it to her, and torment her, she has not let on.

The house is unnaturally quiet this Saturday afternoon, but Yvonne and I are happy to be alone for once. We have some problems to talk over.

NOVEMBER 12 (SUNDAY)

IT IS a temptation, of course, to pull out and return to Europe to live. Yvonne is rather keen on it. She points out that we could live in Versailles in a wing of the big family house. Her parents are getting old. They are ailing. One day the house will be hers. I could write articles from Paris for the British press and the English-language publications in the Empire, including India. I could get my books published in London. She could teach school. We could manage.

We could. And not have to live from day to day under a cloud. It is a temptation, but I say "NO."

To go back to Europe now would be to admit defeat. I do not admit it. A beating, yes; but not defeat. If I went back now, it would be forever. I could never marshal the stamina to make again the readjustment of coming home. And look at Wendell Philpots, I say. His years of misery and hopelessness over there. No, Yvonne, I shall not spend my last years as a lonely, bitter expatriate.

Beides, there are the children. We agreed that they should be American. They already are. I want them to stay that way.

This is my country, Yvonne. This is where I belong. I'm going to stay, and fight — not only to exist, but to live as I like and say and write what I damned please.

Yvonne, with tears in her eyes but also a smile on her lips, agrees. The other thing was just a suggestion, she says, a possible way out. But now that we are determined to stay, how are we to live? she asks. The down-to-earth common sense of the French begins to come out in her. She volunteers part of the answer. She will get a job teaching French.

Perhaps that will not be necessary, I say. I will write books.

[343]

Even a victim of O'Brien can publish books in America. The shabby Senator is not yet in a strong enough position to tell Americans whom and what they shall read, though no doubt, in his crabbed mind, he has visions of book-burning in the near future. I can churn out pieces for the British press and the English-language Empire press better from here than from Paris. The U.N. is a fertile source of stories.

I can do that; or maybe I will take up something quite different, I say, and Yvonne catches the twinkle in my eye. What is that? she asks. You remember that farm we looked at? Steve and I might farm it. There is a decent living in dairying, they say. Have you ever farmed? Yvonne asks. Has Steve? No, but we could learn. And wouldn't it be wonderful to get back to the soil? It would, she agrees.

In the meantime, unfortunately, we have certain expenses, Yvonne, ever the practical Frenchwoman, reminds me. Keeping the children in a private school in New York costs a couple of thousand dollars a year. Well, other children — in fact almost all of them in this country — go to public schools. In the country the public schools would be all right. I went to them myself. Out in Indiana.

What about the expenses of the hearing? Yvonne asks. I had forgotten them. But they have to be faced. The O'Brien committee's verdict not only has wiped out any possibility of my earning a living by the only profession I know, but the hearings which led to the verdict have cost me some $5000, even though Rikind will not take a cent for his own services or those of his law firm.

Aside from those expenses, we have enough in the bank to tide us over through Christmas and New Year's, Yvonne calculates — perhaps a few weeks longer since Steve is contributing his full share to food and rent.

That gives us a couple of months of grace, I say, trying to smile. It is time enough, Yvonne. We go out for a stroll along the East River. It is a mellow November evening and the lights of the bridges sparkle in the sky and down the stream a couple of tugboats hoot at each other with their whistles and there

[344]

are other lovers about in the shadows, arm in arm, gazing, whispering; and under the soft light of a street lamp I catch the profile of my wife, straight and provocative, and see the dark eyes burning with a steady fire that was never stoked and never quenched, and I move my arm free from her ample shoulder and muss her long black hair and kiss her, holding her close and feeling her growing response. Then we turn, and with quickened steps make for home to be wonderfully alone together all through this wondrous night.

NOVEMBER 13

STEVE back, and full of talk about our farm. He went over to see it again yesterday, accompanied by a neighboring farmer, a friend of Chris's. There are one hundred acres in woods, twenty-five in hillside, unimproved pasture, and seventy-five in cultivatable fields, most of which are in fair shape, as are the barns. The owner, a widow whose husband died last summer, will sell it to us cheap if we buy now and pay cash. She will let us have her dairy herd of thirty cows cheap too. About $17,000 for everything — house, land, cattle, equipment.

We sat up with Yvonne discussing how to finance it. Steve says that if he resigns he will be entitled to a pension of about $6500 a year. He could borrow on that and on his life-insurance policies. I could borrow something on my policies. Yvonne thinks her father might lend her a couple of thousand. We could get a mortgage for the rest. Steve is writing right away to the Agriculture Department for all its bulletins on dairy farming.

Apparently Steve and Colette hit it off rather well. He talked about her a good deal. She is also looking for a place in the vicinity.

NOVEMBER 15

MY BIRTHDAY — and I did not think it was one we ought to celebrate. I didn't mention it, and to my relief no one else around the house did either. But when I came in at dusk from a long walk, Yvonne, Steve and the children greeted me with a surprise birthday dinner. There were presents and a large birthday cake with forty-seven candles. I must say I was moved.

Wendell Philpots and Wanda came by for a drink after dinner. They are both in the lower depths of depression. Bert Woodruff and Frederick Newman have been sniping at Wendell with nasty paragraphs in their columns and echoing O'Brien's demand that the State Department hold up approving his appointment at the U.N.

NOVEMBER 17

AFTER school today Dick came up to my study. I was feeling rather pleased with myself; I had just finished the opening chapter of the book and it had turned out surprisingly well.

"Dad, why don't you sue that O'Brien fellow for libel?"

The youngsters must have been discussing my case at school. "I can't, Dick," I said.

"Why not? You've got a good case, haven't you?"

There was just the slightest edge of doubt in his tone.

"Because the findings of the Senate committee are privileged. And because O'Brien, Dick, hasn't got the guts to repeat his charges outside of the committee or outside of the Senate, where they're also privileged. If he did, I'd sue him."

"I see."

But I was not quite sure that he did. There was a moment of silence. Dick shifted uneasily from one foot to the other, but made no move to go.

"What are you going to do now, Pop?" he asked after a while.

"Keep on plugging. Finish this book, for one thing. Write some magazine articles. And . . ."

"What about radio?"

"That's out, for the time being, Dick."

"You're awfully good on the air, Pop. And it isn't just I who think so. The kids at school say so too."

"I'll go back to radio eventually, Dick. Or maybe into TV. I've got some new ideas for TV, you know."

"TV sure needs some new ideas," Dick said. "Especially for the news shows. I'm telling you." He was getting old enough to have his own decided opinions. I looked up at him. He seemed already a grown man.

"Dick," I said, "how would you like to do a little farming?"

"Gee, I think I'd like it, Pop. Why do you ask?"

"We're thinking of buying a farm and maybe doing some dairying."

"You and Steve?"

"Yes. Are you interested?"

"Gee, I certainly am, Pop."

And then he was off. He is week-ending again out at Long Island. I'm glad I talked with him.

NOVEMBER 18 (SATURDAY)

SWEATED all day at the typewriter getting chapter two launched. God knows, writing does not come easy with me. Does it — with the good writers? Didn't it with Dostoevski, Tolstoi, Dickens, Balzac?

If I didn't have this book to occupy my working hours — and most of my thoughts — I would feel awfully adrift. The idea itself, I think, is good. I am combining two themes: a farewell to Europe, and how America looks when you finally come home.

NOVEMBER 19 (SUNDAY)

STEVE wanted me to drive up to Connecticut and have another look at the farm today. Keen as I am about it, I put him off. I've decided to make one more pitch for a job at my old profession. I swallowed my pride and asked Henry Wadsworth Prentice, editor of *U.S.A.*, to lunch tomorrow. If I can combine magazine articles with books, I won't need to worry about being off radio.

Somewhat to my surprise, Steve said he would drive up to Chris Chambers's anyway. Colette, he said, wanted to go.

Thus Yvonne and I have had a day off in town with the four girls. We went for a romp in Central Park at noon, hurried home for sandwiches, and then piled off to hear a concert of the Philharmonic at Carnegie Hall. Marguerite, who reminds me more each day of her wonderful mother, was carried away by the music, as indeed was I. Being almost supersensitive she was a little disturbed, I gather, by Steve's going off alone to Connecticut with Colette Robson. Wouldn't it be rather nice, though, if Steve and Colette did hit it off?

NOVEMBER 20

PRENTICE turned me down rather charmingly. He praised my courage in standing up to O'Brien. He said I had given encouragement to every decent person in the country. He would love to have me back among his regular contributors. But at the moment *U.S.A.* is overstaffed, he said, and "terribly embarrassed" by having more old-time contributors than it can use. Like all magazines, he explained, it has had to turn increasingly to new, young writers — the postwar generation.

"But please keep us in mind," he said affably, "if you ever have anything you think we ought to publish. The country needs to hear your voice, Raymond." Perhaps that was a hint. Why didn't I go back to radio?

Henry Wadsworth Prentice, a sparkling muckraking liberal in the old days, has aged, I thought. He has become rather careful and conservative. Who hasn't, who is still in business?

We had a fine view from the Rainbow Room. The spires of the great city were half enshrouded in fog.

NOVEMBER 21

STEVE BURNETT has been offered a chance to resign from the foreign service, with full pension and "without prejudice" — which means the "disloyalty" charge is thrown out by executive action and the stain on his honor erased. Though he hesitates to quit under fire, he is inclined to accept.

Wait till O'Brien hears about this!

As usual, Steve sees his situation quite realistically.

"Cleared though I may be," he said this evening after dinner while we were talking things over, "I realize I won't be able to do a lot of the things I had contemplated doing after retirement. Teaching history in a university or college in some pleasant New England town, for instance. Or heading some agency at the U.N. No college and not even the U.N. would dare hire me now. Still, I could be worse off, Raymond. I will have a pension of roughly $6500 a year. When the girls are through college that will be quite sufficient for my own requirements. Until then, I will need a little more. How about that farm, Raymond?"

"It's a go, Steve," I said.

My pleasant luncheon with Prentice yesterday had convinced me that the farm was all that was left, except the books. And I could not support a family on books alone.

"I'll write my father tonight," Yvonne said cheerily. "Maybe I can get three thousand dollars out of him. It is a lot of francs, but I am sure Papa has them."

"How about clinching the deal this week end?" Steve said. "We'll all be up at Chris's over Thanksgiving. A thousand dollar down payment will do it. I think I've got that much in the bank."

I got out a small bottle of champagne to celebrate. We all feel relieved that we have at last made up our minds. The land is one place even O'Brien can't drive us off. There is not a subversive clump of sod on the whole two hundred acres. On the land we can find fruitful work again, and thrive and live in peace.

NOVEMBER 22

A SPECIAL-DELIVERY letter arrived before breakfast from Elsie McCabe.

"I wanted you to be the first to know. Frederick Newman and I are getting married! He is getting his divorce next month. At last, Raymond, I have found happiness!"

Well, I don't begrudge anyone happiness, not even Elsie.

If I was the first to know, "Betty and Bob" were a close second. At breakfast the Collier couple fairly gushed over Elsie McCabe's coming marriage to Newman. We caught their program while we sipped our coffee.

"And Senator O'Brien," Betty chirped, "will be the best man!"

Sandwiched in between the almost continuous commercials was a news item about Bob Fletcher. "Incidentally" — Collier squeezed a word in, while his ebullient wife was catching her breath — "all our listeners will be pleased to hear — and I believe we are privileged to be first with the announcement — that Mr. Mark Robson has just named Mr. Robert A. Fletcher president of F.B.C. Mr. Robson himself relinquishes the post to become chairman of the board. Our congratulations to Bob Fletcher!"

So Bob had climbed to the top.

WEST CORNWALL, CONNECTICUT, NOVEMBER 23 (THANKSGIVING)

WE AGREED — a bit sentimentally, no doubt, as is natural on this day after the lavish feasting — that we had something to be thankful for: the bright happiness of the day itself, the high spirits of the children, the conviviality and comradery that prevailed among us all, the haunting beauty of the late autumn landscape and the stirring of new hope in our limbs.

NOVEMBER 24

A DAY of decision, accomplishment and of a pleasant surprise. We spent the morning — there was a fine nip in the air that made your spirits soar at once — galavanting over our new fields, traipsing through the woods, inspecting, with the aid of two local farmers, the barns, the cows, the machinery, the well, the springs, the brook and the big sprawling white-frame house. For they are *ours* — at the close of this exciting day. All but ten acres of the two hundred. We sold the ten. That was the day's surprise. And it enabled us to pay down not only the thousand dollars Steve had raised but an additional $5000, which sprouted up out of the blue, as if in a fairy tale.

Colette Robson turned out to be the fairy godmother, though she stoutly rejects any claim to the role. She had joined us — Steve, Chris Chambers, Yvonne, the children, the two farmers and me — after breakfast as we set out to see the farm and come to a momentous decision. There was a wooded hill at one corner of the property which I had not seen before. It was just surplus land so far as dairying is concerned, but it commanded a superb view over the hills and looked down upon the racing, winding Housatonic River. Colette was enchanted by it. She sat down on a log, lit a cigarette, gazed across the hills and down at the river below. We could not pull her away.

"You go on and look at your smelly old barns," she said. "I'm going to sit here for a while." Marguerite Burnett remained with her.

She came in late to lunch. We had made up our minds to buy and were going over final details, adding up how much hay there was in the barns, how much feed, and so on, while Chris kidded us about how on earth we were ever going to milk a cow.

"That's simple," Steve and I maintained. "You do it with machines." Neither of us had the faintest idea of how to milk a cow by hand.

"Have you bought the place?" Colette asked rather eagerly as she sat down.

"We're going to," Steve said, grinning. "In fact, as soon as lunch is finished, Raymond and I are going over and present Mrs. What's-her-name with a certified check, which I have been nursing in my wallet, for a $1000 down payment."

"Then, I have an offer to make," Colette said impishly. "Not to the lady, but to you."

"You have a what to make?" Steve stuttered. It was all a joke, of course, I thought.

"I want that hill, gentlemen!" Colette said, raising her low voice, theatrically.

"How much you pay?" Steve fairly shouted. It was all in fun. Or so we thought.

"How much you want?" Colette said, with mock sharpness.

"I do believe the lady is serious," Chris Chambers said ironically.

"Of course, I'm serious. Listen, my dears. I'm not joking. I've found my mountaintop!"

"It's only a hill," Chris taunted her. "Not an inch over 1500 feet. A mere knoll, you might say."

"I say it's a mountain," Colette said. "And I want it. About ten acres of it. And since you two city suckers are too dumb to know how much you want I'll make you an offer! Five thousand, cash. Payable this moment."

She actually reached for her bag and pulled out a checkbook.

Colette is really subsidizing us. Five thousand dollars for ten acres is too much. But once she had convinced us she was serious, she went on to explain what had suddenly come into her mind and why, as she argued, she thought $5000 was a bargain price.

"I'll build a simple little cottage on it," she said. "But with modern improvements. I love these old Connecticut farmhouses. They're beautiful. They have charm, character. But I'm too old to put up with them, especially in winter. They're drafty, even when the furnace functions; and the plumbing is always freezing or otherwise breaking down. . . ."

"But Colette," I protested, "you could go down the road this minute and buy your mountain from the widow for a fifth of $5000."

"I could, but I won't. You two city fellows might get cold feet, and not buy after all. Where would that leave me? With a lonely hilltop on the widow's acres. With Christopher Chambers the only neighbor I knew — and he here only week ends, holidays and summers. Don't get me wrong, Steve and Raymond. I won't interfere with your farming, if that's what you're going to do. But I insist on having some old friends at the bottom of my hill. So, gentlemen, as soon as you sign with the widow, I'll sign with you. And I assure you, I consider it a bargain. Five thousand dollars for the finest view in Connecticut!"

LAST evening was even gayer than Thanksgiving. Chris got out his finest French champagne and we celebrated. He kept toasting his "new neighbors."

"To have Yvonne, not to mention Raymond and Steve, and not forgetting the children, here is just about the nicest thing that ever happened to me," Chris said, his boyish eyes lighting up. "But to have you, my beautiful Colette, in addition! I don't deserve it!"

There was only one thing he didn't like about it, Chris said, puckering his lips and trying to look distressed.

"And what is that, my dear?" Colette smiled.

Chris looked searchingly into her finely chiseled face, and we could see he really was serious, for the moment.

"Does it mean you will never return to the theater?" he said earnestly.

Colette's eyes narrowed. For just a second a sadness came over them, and then it passed and the smile returned.

"Not necessarily, Chris," she said. "Find me the right play, and I'll go back."

Whether she meant it or not, I wasn't quite sure. Did not all the great artists of the theater say that, even after they knew they would never step before the spotlights again? She had been away from Broadway so long. Mark Robson had insisted on that. And now she was forty-five or so. Watching her, I suddenly thought of something else: Had she not taken her hilltop so as to be near to Steve? The answer might come when she came to build her house. If the simple little cottage she spoke of turned out to be rather roomy and large, would it not be because she and Steve were planning to live together there one day? . . .

The joy of the children — Steve's and ours — was indescribable today. They spent most of the afternoon patting the cows and the pair of horses and romping with the dogs. They have already fallen in love with the animals. And Dick! He spent the afternoon tinkering with the tractor and the farm machinery. We could hardly get him away from the machine shed to

[*353*]

come to dinner. Only Marguerite failed to share the enthusiasm of all the rest. She spent the afternoon in Chris's library reading.

Tonight Steve suddenly broke away from our celebration. He said he had to make a telephone call. Soon he was back, beaming from ear to ear.

"I've done it!" he announced.

"What?" Yvonne asked.

"Telephoned a telegram to Washington. Ladies and gentlemen, I've resigned!"

NEW YORK, NOVEMBER 26 (SUNDAY)

THE noisy household finally subsided after the tumultuous Thanksgiving week end. We had to practically sit on the children to get them to bed. We tried to remind them there is school tomorrow. But as Maria said:

"Who cares about that darned old New York school?"

The children are already excited about going to school in the country.

Chris Chambers, who drove in with us, has a bright idea. He proposes that the three of us — he, Steve and I — write a play for Colette. All the way in we tossed possible stories and plots back and forth — with reckless abandon. Chris leans toward making the story rather autobiographical. He paused here long enough to grab a highball and take along to read the first two chapters of my book.

Steve and I up late tonight poring over a pack of bulletins from the Department of Agriculture on dairying. We couldn't make head nor tail of them.

"My God, Steve," I groaned. "What have we gone and done?"

NOVEMBER 27

CHRIS phoned this morning and said he had become so absorbed in my first couple of chapters that he would like to show them to his publishers. I told him to go ahead. I do not recall having heard from my own publisher since I re-

[354]

turned. Not that I blame him. He didn't do very well on my previous two volumes, though they sold rather well in England; and my current reputation probably does not encourage him to speculate a third time.

Our new offensive in Korea against the Chinese Reds has revived spirits out at the U.N., though Wendell Philpots, whom I saw for just a moment today, is still plunged in gloom over his personal troubles. He doesn't know whether he has a job or not, and won't know until the State Department okays him. He seems to think O'Brien is not through with him. Could be. It gives me a heartache to see Wendell in such a state so soon after his promising return.

NOVEMBER 28

STEVE BURNETT'S resignation is on the front pages today. The local morning newspapers even carry a photograph, which looks as if it were lifted from a rogue's gallery — no resemblance to Steve. The headlines, though, pleased him.

BURNETT IS CLEARED
ON LOYALTY. RESIGNS

But this afternoon in Washington Senator O'Brien reacted to the news like a bull in a china shop. He calls the State Department's action "outrageous!" "criminal!" and so on. In fact he hurriedly introduced a bill, which is surely unconstitutional, to deny Steve his pension. "I do not believe," he is quoted as shouting, "that this country owes one single red cent to a Red civil servant who has been found disloyal to it!"

Steve points out that his pension is not exactly a gift, at least not all of it. For twenty-five years he has been paying into the pension fund a nice little slice of his annual salary.

DECEMBER 1

AN EVENTFUL day. Chris Chambers took me down to his publishers, Woodbury & Sons, this afternoon. We emerged from the pleasantest of conversations with a contract for the book and a check for $2500 as an advance on it. But most encouraging of all was Woodbury's attitude. They are not afraid of anybody, including Senator O'Brien. They asked me not to pull any punches.

DECEMBER 3 (SUNDAY)

WENDELL dropped by to fill us in on the catastrophic news from Korea. The Chinese Communists have struck back, smashed our offensive, launched a mighty one of their own, broken through our lines on a wide front, surrounded whole divisions of our troops, and now threaten us with a disastrous defeat. Tomorrow, Wendell says, the American public will be told the worst news it has had since Pearl Harbor: two whole U.S. divisions trapped in North Korea, and the rest retreating for their lives! He was too full of this news to mention his difficulties with O'Brien.

DECEMBER 4

A LETTER from my English publisher, from old Hamilton J. Smith, himself.

DEAR RAYMOND:

We have followed with interest and much anguish, believe me, your news. . . . Yesterday I read in one of the gossip columns that you were at work on a new book. Please let us know about it and whether you want an advance. What we would like from you — in this book or the next, and the sooner the better — is something about America. We are very puzzled over here at what is happening over there. Perhaps you could explain, for one thing, what the newspapers here refer to as "O'Brienism." Some people in London speak of it in terms they have previously reserved for "Stalinism." . . . At any rate, do let us hear from you soon.

DECEMBER 5

YVONNE announced this morning that her father had generously come through with a $3000 "loan." With this plus $2000 from my book advance plus Steve's $4000 we have enough to complete payment on the farm, except for $2000 we are going to borrow on a mortgage. Colette's $5000 really put us into business. Probably we will need a little cash reserve at first. But income from the milk will begin at once. That is, if we can manage to extract milk from the cows.

DECEMBER 6

WE ARE going to move to our farm for Christmas! Steve, loaded with our money, drove up to West Cornwall today, made the final payment and arranged for the mortgage. Bill Rikind has bullied our landlord here into letting us out of our lease. Bill threatened to sue him for damages for giving us six months' notice during my hearing. Apparently it was also a breach of contract.

I told Bill I would be able to pay off our expenses for the hearing. Milk prices are going up. Also, once we are settled in the routine of dairying, I'll finish the book. It could be a best-seller. You never know.

Much noisy rejoicing in this house tonight at the news.

DECEMBER 7

WENDELL PHILPOTS'S affairs reached what, I suppose, was the inevitable crisis today, and tonight we are worried sick over him.

Senator O'Brien has given him the full treatment. Though legally and constitutionally and every other way it is none of O'Brien's business whom the U.N. Secretariat hires, the Senator today subpoenaed Wendell to appear before his committee to answer "certain charges" in connection with his employment, "as an American citizen," at the U.N. The Grand Inquisitor says he wants a full explanation from Philpots of why he stayed away from America so long, and a frank account (!) of his relations with such "Communists" as Raymond Whitehead and Stephen A. Burnett.

He also demands that Philpots answer the "grave charges"

[357]

that "sinister foreign influences were responsible for getting this American citizen his high post in the U.N. Secretariat."

The Clark press carries the story in flaming red headlines. Even the other journals display it prominently on page one.

We had Wendell and Wanda over for cocktails and dinner, and worked on them all evening. Wanda is in the depths of a Slavic depression which only a Dostoevski could fathom. She is in a murky daze, says nothing, but weeps frequently.

Wendell is simply down, and is too weary, too discouraged, too hurt, too proud, to care about getting up and knocking O'Brien down. Not that he has surrendered. Far from it. He keeps saying he did not come back to his native land to be destroyed by charlatans.

"If the people of this country," he said, "want to be dominated by political hoodlums, that's their business. I don't."

"Wendell," I said, "you can't go back to Paris now."

"We'll see what I can do," he said, with some heat. "One thing I won't do is to obey this ridiculous subpoena."

We frantically summoned Bill Rikind, who talked with his usual bubbling optimism.

"Why, Mr. Philpots," Bill said, "we'll make mincemeat of that crawling worm."

But Wendell was not interested. "I've been a fairly patriotic and perhaps a little too conservative American all my life. But I don't intend to prove it to a know-nothing Senator," he said. "Maybe the America I grew up in," he said, with a sad smile, "has ceased to exist. It had great virtues, and I believed in them. But if it's dead, as it now seems to be, I don't care, gentlemen, to stay around in it any longer."

"Wendell, you've got to stay around and fight to bring it back!" I said, trying to arouse him.

"You fought, Raymond," he said, not maliciously, "and I'm glad you did. But I'm too old."

It was midnight when Wendell and Wanda got up to go. Wanda frightened me. She had dried her eyes for the last time. They were bloodshot and glassy. This usually so friendly and warm and vital woman glared at us, her old friends, as if she were in a trance and saw in us her dread enemies. She clung to Wendell's arm and neither shook hands in parting, as she customarily did, nor said good-by.

Wendell, outwardly at least, seemed composed. He had made up his mind to several things, he said. For one, he would not obey the O'Brien subpoena.

"Let them come and arrest me — if they can," he said, and though he pressed his lips grimly and his eyes flashed, I felt he was trying to smile.

"How about lunch tomorrow, Wendell?" I said, as I saw them to the door. I would have to work on him some more.

"Good."

"I'll pick you up at your office. Shall we say about noontime?"

"Fine."

I wrung his hand warmly, kissed Wanda on both cheeks, though she did not respond, and saw them out into the cold, blustery, December night.

DECEMBER 8

I HURRIED down First Avenue, turning into the U.N. Secretariat some minutes before twelve, but it was too late.

When I got into the lobby I sensed the excitement. Through the big glass windows I could see a crowd milling about on the terrace above the river. My heart sank. For what must have been several minutes I stood there by a pillar, unable to move one foot before the other. I clutched at a guard hurrying by. I asked him what had happened out there. He rushed on, without replying. But I knew, without asking, without forcing myself out on the terrace to see. If I had only come a little sooner! My God, why had I not come a half hour sooner! . . .

Wanda and Wendell jumped from his tenth-story office in the U.N. Secretariat at 11:42 A.M. Her body slid into the East River and was dragged out by a fire department boat. Wendell had not leapt so far. His remains were found on the terrace.

[359]

There were two brief notes on his desk, both addressed to me.

Wendell's handwriting was neat:

Sorry, my friend, about the lunch. We are tired. We are going away — for good. Bless you and Yvonne and the children. We both think of you fondly.

Wanda had scrawled, almost illegibly, in large characters that filled a sheet of U.N. stationery:

Raymond! Raymond! Raymond! Why? You know! Forgive! Love! Love — Wanda.

DECEMBER 10 (SUNDAY)

A GRAY, cold day with a North wind whistling down the river. Steve and Yvonne and I tried Friday and yesterday to find out through the Polish consulate whether Wanda had any relatives in Poland whom we could notify. Apparently her family was liquidated by the Communists. The consulate advised that its queries in Warsaw were fruitless.

I knew that both of Wendell's parents, of course, were dead, and I had understood vaguely that a brother and sister of his had passed away years ago. I phoned up to his village in Connecticut. The Congregational minister said he did not know of any relatives. He scarcely knew of the family. They were not buried there. He would inquire around however. Could we bring the bodies up tomorrow for burial? I asked. Yes, we could, if we had no place else to go. He would see whether they could get the graves dug, he said.

Yvonne remembered that Wendell had been married previously. His first wife had divorced him immediately after the First World War because he would not return with her to Chicago. A daughter of one of the big meat packers, I believe she was. Perhaps she would be interested in the funeral arrangements. We got the A.P. bureau in Chicago to try to track her down. It couldn't find her. Perhaps she too was dead. . . .

Those two rare creatures must have been quite alone in this

world. The last survivors of families that once had been substantial and prosperous and no doubt highly respected in their respective lands.

DECEMBER 11

WE DROVE up to Connecticut behind the two black hearses, speeding past the bare, frozen fields and slowing down through the bustling towns and sleepy villages. There was not much traffic on a Monday and we reached Wendell's little town shortly after 2 P.M. I stopped our cortege at one end of the square while I went into a filling station to phone the Congregational minister of our arrival and to inquire the way to the cemetery.

He joined us there. It was a lonely spot on a slope by the edge of a woods, though in summer, perhaps, when the leaves were out and the grass green and cut, it had its beauty. No one came out from the village except the caretaker, who boasted that he had dug the twin graves himself out of the hard, frozen soil. He was a wizened old man, with a straggly white goatee on his small chin and no teeth that I could see.

The minister, a tall, lean man in a frayed, dark overcoat had a troubled expression on his thin, angular, Yankee face. He had bundled himself up with a gray, wool muffler twisted untidily about his neck.

He came up to us — Steve, Yvonne, Marguerite Burnett and me — singled me out and, his teeth chattering from the cold, whispered:

"May I ask, sir, what religion were the deceased?"

Wanda, being Polish, had undoubtedly been born a Catholic, but there was a gaunt look in the preacher's face which made me think better of telling him so.

"Mr. Philpots belonged to your church, sir," I said. Probably he did once. It seemed to be the only church in the village.

The minister was obviously relieved, his curiosity satisfied, his conscience cleared. He pulled out a New Testament from one of his overcoat pockets, pulled his woolen mittens off his hands, turned a few pages, mumbled the familiar lines — *The Lord Giveth and the Lord Taketh Away* — intoned a prayer that suddenly moved us all, and then, stooping down, tossed a handful of frozen sod on the two coffins which we had bedecked with flowers. Yvonne and I stepped forward and kissed them, and then all four of us turned to go.

When we glanced back we saw that the bent old caretaker and the minister, who had buttoned himself up again against the icy blasts, were having trouble working the leather straps which lowered the coffins. Steve and I turned to give them a hand. It took us some time, and before we had finished a light snow began to fall. In the early December dusk against the stately, cathedral-like, dark green hemlock trees which, I now noticed, dotted one corner of the woods directly behind us, the snow seemed a pure, white offering drifting down gently, beautifully from the gray heavens which watched over us from above.

DECEMBER 13

WHILE I toil away at the typewriter Yvonne and Steve labor at the dismantling of this household. I fret at not being able to give them more of a hand, but they will not allow it. Actually Steve must be anxious to get started on a book of his own, though so far he has merely joked about it. He says it will be entitled: "The Rise and Fall of a Yankee Diplomat."

We shall probably be the scribblingest pair of farmers in New England.

Impossible to believe that Wendell Philpots and Wanda are gone forever.

DECEMBER 14

A PARTING quip from the magnificent Woodruff in his inestimable column today: "This is probably the last time those bum Americans Raymond Whitehead and Stephen Burnett will be mentioned in this column. At long last they are retiring from the public eye — and this is good riddance. Our intelligence reports they have taken to the country and — believe it or not — are going to try to farm for a living. Well, it is better that they pollute the soil of a few barren New England acres than the body politic of our nations. Farewell, you un-Americans!"

DECEMBER 15

IT BURNS me up that there is no appeal against the O'Brien committee findings. I must try to forget it. . . . We move to the country next Monday, the eighteenth!

DECEMBER 16

THE President today proclaimed the existence of a "national emergency." It is the consequence of our disastrous defeat in Korea at the hands of the Chinese Communists and of what the President warns is "the increasing menace of the forces of Communist aggression." The intervention of Red China in Korea, like the original aggression of the North Koreans, has once more wakened us up. Says the President: "Our homes, our nation, all the things we believe in, are in a great danger . . . created by the rulers of the Soviet Union."

He orders further mobilization. We must call up another million men to the armed forces. Will we ever see peace and normal living again? The prospect seems dim tonight. . . .

And in the midst of this crisis, this new national emergency, we move to the country! To live bucolically milking cows! Steve and I, who have spent an exciting lifetime reporting one upheaval after another all over the world! My blood revolts against withdrawing from it all. But for the moment I have been forced to, and must accept it. I shall miss, though, writing and broadcasting about all the turmoil. . . . I am going to make right now one unbreakable promise with myself: that from this moment on I shall *not — ever —* start feeling sorry for myself. Why should I? Farming, if we can do it, will provide a decent living. But it will not be all. There will be the books to write — and maybe, for Colette, a play. I shall not be really silenced. I still shall be a free man.

DECEMBER 17 (SUNDAY)

WEARY from the packing but full of excitement — all of us — about tomorrow's moving. Yvonne and I were alone in the bare house this evening. Steve had driven up to the country this afternoon with all our offspring. It was one of those clear, cold winter nights, the air crisp and clean. We stood by the window in what has been my study and watched the lights of the bridges and of Long Island sparkle beyond the water. We have met disaster since we came to dwell here. But we both feel a little sad at leaving. It was a home — our first together in America — and there were some stirring moments lived here.

THE FARM (!) DECEMBER 19

THE big, sprawling, old house a joy, but in somewhat of a turmoil. Yvonne, however, establishes a little order and keeps us at work unpacking, uncrating, hanging, unhanging, and heaving the furniture (Steve's and ours) about. Meanwhile there are thirty cows to tend.

DECEMBER 20

MAYBE we will learn eventually how to milk cows, not to mention how to feed and water and humor them, and remove and dispose of their manure. At the moment, after a couple of days' toil, I would rather climb Mount Everest. Luckily, the widow's uncle, Sykes — a patient old man of New England, who has been wrestling for half a century with stubborn bovines and the even more stubborn boulder-strewn fields from which they live in these parts — has agreed to stay on with us.

Funny — I had forgotten, if I ever knew, that you had to get up long before dawn, even in winter, indeed especially in winter, when the days are short, if you keep a herd. My back has a hundred aches and my pretty, citified hands are bulging with blisters. But, oh, how I sleep at night!

DECEMBER 22

A CHEERING note came from Lawyer Rikind today. I can stop worrying, he says, about the Justice Department asking the grand jury to bring perjury charges against me for my testimony during the O'Brien hearing. In the first place, says Bill, there's no case for an indictment. Secondly, Senator Jones effectively spiked O'Brien's game by his request that the Justice Department ask the grand jury to consider perjury charges against Elsie McCabe and Frederick Newman. The Justice Department, says Bill, doesn't wish to involve the two ex-Communists that way. Hence, he learns, it will press neither the charges against them nor against me.

DECEMBER 23

YVONNE and the girls went into the village today to shop for our Christmas feast. While they were gone Steve, Dick and I stole into the far end of the chicken coop, snared a big, fat turkey — one of a dozen the widow kindly left for us with the chickens — took it to the barn and, after much hesitation, managed to kill it. (The girls won't stand for us killing any living thing on the place, so we all swore secrecy.) None of us has the faintest idea how to dress it — and Sykes has taken the afternoon off — but we shall consult the book. (We have a library to tell us how to do everything imaginable about the place.)

Colette arriving tomorrow to stay with us over the holidays — it is touching to see Steve try to hide his joy. Chris Chambers is coming over tomorrow to help celebrate Christmas Eve. He may have to wade through a lot of snow. It has been snowing hard this evening. We shall have a white Christmas.

DECEMBER 24 (SUNDAY AND CHRISTMAS EVE)

THE whole brood of Whiteheads and Burnetts went trudging through the snow this afternoon to the edge of the woods where we hacked down a beautiful young pine for our Christmas tree. We agreed you couldn't buy such a magnificent specimen in any store in New York. After we had dragged it to the house we all piled into an old sledge we have been fixing up to haul the milk to the creamery — though we probably could have got through in the car if we'd used chains — and drove down to the village to meet Colette's train from New York. She cried out with excitement when she saw the old relic hitched to our pair of nags behind a snowdrift by the little frame station. It was the sound of the sleigh bells that touched all of us old folk, for we had not heard that gay, tinkling tone in many a year, and it brought back, sentimentally, our magic youth in a young, unspoiled, unmotorized America that is only a memory now.

We have had in our family many memorable Christmas Eves — in the Old World and last year in the New — but I feel that tonight's is going to be the best of all.

DECEMBER 25

THERE was never anything quite like it, we agreed: our home-grown candlelit pine tree stretching its needled boughs gracefully over one corner of the room; and the roaring fire of hard maple logs in the big Dutch fireplace; and Colette (one of the most sophisticated as well as beautiful women who ever lived) leading us spiritedly in singing Christmas carols to the accompaniment of Dick's accordion; and Chris Chambers (the cynical, worldly critic), lounging on the floor before the fire reading Dickens's *Christmas Carol* with all the fire and fervor and finesse one imagined the great author himself showed when he read it, with laughter and tears, to his own large brood of children in London many Christmases ago. . . .

After the younger children had gone to bed last night — Dick and Marguerite stayed up with us — we exchanged our few simple presents, though Colette had brought some rather elegant ones, a whole suitcaseful. And then at midnight we listened, like millions of other Americans, I suppose, to someone — an opera star, but we didn't catch her name — sing "Stille Nacht" (recalling earlier times when Madame Schumann-Heink used to sing it) on the air. Yvonne then produced from the icebox some champagne her parents had sent from France, and we toasted the holiday and one another around the fire. It was a merry gathering, and outside, the barns and the woods and the fields, under the thick mantle of snow, looked in the moonlight like the nostalgic view on an old Christmas card.

Today we feasted on our turkey in the big dining room and this afternoon, with a bright sun sparkling on the snow, we swept a corner of the pond and took to ice skating. In the general merriment, Steve and Colette performed a waltz on ice!

DECEMBER 26

YVONNE and I touched by a Christmas card from Barbara Fletcher. Underneath the engraved holiday greetings she writes: "— and love, as always, to you both. If, for the moment, we are out of touch please remember that my feelings toward you have not changed — nor will they ever!"

DECEMBER 27

STEVE and I, with Dick generously assisting, did our first milking operation alone today, with old Sykes looking on apprehensively. He is taking a few days off and wanted to be sure we could hold the fort without him. We were nervous as old hens and perspired profusely, but it went off with scarcely a hitch. My back aches, though, from shoveling manure and forking hay and shouldering hundred-pound bags of feed. Dick, being very apt with the tractor, has taken on himself the arduous job of hauling the manure out to the fields and spreading it.

DECEMBER 28

I HAVE discovered that after we have milked, fed and watered the cows in the morning I have several hours free until the evening chores. After the aches have subsided —

or rather, right away, right next week — I must get to work and finish the book. Farming and writing — that will be a life!

DECEMBER 29

COLETTE had an architect in today to look over her mountaintop and plan her cottage. To judge by her talk, it will be quite an affair. "I don't want anything skimpy, sir!" I heard her say. She and Steve walk over daily to see her place.

DECEMBER 30

OUR first milk check — nearly $200 for the week! We feel eminently successful and unbelievably well off.

DECEMBER 31

EVERYONE in a fine fettle to see the New Year in tonight. Some theater people, friends of Chris and Colette, are coming over from Chris's later on to help us celebrate.

This afternoon, until it was time for the chores and the milking, Steve and I relaxed in the second-floor study which we have fixed up for our nonagricultural pursuits. He seemed amused at the idea of settling down to do his "memoirs." He had some weird stories to tell, he thought. Thinking about some of them, he said, had given him a fresh idea for our play for Colette. It would be good for our souls as well as for her to do a comedy. We could take one of our lady ambassadors he had known in Europe — this one was not only rich but youngish and beautiful — and set her down as our representative in a mythical kingdom in Asia, one in which the bachelor king had a hundred mistresses, but none so attractive as the ambassadress. There could be a complication there, and perhaps another with the Soviet Ambassador, who would lose his head at the first sight of our dazzling envoy, with results as dizzily catastrophic to the Kremlin as to the State Department. . . .

After a while Chris Chambers dropped by. He thought maybe Steve had something there. Colette was a genius at comedy, he said. Or perhaps it would make a musical — Colette had always wanted to do a musical. We would spring the idea on one of Chris's friends, a producer, who would be coming over this evening. We might even get a rise out of Colette.

We were so full of our talk that none of us noticed it getting dark outside until Marguerite Burnett and young Richard barged in, their ski suits plastered with snow, their faces glowing from the winter air.

"Is it too late to help with the milking?" Dick asked tauntingly.

"We were just going out to do it," Steve lied. We had somehow forgotten all about it.

"Can I help too?" Marguerite asked.

"Sure, and Chris also," I said.

"If it's just the same with you, I'll skip it," Chris smiled.

Downstairs Yvonne was pouring hot rum toddy into several glasses. "It's freezing out there," she said, greeting us. "Take this first." There was a certain knowing gleam in her eye.

"Mama," young Maria blurted out. "Tell them what you just told us." Maria, joined by Irita and Marcia — Steve's youngest — gathered around excitedly. From their shoes I could see they had just come in from the barn.

"I think Starry Eyes is going to calve tonight," Yvonne said.

"My God! What do we do?" I cried.

"Call the vet," Chris said. "Or, if you prefer, trust to nature."

"I think this will be quite a nice New Year's Eve, don't you?" Yvonne smiled. "A fitting conclusion to an eventful year."

Steve and I pulled on our overshoes, donned our old jackets and followed by the whole yelping Burnett and Whitehead broods traipsed out into the snow toward the barn.